Introduction to Modern Algebra and Matrix Theory

C. V. NEWSOM, *Consulting Editor*

Ambrose and Lazerowitz *Fundamentals of Symbolic Logic*

Beaumont and Ball *Introduction to Modern Algebra and Matrix Theory*

Britton *Calculus*

Britton and Snively *Algebra for College Students*, Revised; *College Algebra; Intermediate Algebra*

Eves *An Introduction to the History of Mathematics*

Goffman *Real Functions*

Johnson, McCoy, and O'Neill *Fundamentals of College Mathematics*

Jones *The Theory of Numbers*

Kinney and Purdy *Teaching Mathematics in the Secondary School*

Larsen *Rinehart Mathematical Tables; Rinehart Mathematical Tables, Formulas, and Curves*, Enlarged

Levinson *The Science of Chance*

McCoy and Johnson *Analytic Geometry*

Miller *Engineering Mathematics*

Morrill *Plane Trigonometry*, Revised

Northcott *Mathematics of Finance; Plane and Spherical Trigonometry*, Revised

Reagan, Ott, and Sigley *College Alegbra*, Revised

Rider and Fischer *Mathematics of Investment*

Swain *Understanding Arithmetic*

Tintner *Mathematics and Statistics for Economists*

Varner *Computing with Desk Calculators*

INTRODUCTION TO MODERN ALGEBRA AND MATRIX THEORY

by ROSS A. BEAUMONT

Professor of Mathematics

University of Washington

and RICHARD W. BALL

Associate Professor of Mathematics

Alabama Polytechnic Institute

Rinehart & Company, Inc. | New York

Third Printing June, 1957

Printed in the United States of America

Library of Congress Catalog Card Number: 54-8194

PREFACE

Three principal goals have been kept in mind in the writing of this book. The first is to present to the student whose interest is in mathematics, the physical sciences, or certain of the social sciences, a basic knowledge of linear algebra, the number systems of mathematics, and the theory of polynomial equations, which he will certainly need for advanced work in these fields. The second is to present this classical material in conjunction with the fundamental concepts of modern algebra which serve as the central theme of the book. The study of the abstract algebraic concepts which are introduced is carried far enough to allow a graduate course in algebra to be given at a more sophisticated level than is generally possible. The final goal, which is possibly the most important one of all, is to give the student, who in his first two years of college mathematics has been primarily concerned with learning techniques, an appreciation for precise mathematical statements and for proofs which meet current standards of rigor.

In the Introduction to the book, a discussion of the positive integers is given; this is needed for an understanding of inductive proofs and other proofs based on simple number theory.

The contents of Chapter I are the algebra of matrices and the properties of determinants. In order to avoid introducing unnecessary abstractions at the outset, the elements of the matrices are numbers, but care is taken to emphasize that the algebraic identities of the matrix operations are consequences of similar identities which are assumed for numbers. We believe that the student can more readily appreciate the importance of these identities when they are discussed in connection with objects like matrices, which are new to him, than when they are first discussed in detail as the familiar properties of number systems, which he regards as obvious.

In Chapter II, the general discussion of a group of transformations leads in a natural way to the introduction of the concept of an equivalence relation, which is stressed throughout the book. Here it is used to explain the meaning of canonical forms for matrices as the representatives of equivalence classes. The general results of this chapter are applied to the study of the equivalence of matrices and the solution of linear equations. Number fields are introduced when considerations of rationality occur in the discussion of the equivalence of matrices. Vector spaces, defined as sets of row matrices with elements in a number field, are discussed in Chapter III, and a matrix is interpreted as a representation for a linear mapping.

With many examples at hand from the preceding chapters, and with motivation having been supplied by the study of groups of transformations, an introduction to the theory of abstract groups is given in Chapter IV. This study, which begins with a discussion of binary operations and isomorphism, continues through the homomorphism theorems and a simple structure theorem for abelian groups. Rings, integral domains, and fields are introduced in Chapter V as abstract models of the number systems, which are systematically developed in this chapter.

In Chapter VI, we have tried to avoid the standard treatment of polynomials by approaching the subject through a discussion of the general problem of field extensions. In this way, a common introduction is provided for a study of the properties of polynomials, the theory of polynomial equations, and an introduction to the algebraic theory of fields.

Matrices with polynomial elements are treated in Chapter VII, and the book concludes with Chapter VIII, which contains classical results on the reduction of matrices to canonical form by various groups of matrix transformations. We have tried in this chapter to give a careful treatment of the relation between the matrix transformations involved in the reduction and the corresponding coordinate transformations in a vector space over a number field.

The book has been designed so that material for a course on the theory of matrices can be given independently. Thus, a one-quarter course meeting five hours a week or a one-semester course meeting three or four hours a week can be based on the contents of Chapters I, II, III, VII, and VIII. Since such a course is popular with students whose major interest is in the application of this theory to other fields, abstract concepts are not emphasized in these chapters. This course may be followed by one on abstract algebra based on the remaining three chapters of the book. The complete book is intended as a textbook for an introductory course in modern algebra meeting three or four hours a week throughout the year. The material in the final two chapters is often omitted in such a course. The courses outlined above can be given in the fourth college year, although some schools will offer them in the third year of the curriculum, or even at the first-year graduate level.

We have, of course, been influenced by the available textbooks on algebra and matrix theory, and we wish to express our indebtedness to the authors of these books. Our thanks are due to our colleagues at the University of Washington and the editorial consultants for the publisher, who have offered many helpful suggestions in the preparation of the book, and also to our many classroom students who were the final critics of this work. Finally, we wish to acknowledge the help and encouragement of the Department of Mathematics of the University of Washington in providing secretarial assistance in the preparation of the manuscript for classroom use and for publication.

ROSS A. BEAUMONT
RICHARD W. BALL

Seattle, Washington
April, 1954

CONTENTS

Introduction to Modern Algebra and Matrix Theory

INTRODUCTION

It is the purpose of this book to introduce to the reader the fundamental concepts and methods of modern algebra, as well as to give a selection of classical results from the theory of matrices and the theory of equations which are useful in other branches of mathematics and in other sciences. While acquiring new information and techniques, the reader should be rewarded by a unification of ideas which were previously disconnected, and by a new understanding of familiar things. Perhaps the most important attainment to be gained is an appreciation for precise mathematical statements and logical clarity of exposition. The previous knowledge of the reader will be called upon chiefly for the construction of examples and to suggest possible approaches to an abstract problem.

Undoubtedly the first set of mathematical objects which the reader encountered was the set of positive integers 1, 2, 3, · · · . Later this set was extended to the set of all integers 0, ± 1, ± 2, · · · . It is not our intention here to develop the properties of the integers systematically from a set of postulates for the positive integers.* We will assume that the fundamental properties of the integers are known, and will begin our discussion by deriving some additional properties which will be used in our later work. A knowledge of these properties is necessary in most mathematical discussions, for, among other things, integers are used as exponents to indicate repeated operations and as subscripts to count the elements in a given set.

One property of the positive integers which, in one form or another, must be assumed as a postulate in a logical development of the properties of the integers is known as the well-ordering principle. It is given here since it is the basis for proofs by "mathematical induction," and since the reader, although he has certainly used this principle many times, may not be familiar with its formal statement.

(0.1)† Well-Ordering Principle for Positive Integers. Every non-empty set of positive integers contains a least positive integer.

We will use this principle to obtain several fundamental theorems

---

*See B. L. van der Waerden, *Modern Algebra* (New York, 1949), I, 3.

† The definitions and theorems in this text will be numbered consecutively, giving first the section in which the item occurs.

concerning the integers. The first two of these theorems formulate the alternative methods of inductive proof.

(0.2) Theorem. If S is any set of positive integers which contains the integer 1 and which contains the integer $n + 1$ for every integer n in S, then S contains every positive integer.

PROOF. Let T be the set of all positive integers not in S. Then 1 is not in T by hypothesis. Assume that the theorem is false, that is, assume that T is non-empty. Then by (0.1), T contains a least positive integer $m > 1$. This means that $m - 1$ is a positive integer, and that $m - 1$ is in S since $m - 1 < m$. But by hypothesis, if $m - 1$ is in S, then $(m - 1) + 1 = m$ is in S. This is a contradiction, which arose from the assumption that T is not empty. Therefore, T can contain no positive integers, and the theorem is true.

This theorem is known as the First Principle of Finite Induction. It is used to prove propositions which can be expressed in terms of cases $n = 1, 2, 3, \cdots$. Let S be the set of all positive integers n for which the corresponding case of the proposition is true. If we can prove that 1 is in S, that is, if we can prove that the proposition is true for the case $n = 1$, and if we can prove that $n + 1$ is in S whenever n is in S, that is, if we can prove that the case $n + 1$ of the proposition is true whenever the case n is true; then the proposition is true for all cases since the set S is the set of all positive integers by Theorem (0.2).

It is often convenient to apply an alternate form of Theorem (0.2).

(0.3) Theorem. If S is any set of positive integers which contains the integer n whenever it contains all positive integers $m < n$, then S contains every positive integer.

The proof of this theorem is similar to that of (0.2). The reader should note that this theorem still requires that we be able to prove explicitly that 1 is in S since there are no positive integers less than 1.

A second use of (0.1) is in the proof of the division algorithm. We will prove this result for positive integers and leave it for the reader to extend the result to all integers.

If a and b are any two integers, we say that b is a *factor* of a, or that b divides a, if there exists an integer c such that $a = bc$. If a and b are any two integers, $b \neq 0$, we may divide b into a to get a unique quotient and a unique non-negative remainder which is smaller than $|b|$, and equal to zero if b divides a. The following theorem proves the existence of this division process.

(0.4) Division Algorithm for Positive Integers. If n and m are positive integers, there exist unique non-negative integers q and r such that $n = qm + r$ where $0 \leq r < m$.

PROOF. Consider the set S of all non-negative integers of the form $n - qm$ for q a non-negative integer. Since $n = n - 0 \cdot m > 0$, n is in S, and S contains at least one positive integer. By (0.1), S contains a least positive integer $r = n - qm$ for some non-negative integer q. If $r > m$, then $0 < r - m = n - qm - m = n - (q + 1)m$, so that $r - m$ is in S. Since $r - m < r$, this contradicts the fact that r is the smallest positive integer in S. Therefore $r \leq m$. If $r < m$, we are finished since $n = qm + r$ is the required expression. If $r = m$, $n = qm + m = (q + 1)m + 0$ is the required expression.

To show that q and r are unique, assume that $n = q'm + r'$ is any division with $0 \leq r' < m$. Then $qm + r = q'm + r'$ or $(q - q')m = r' - r$. This means that m is a factor of $r' - r$. But since $0 \leq r < m$ and $0 \leq r' < m$, we have that $0 \leq |r' - r| < m$. Therefore $r' - r = 0$ and $q' - q = 0$ since $m \neq 0$. Thus $r' = r$ and $q' = q$, so that the quotient and remainder are unique.

(0.5) Definition. A *greatest common divisor* (g.c.d.) of the integers a and b, not both zero, is a positive integer d such that

(i) d divides both a and b;

(ii) every integer c which divides both a and b also divides d.

(0.6) Theorem. Every pair of integers a and b, not both zero, has a unique g.c.d. d, which can be written in the form $d = au + bv$ for integers u and v.

PROOF. Let S be the set of all positive integers $ax + by$, where x and y are integers. The set S is not empty since at least one of the four integers, $1 \cdot a + 0 \cdot b$, $(-1) \cdot a + 0 \cdot b$, $0 \cdot a + 1 \cdot b$, $0 \cdot a + (-1) \cdot b$, is positive. Let $d = au + bv$ for integers u and v be the smallest positive integer in S. Then d is a g.c.d. of a and b:

(i) By (0.4) there exist unique q and r such that $a = qd + r$, where $0 \leq r < d$. Thus $r = a - qd = a - q(au + bv) = a(1 - qu) + b(-qv)$ is either 0 or in S. This implies that $r = 0$ since $r < d$, the smallest positive integer in S. Therefore $a = qd$, and d divides a. Similarly d divides b.

(ii) Let c be any common divisor of a and b, say $a = mc$, $b = nc$. Then $d = au + bv = mcu + ncv = (mu + nv)c$, so that c divides d.

By (0.5), d is a g.c.d. of a and b. Let d' be any g.c.d. of a and b. Then d divides d' since d' is a g.c.d., and d' divides d since d is a g.c.d. These two statements imply that $d = d'$ since both integers are positive.

The special case with $d = 1$ will be of particular importance.

(0.7) Definition. Two integers are *relatively prime* if their g.c.d. is 1.

We will now use inductive proofs to obtain the unique factorization theorem for integers.

(0.8) Definition. An integer $p > 1$ is called a *prime* if ± 1 and $\pm p$ are the only divisors of p.

(0.9) Theorem. Every positive integer $n > 1$ can be written as a product of prime factors.

PROOF. Let n be any integer greater than 1, and assume that the theorem is true for all integers less than n. If n is a prime, we are finished. Otherwise, $n = ab$ with $0 < a < n$ and $0 < b < n$. But by the induction hypothesis, $a = p_1p_2 \cdots p_r$ and $b = p_{r+1}p_{r+2} \cdots p_s$, where the p_i are primes. Therefore, $n = p_1p_2 \cdots p_r\, p_{r+1}p_{r+2} \cdots p_s$ is a factorization of n, and by Theorem (0.3), the theorem is true.

The customary statement of the uniqueness of this factorization depends on the following result.

(0.10) Theorem. If a is a factor of the product bc and if a and b are relatively prime, then a is a factor of c.

PROOF. By the hypothesis there exist integers m, u, and v such that $bc = am$ and $1 = au + bv$. Therefore, $c = 1 \cdot c = (au + bv)c = auc + bvc = auc + (bc)v = auc + (am)v = a(uc + mv)$, which means that a is a factor of c.

(0.11) Corollary. If a prime p divides a product $a_1a_2 \cdots a_n$, then p divides at least one a_i.

This corollary is proved by induction on n, noting that if a prime does not divide an integer a, it is relatively prime to a.

(0.12) Unique Factorization Theorem for Positive Integers. Every positive integer $n > 1$ can be written uniquely as a product of primes, except for the order of the factors.

PROOF. By Theorem (0.9), every $n > 1$ can be factored in at least one way. To prove uniqueness we shall use the first form of induction on the number k of prime factors in a factorization of n. If $k = 1$, then n is itself a prime and has no other factors. Assume the theorem for all integers which can be factored in any way as a product of $k - 1$ prime factors, and let n be an integer which can be written as a product $p_1p_2 \cdots p_k$ of k prime factors. If $n = q_1q_2 \cdots q_s$ is any factorization of n into prime factors, then $p_1p_2 \cdots p_k = q_1q_2 \cdots q_s$, which means that p_1 divides the product $q_1q_2 \cdots q_s$. By Corollary (0.11), p_1 divides some q_i, and therefore $p_1 = q_i$ since the q_j are themselves primes. Thus $n/p_1 = p_2 \cdots p_k = q_1 \cdots q_{i-1}q_{i+1} \cdots q_s$, and by the induction hypothesis the factors p_i and q_j are the same except for their order. This means the theorem is true by Theorem (0.2).

Exercise (0.1). Prove Corollary (0.11).

Exercise (0.2). Prove (0.9) and (0.12) directly from (0.1).

Exercise (0.3). Prove (0.3) and discuss the corresponding method of inductive proof. Show that in the proof of (0.9) the case $n = 2$ is included implicitly.

Exercise (0.4). Using (0.4), prove the division algorithm for any two integers a and b, $b \neq 0$. Here $a = qb + r$ with integers q and r, $0 \leq r < |b|$.

Exercise (0.5). Write out the division algorithm for the following pairs of integers: $a = 10$, $b = 3$; $a = 40$, $b = 4$; $a = -20$, $b = 30$.

Exercise (0.6). Find the g.c.d. and express it in the form $d = au + bv$ for each of the pairs of the preceding exercise.

Exercise (0.7). Using (0.1), prove that there is no integer between 0 and 1. [*Hint:* If $0 < a < 1$, then $0 < a^2 < a < 1$.]

Exercise (0.8). Using (0.1), show that every positive integer may be expressed as a finite sum of the integer 1 with itself.

Exercise (0.9). A closed plane polygon is convex if each of its interior angles is less than 180°. Prove by induction that the sum of the interior angles of an n-sided convex polygon ($n \geq 3$) is $(n - 2) \cdot 180°$.

I MATRICES AND DETERMINANTS

Section 1. Rectangular Matrices

The reader has had experience in college algebra in solving systems of n linear equations in n unknowns. A system of two linear equations in two unknowns, such as

$$\begin{aligned} 7x + 4y &= 12 \\ 2x - 3y &= -5, \end{aligned}$$

can easily be solved by successively eliminating x and y between the two equations, and solving the resulting equations

$$\begin{aligned} 29y &= 59 \\ 29x &= 16 \end{aligned}$$

separately, for the unknowns x and y. The questions which arise in the solution of systems of linear equations can be answered without difficulty by this method of successive elimination if only two or three equations are involved, but the method becomes practically unworkable as the number of equations increases. The method of determinants is introduced to answer more readily questions about the nature of the solution, and to systematize the procedure for solving the equations when a solution exists.

The study of m linear equations in n unknowns leads naturally to the concept of a rectangular matrix. Consider, for example, the system of equations

$$\begin{aligned} 2x - 3y + 5z - w &= 0 \\ x + 6y - 3z + 2w &= 5 \\ 4x - y + 7z - 3w &= 2. \end{aligned}$$

Since the letters x,y,z, and w are merely symbols which stand for possible numerical solutions, the only significant features of this system are the numbers which appear in the equations and their relative positions. Therefore, these equations are completely described by the rectangular array

$$\begin{pmatrix} 2 & -3 & 5 & -1 & 0 \\ 1 & 6 & -3 & 2 & 5 \\ 4 & -1 & 7 & -3 & 2 \end{pmatrix},$$

which is called a matrix.

By a solution of such a system of equations, we mean any set of numbers x,y,z,w which satisfy the three equations. As we have indicated earlier, there are several important questions which arise in the discussion of the system. Are there any solutions at all, and if there are solutions, how many? How are the solutions related to the coefficients of the equations, and, in particular, what is the technique for

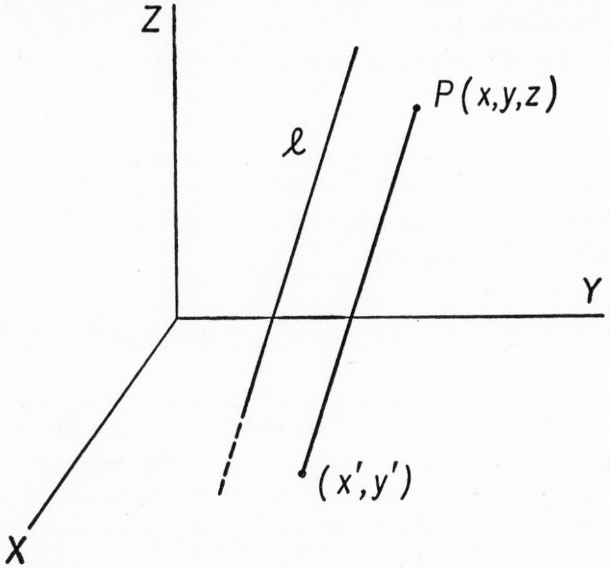

Fig. 1

finding solutions? Since the system of equations is described by a matrix, the answers to these questions can be found in the study of this matrix. We shall see that the algebraic operations involved in finding the answers to these questions can be conveniently interpreted as operations on the matrix of the system.

Closely related to a system of m linear equations in n unknowns is the concept of a linear mapping. An example of a linear mapping known to the reader is the pair of equations which describes a rotation of axes of a Cartesian coordinate system in the plane through an angle θ. The equations are

$$\begin{aligned} x &= x' \cos \theta - y' \sin \theta \\ y &= x' \sin \theta + y' \cos \theta, \end{aligned}$$

where the coordinates of a point P are (x,y) when referred to the original axes, and (x',y') when referred to the new axes. The properties of this mapping are completely determined by the matrix

$$\begin{pmatrix} \cos\theta & -\sin\theta \\ \sin\theta & \cos\theta \end{pmatrix},$$

which is called the matrix of the mapping.

As a second example of a linear mapping, consider the projection of a point (x,y,z) in space onto the XY-plane, where we project parallel to a line l with direction angles α, β, γ. (See Figure 1.) Given the point P with coordinates (x,y,z), the coordinates (x',y') of its projection in the XY-plane are found by setting z' equal to zero in the equations

$$\frac{x'-x}{\cos\alpha} = \frac{y'-y}{\cos\beta} = \frac{z'-z}{\cos\gamma},$$

which are the equations of the line through P which is parallel to l. The result is a linear mapping

$$x' = x - \frac{\cos\alpha}{\cos\gamma}z$$

$$y' = y - \frac{\cos\beta}{\cos\gamma}z$$

with matrix

$$\begin{pmatrix} 1 & 0 & -\dfrac{\cos\alpha}{\cos\gamma} \\ 0 & 1 & -\dfrac{\cos\beta}{\cos\gamma} \end{pmatrix}.$$

In general, a linear mapping is given by a system of linear equations

$$\begin{aligned} x_1 &= a_{11}y_1 + a_{12}y_2 + \cdots + a_{1n}y_n \\ x_2 &= a_{21}y_1 + a_{22}y_2 + \cdots + a_{2n}y_n \\ &\cdots \\ x_m &= a_{m1}y_1 + a_{m2}y_2 + \cdots + a_{mn}y_n, \end{aligned}$$

which give the values of the m variables $x_1, x_2, \cdots, x_m$ in terms of the values of the n variables $y_1, y_2, \cdots, y_n$. If we let A be the rectangular array

$$\begin{pmatrix} a_{11} & a_{12} & \cdots & a_{1n} \\ a_{21} & a_{22} & \cdots & a_{2n} \\ \cdot & \cdot & \cdots & \cdot \\ \cdot & \cdot & \cdots & \cdot \\ \cdot & \cdot & \cdots & \cdot \\ a_{m1} & a_{m2} & \cdots & a_{mn} \end{pmatrix},$$

we can determine the properties of the mapping by studying the matrix A. Moreover, the equations of the mapping can be indicated by the concise notation $x = Ay$.

The problems discussed above are two examples of the many applications of the theory of matrices which provide motivation for the present study.

(1.1) Definition. If S is an arbitrary set of elements, then an *m by n S-matrix* A is a rectangular array

$$A = \begin{pmatrix} a_{11} & a_{12} & \cdots & a_{1n} \\ a_{21} & a_{22} & \cdots & a_{2n} \\ \cdot & \cdot & \cdots & \cdot \\ \cdot & \cdot & \cdots & \cdot \\ \cdot & \cdot & \cdots & \cdot \\ a_{m1} & a_{m2} & \cdots & a_{mn} \end{pmatrix}$$

of m rows and n columns, where the elements a_{ij} are in the set S. If $m = n$, we call A a *square matrix of order n*, or an *n-rowed square matrix.*

Since we want to think of a matrix as a single entity, we indicate this by enclosing the array of elements in large parentheses. The rows of a matrix are always numbered from the top down and the columns from left to right. The position of each element in the array is given by its subscripts; that is, a_{ij} is the element in the ith row and jth column. The elements a_{ij} for which $i = j$ are called *principal diagonal elements.*

Since every element of A is represented by a_{ij} as i takes on the values $1, 2, \cdots, m$ and j the values $1, 2, \cdots, n$, we call a_{ij} the *typical element* of A. This suggests the simpler notation

$$A = (a_{ij}) \qquad i = 1, 2, \cdots, m; \qquad j = 1, 2, \cdots, n$$

for an m by n S-matrix.

The matrix $\begin{pmatrix} 2 & -3 & 5 & 0 \\ 1 & 6 & -3 & 5 \\ 4 & -1 & 7 & 2 \end{pmatrix}$ of the system of equations considered earlier in this section is a 3 by 4 matrix where we can take S to be the set of all integers, positive, negative, and zero. The matrices

$\begin{pmatrix} \cos\theta & -\sin\theta \\ \sin\theta & \cos\theta \end{pmatrix}$ and $\begin{pmatrix} 1 & 0 & -\dfrac{\cos\alpha}{\cos\gamma} \\ 0 & 1 & -\dfrac{\cos\beta}{\cos\gamma} \end{pmatrix}$, of the examples of linear mappings, have real numbers as elements, the first being a square matrix of order 2, and the second a 2 by 3 matrix.

It should be noticed that Definition (1.1) does not assign a value, or magnitude, to an S-matrix. As our examples indicate, the usefulness of a matrix is derived from the positional relationships among its elements. These remarks are implicit in the following definition.

(1.2) Definition. If $A = (a_{ij})$ is an m by n S-matrix and $B = (b_{ij})$ is a p by q S-matrix, then A and B are *equal* if $m = p$, $n = q$, and $a_{ij} = b_{ij}$ in S for all pairs i,j.

In other words, two matrices are equal if and only if they are identical.

Exercise (1.1). If $A = (a_{ij})$ for $i = 1, 2, \cdots, m$; $j = 1, 2, \cdots, n$, where are the elements a_{ij} with constant i? Those with constant j? Those with $i = j$?

Exercise (1.2). Construct a 2 by 6 matrix (a_{ij}) with $a_{13} = a_{25} = 1$, $a_{23} = -1$, and all other elements zero.

Exercise (1.3). Construct a 3 by 5 matrix (a_{ij}) with $a_{ij} = i + j$ for all pairs i,j.

Exercise (1.4). A certain automobile company has its salesmen send in 3 by 4 matrices as sales reports, where the rows stand in order for the number of coupes, sedans, and convertibles sold, and the columns in order for the colors red, green, blue, and black. It receives reports from two salesmen as follows:

$$\text{A:}\begin{pmatrix} 2 & 3 & 3 & 4 \\ 3 & 2 & 1 & 5 \\ 5 & 0 & 0 & 0 \end{pmatrix} \qquad \text{B:}\begin{pmatrix} 2 & 2 & 3 & 1 \\ 3 & 4 & 2 & 6 \\ 2 & 2 & 1 & 0 \end{pmatrix}.$$

How many blue sedans did A sell? Which man sold more green convertibles? Which sold more sedans? How many cars did B sell?

Exercise (1.5). Write out systems of linear equations which have the following matrices:

(a) $\begin{pmatrix} 2 & -3 & 0 \\ 5 & 0 & 1 \end{pmatrix}$, (b) $\begin{pmatrix} -6 & 7 & 4 \\ 0 & -5 & 11 \\ 2 & -3 & 7 \end{pmatrix}$,

(c) $\begin{pmatrix} 7 & -3 & 2 & -1 & 5 \\ -9 & 6 & 0 & 2 & 0 \\ 4 & -3 & 11 & 2 & 6 \end{pmatrix}$, (d) $\begin{pmatrix} 2 & -1 & 6 & 0 \\ 0 & -5 & 4 & 0 \\ 0 & 0 & 3 & 0 \end{pmatrix}$.

Exercise (1.6). Solve the systems of equations which have the matrices of Exercise (1.5).

Exercise (1.7). The equations which describe a rotation of axes in the plane are given in the text. Find the matrix of the linear mapping which gives the new coordinates (x',y') of a point in terms of the old coordinates (x,y).

Section 2. The Addition of Matrices

In order that the rectangular matrices defined in Section 1 may be useful in a wide variety of applications, it is necessary that we be able to combine these matrices in certain definite ways. The particular combining operations which we wish to define require that similar operations be defined for the elements of the set S. If we take S to be the set of ordinary complex numbers, then all of the rational operations (addition, subtraction, multiplication, and division by a non-zero quantity) will be available for the elements of our S-matrices. Therefore, to fix the ideas of this chapter, we will restrict our attention to matrices with complex number elements. We shall later see that the results obtained in this chapter remain valid for matrices with elements in more general algebraic systems.

A force F, acting at a point P in space, can be described by the components of the force, F_x, F_y, and F_z, acting in the x, y, and z directions of a Cartesian coordinate system. Thus F can be represented by the 1 by 3 matrix of its components, and we write $F = (F_x,F_y,F_z)$. If a second force G acting at P is given by $G = (G_x,G_y,G_z)$, the sum, or resultant, of the forces F and G at P has components $F_x + G_x$, $F_y + G_y$, and $F_z + G_z$, and is given by

$$F + G = (F_x + G_x,\ F_y + G_y,\ F_z + G_z).$$

Therefore, the matrix which represents the sum of the forces is obtained by adding the correspondingly placed elements in the matrices representing each force.

As in the example described above, matrices are used to represent objects which are added component by component. Therefore, we define addition of matrices in this way. We will show that the operation of matrix addition satisfies the same formal rules as those satisfied by the addition of complex numbers. In fact, we derive each property of matrix addition from the corresponding property of complex number addition.

(2.1) Definition. If $A = (a_{ij})$ and $B = (b_{ij})$ are both m by n matrices, their *sum* $A + B$ is the m by n matrix $C = (c_{ij})$ where $c_{ij} = a_{ij} + b_{ij}$ for all pairs i,j.

We define $A + B$ only if A and B have the same size, that is, the same number of rows and the same number of columns. The sum $C = A + B$ is a unique m by n matrix with typical element c_{ij} which is the sum of the numbers in the i,j position of A and of B.

Addition of complex numbers is associative; thus if a, b, and c are any three complex numbers, then $(a + b) + c = a + (b + c)$. Using this property we obtain

(2.2) The Associative Law of Matrix Addition. If A, B, and C are any three m by n matrices, then

$$(A + B) + C = A + (B + C).$$

PROOF. Let $A = (a_{ij})$, $B = (b_{ij})$, and $C = (c_{ij})$. Then $A + B = (a_{ij} + b_{ij})$ is an m by n matrix, so that $(A + B) + C$ exists and is the m by n matrix $([a_{ij} + b_{ij}] + c_{ij})$ by Definition (2.1). Similarly $B + C = (b_{ij} + c_{ij})$ and $A + (B + C)$ is the m by n matrix $(a_{ij} + [b_{ij} + c_{ij}])$. But $[a_{ij} + b_{ij}] + c_{ij} = a_{ij} + [b_{ij} + c_{ij}]$ for all pairs i,j by the associative law of complex number addition. Hence $(A + B) + C = A + (B + C)$ by Definition (1.2).

Addition of complex numbers is also commutative; thus if a and b are any two complex numbers, then $a + b = b + a$. Using this we prove

(2.3) The Commutative Law of Matrix Addition. If A and B are any two m by n matrices, then

$$A + B = B + A.$$

PROOF. Let $A = (a_{ij})$ and $B = (b_{ij})$. Then $A + B = (a_{ij} + b_{ij})$ and $B + A = (b_{ij} + a_{ij})$ are m by n matrices by (2.1). But $a_{ij} + b_{ij} = b_{ij} + a_{ij}$ for all pairs i,j by the commutative law of complex number addition, so that $A + B = B + A$ by (1.2).

Since for m by n matrices A, B, and C, the two calculations $(A + B) + C$ and $A + (B + C)$ result in the same m by n matrix, we may use the notation $A + B + C$ for their uniquely determined sum. It requires only a simple inductive proof in any algebraic system to show that the associative and commutative laws of addition imply that the grouping and ordering of the summands in any finite sum may be changed in any manner whatever without changing the sum. We will assume this result for matrix addition. (See Section 31.)

The proofs of the associative and commutative laws of addition, simple as they are, illustrate the method for verifying matrix identities. After checking that the matrix in the left member of the identity has the same size as the matrix in the right member, we show that these matrices have the same typical element. Then the matrices will have the same element a_{ij} for all pairs i,j, and are equal by (1.2).

Let us denote by O the m by n matrix which has the number 0 in every position. Then for any m by n matrix $A = (a_{ij})$, we have

$$A + O = O + A = A. \tag{2.4}$$

This follows from the fact that $A + O = O + A = (0 + a_{ij}) = (a_{ij}) = A$.

We see that the matrix O has the same property as the number zero and we call it a *zero matrix*.

If we define $-A$ to be the matrix $(-a_{ij})$, then $A + (-A) = (a_{ij} - a_{ij}) = (0) = O$. Subtraction of m by n matrices is defined by

$$B - A = B + (-A). \tag{2.5}$$

It is clear from this definition that subtraction of m by n matrices is always possible and is unique.

EXAMPLE. Let $A = \begin{pmatrix} 1 & 0 & -1 \\ 3 & 5 & 7 \end{pmatrix}$ and $B = \begin{pmatrix} 2 & -6 & 0 \\ 7 & 1 & 2 \end{pmatrix}$.

Then $A + B = \begin{pmatrix} 3 & -6 & -1 \\ 10 & 6 & 9 \end{pmatrix}$, $-A = \begin{pmatrix} -1 & 0 & 1 \\ -3 & -5 & -7 \end{pmatrix}$, and $B - A = \begin{pmatrix} 1 & -6 & 1 \\ 4 & -4 & -5 \end{pmatrix}$.

Exercise (2.1). Perform the indicated operations.

(a) $\begin{pmatrix} 3 & 5 & -2 \\ 4 & 0 & 2 \\ 2 & 1 & 0 \end{pmatrix} + \begin{pmatrix} 2 & 6 & -1 \\ -3 & 2 & -2 \\ -3 & 1 & 0 \end{pmatrix}$,

(b) $\begin{pmatrix} 3 & 4 & 2 & 7 \\ 0 & 2 & -1 & 3 \end{pmatrix} - \begin{pmatrix} 2 & 3 & 1 & 6 \\ -1 & -2 & 0 & 1 \end{pmatrix}$,

(c) $\left[\begin{pmatrix} 1/2 & 0 \\ -3/5 & 2 \\ 1 & 6 \end{pmatrix} + \begin{pmatrix} 3 & 1 \\ 2/5 & 1/3 \\ -1 & 5 \end{pmatrix}\right] - \begin{pmatrix} 5/2 & 1 \\ -1/5 & 4/3 \\ 0 & 11 \end{pmatrix}$,

(d) $(-2 \quad i \quad 1+i) + [(i \quad 1 \quad -i) + (5-3i \quad 2 \quad 5)]$,

(e) $\begin{pmatrix} \sin^2\theta & \sec^2\theta \\ \csc^2\theta & \cos^2\theta \end{pmatrix} + \begin{pmatrix} \cos^2\theta & -\tan^2\theta \\ -\cot^2\theta & \sin^2\theta \end{pmatrix}$.

Exercise (2.2). Verify the associative law of addition in the special case

$$A = \begin{pmatrix} 2 & 3 & 1 \\ 3 & 1 & 4 \end{pmatrix}, B = \begin{pmatrix} -1 & 2 & 0 \\ 3 & -1 & -2 \end{pmatrix}, C = \begin{pmatrix} 3 & -2 & -3 \\ 0 & 0 & 2 \end{pmatrix}.$$

Exercise (2.3). Prove that $B - A$ is the unique solution of the matrix equation $A + X = B$.

Exercise (2.4). Solve the following matrix equations:

(a) $$\begin{pmatrix} 3 & 2 & 3 \\ -2 & 4 & -1 \end{pmatrix} + X = \begin{pmatrix} 2 & -1 & 4 \\ -3 & 0 & 1 \end{pmatrix},$$

(b) $$\begin{pmatrix} 1 & 0 \\ -2 & 5 \\ 6 & 3 \end{pmatrix} + X = \begin{pmatrix} 0 & 1 \\ -2 & 5 \\ 6 & 3 \end{pmatrix},$$

(c) $$\begin{pmatrix} i & 0 \\ 1 & -i \end{pmatrix} + X = \begin{pmatrix} i & 2 \\ 3 & 4+i \end{pmatrix} - X.$$

Exercise (2.5). Write out the sum of the reports in Exercise (1.4). Interpret the entries.

Exercise (2.6). Let $F = (-4, 5, -1)$ and $G = (0, 2, 5)$ be forces acting at a point P in space as described in the example of the text. Find the magnitude and direction of the resultant of these forces at P.

Exercise (2.7). If addition of the m by n matrices $A = (a_{ij})$ and $B = (b_{ij})$ were defined by $A + B = (2a_{ij} + 2b_{ij})$, could we prove the associative and commutative laws? Could we prove these laws if we define $A + B = (a_{ij}b_{ij})$?

Section 3. Multiplication of Matrices

The linear mapping

$$\begin{aligned} x_1 &= a_{11}y_1 + a_{12}y_2 + \cdots + a_{1n}y_n \\ x_2 &= a_{21}y_1 + a_{22}y_2 + \cdots + a_{2n}y_n \\ &\cdots \\ x_m &= a_{m1}y_1 + a_{m2}y_2 + \cdots + a_{mn}y_n \end{aligned}$$

with m by n matrix $A = (a_{ij})$, which we discussed in Section 1, can be written

$$x_i = \sum_{k=1}^{n} a_{ik}y_k, \qquad i = 1, 2, \cdots, m,$$

where $\sum_{k=1}^{n} a_{ik}y_k$ is an abbreviated notation for the sum $a_{i1}y_1 + a_{i2}y_2 + \cdots + a_{in}y_n$. The symbol $\sum_{k=1}^{n}$ is read "the sum from $k = 1$ to $k = n$."

If a second linear mapping

$$y_k = \sum_{j=1}^{q} b_{kj}z_j, \qquad k = 1, 2, \cdots, n,$$

with n by q matrix $B = (b_{ij})$, gives the values of $y_1, y_2, \cdots, y_n$ in terms of the variables $z_1, z_2, \cdots, z_q$, then the values of the x's in terms of the z's are obtained by substituting the second set of equations into the first:

$$x_i = \sum_{k=1}^{n} a_{ik}y_k = \sum_{k=1}^{n} a_{ik}\left(\sum_{j=1}^{q} b_{kj}z_j\right)$$

$$= \sum_{j=1}^{q}\left(\sum_{k=1}^{n} a_{ik}b_{kj}\right) z_j, \qquad i = 1, 2, \cdots, m.$$

The result is a linear mapping with m by q matrix $C = (c_{ij})$, where $c_{ij} = \sum_{k=1}^{n} a_{ik}b_{kj}$. This result is the basis for the definition of the product AB of an m by n matrix A and an n by q matrix B. Then, when we write the given mappings in the form $x = Ay$ and $y = Bz$, the composite mapping $x = Cz$ can be written $x = ABz$. We will make these notions precise in the present section.

(3.1) Definition. If $A = (a_{ij})$ is an m by n matrix and $B = (b_{ij})$ is an n by q matrix, then their *product* AB is the m by q matrix $C = (c_{ij})$, where $c_{ij} = \sum_{k=1}^{n} a_{ik}b_{kj}$ for all pairs i,j.

Thus to obtain the element in the i,j position of the product AB, we multiply the n elements of the ith row of A into the n elements of the jth column of B, term by term, and add these products. This definition is called the "row-by-column rule" for multiplying matrices. In the expression $\sum_{k=1}^{n} a_{ik}b_{kj}$ for the typical element of the product, the integers i and j give the row and column position of the element, while k is only an index symbol which can be replaced by any other letter.

The matrix B is said to be *conformable* with respect to a matrix A if B has the same number of rows as A has columns. Thus, if B is an n by q matrix, and if A is an m by n matrix for any m, B is conformable with respect to A and the product AB exists. It should be emphasized that the product AB is defined only when B is conformable with respect to A (in that order!).

EXAMPLE 1. $A = \begin{pmatrix} 2 & 0 & i \\ 4 & 1 & 1/2 \end{pmatrix}$ and $B = \begin{pmatrix} 1/2 & 0 & 5 \\ 0 & 2 & 1 \\ -i & 3 & 1+i \end{pmatrix}$.
Since A is a 2 by 3 matrix and B is a 3 by 3 matrix, B is conformable with respect to A. However, A is not conformable with respect to B. Thus the product BA is not defined, while AB is defined, and is the 2 by 3 matrix

$$AB = \begin{pmatrix} 2 & 3i & 9+i \\ 2 - i/2 & 7/2 & 43/2 + i/2 \end{pmatrix}.$$

EXAMPLE 2. $A = \begin{pmatrix} 1 \\ 2 \\ 0 \end{pmatrix}$ and $B = (3 \quad 1 \quad 2)$. Then $AB = \begin{pmatrix} 3 & 1 & 2 \\ 6 & 2 & 4 \\ 0 & 0 & 0 \end{pmatrix}$
and $BA = (5)$. Since A is a 3 by 1 matrix and B a 1 by 3 matrix, both of the products AB and BA exist. But they are unequal since they do not have the same size.

If A and B are square matrices of order n, then both products AB and BA are defined and are square matrices of order n. These products are not necessarily equal, as the following example shows.

EXAMPLE 3. $A = \begin{pmatrix} 1 & 0 & 3 \\ 4 & 2 & 0 \\ 1 & 2 & 1 \end{pmatrix}$ and $B = \begin{pmatrix} 0 & 1 & 0 \\ 4 & 1 & 0 \\ 2 & 0 & 1 \end{pmatrix}$. Then

$$\begin{pmatrix} 6 & 1 & 3 \\ 8 & 6 & 0 \\ 10 & 3 & 1 \end{pmatrix} = AB \neq BA = \begin{pmatrix} 4 & 2 & 0 \\ 8 & 2 & 12 \\ 3 & 2 & 7 \end{pmatrix}.$$

But if $C = \begin{pmatrix} 3 & 0 & 0 \\ 0 & 3 & 0 \\ 0 & 0 & 3 \end{pmatrix}$ and $D = \begin{pmatrix} 2 & 1 & 2 \\ 1 & 0 & 3 \\ -1 & 2 & 1 \end{pmatrix}$, then

$$CD = DC = \begin{pmatrix} 6 & 3 & 6 \\ 3 & 0 & 9 \\ -3 & 6 & 3 \end{pmatrix}.$$

The complex numbers, which are the elements of our matrices, satisfy the commutative law of multiplication:

$$ab = ba;$$

the associative law of multiplication:

$$(ab)c = a(bc);$$

and the distributive law of multiplication with respect to addition:

$$a(b + c) = ab + ac.$$

We have seen in the above examples that matrix multiplication is not commutative, although a particular pair of matrices may commute, as in the last example. This means that this property of complex number multiplication is not carried over by Definition (3.1) to matrix multiplication. The other properties listed above do carry over, and much of the utility of Definition (3.1) depends upon the fact that matrix multiplication is associative.

(3.2) The Associative Law of Matrix Multiplication. If A, B, and C are m by n, n by p, and p by q matrices respectively, then $(AB)C = A(BC)$.

PROOF. By Definition (3.1), AB is an m by p matrix which is given by

$$AB = (a_{ij})(b_{ij}) = \Big(\sum_{k=1}^{n} a_{ik}b_{kj}\Big).$$

Since C is conformable with respect to the matrix AB, using (3.1) again, $(AB)C$ is an m by q matrix which is given by

$$(AB)C = \Big(\sum_{k=1}^{n} a_{ik}b_{kj}\Big)(c_{ij}) = \Big(\sum_{l=1}^{p}\Big[\sum_{k=1}^{n} a_{ik}b_{kl}\Big]c_{lj}\Big).$$

Thus the typical element of $(AB)C$ is the sum

$$\sum_{l=1}^{p}\Big[\sum_{k=1}^{n} a_{ik}b_{kl}\Big]c_{lj} = \sum_{k=1}^{n}\sum_{l=1}^{p}(a_{ik}b_{kl})c_{lj},$$

where the equality follows from the distributive law and the rules for addition which are satisfied by our elements.

Similarly we obtain

$$A(BC) = (a_{ij})\Big(\sum_{l=1}^{p} b_{il}c_{lj}\Big) = \Big(\sum_{k=1}^{n} a_{ik}\Big[\sum_{l=1}^{p} b_{kl}c_{lj}\Big]\Big),$$

where $A(BC)$ is an m by q matrix with typical element

$$\sum_{k=1}^{n} a_{ik}\left[\sum_{l=1}^{p} b_{kl}c_{lj}\right] = \sum_{k=1}^{n}\sum_{l=1}^{p} a_{ik}(b_{kl}c_{lj}).$$

Now since $(a_{ik}b_{kl})c_{lj} = a_{ik}(b_{kl}c_{lj})$ by the associative law of complex number multiplication, the typical elements of the m by q matrices $(AB)C$ and $A(BC)$ are equal. Therefore the matrices are equal by the definition of equality.

Thus we may use the single symbol ABC to stand for either product $(AB)C$ or $A(BC)$; and in general, the product $A_1A_2 \cdots A_s$ is defined for any pair-wise multiplication provided only that each matrix A_k is conformable with respect to A_{k-1} for $1 < k \leq s$.

Another property of the multiplication of constants which is not satisfied for matrix multiplication is the cancellation law:

$$\text{If } ab = ac \text{ and } a \neq 0, \text{ then } b = c.$$

For example, if $A = \begin{pmatrix} 0 & 0 & 0 \\ 0 & 0 & 0 \\ 1 & 1 & 1 \end{pmatrix}$, $B = \begin{pmatrix} 2 & 3 & 1 \\ 5 & 0 & 1 \\ -4 & 2 & 1 \end{pmatrix}$, and $C = \begin{pmatrix} 1 & 2 & 1 \\ 6 & 0 & 0 \\ -4 & 3 & 2 \end{pmatrix}$,

then $A \neq 0$ and $B \neq C$, but $AB = \begin{pmatrix} 0 & 0 & 0 \\ 0 & 0 & 0 \\ 3 & 5 & 3 \end{pmatrix} = AC$. And if $D = B - C = \begin{pmatrix} 1 & 1 & 0 \\ -1 & 0 & 1 \\ 0 & -1 & -1 \end{pmatrix}$, we find that $AD = O = \begin{pmatrix} 0 & 0 & 0 \\ 0 & 0 & 0 \\ 0 & 0 & 0 \end{pmatrix}$.

Thus the product of two non-zero matrices may be zero!

(3.3) Definition. The square matrix of order n defined by $I_n = (\delta_{ij})$ where* $\delta_{ii} = 1$ and $\delta_{ij} = 0$ for $i \neq j$ is called an *identity matrix of order n*.

The matrix I_n has ones on the principal diagonal and zeros elsewhere. By Definition (3.1)

$$AI_n = \left(\sum_{k=1}^{n} a_{ik}\delta_{kj}\right) = (a_{ij}) = A$$

and

$$I_nB = \left(\sum_{k=1}^{n} \delta_{ik}b_{kj}\right) = (b_{ij}) = B,$$

* The symbol δ_{ij} satisfying these relations is called the Kronecker delta.

when these products exist. Thus I_n is an identity with respect to matrix multiplication.

When the size of I_n is apparent from the context, we will simply write I.

Exercise (3.1). Find the x's in terms of the z's by direct substitution for the following pairs of linear mappings:

(a) $$\begin{aligned} x_1 &= y_1 \cos\theta - y_2 \sin\theta \\ x_2 &= y_1 \sin\theta + y_2 \cos\theta \end{aligned} \qquad \begin{aligned} y_1 &= z_1 \cos\phi - z_2 \sin\phi \\ y_2 &= z_1 \sin\phi + z_2 \cos\phi, \end{aligned}$$

(b) $$\begin{aligned} x_1 &= 3y_1 - 4y_2 \\ x_2 &= 2y_1 + y_2 \\ x_3 &= \quad\;\; - y_2 \\ x_4 &= y_1 \end{aligned} \qquad \begin{aligned} y_1 &= z_1 + 2z_2 + 3z_3 \\ y_2 &= 5z_1 \qquad\;\; - 6z_3. \end{aligned}$$

Also find the x's in terms of the z's by multiplying the matrices of the given mappings.

Exercise (3.2). Compute the product AB for the following matrices A and B:

(a) $$A = \begin{pmatrix} 2 & -1 & 0 & 3 \\ 4 & -5 & 0 & 0 \end{pmatrix}, \quad B = \begin{pmatrix} 0 & -3 \\ 1 & 2 \\ 6 & 1 \\ -5 & 0 \end{pmatrix};$$

(b) $$A = \begin{pmatrix} i & 3 & 1/2 \\ 0 & 1+i & 1 \\ 0 & 0 & 1 \end{pmatrix}, \quad B = \begin{pmatrix} i & 1-i \\ 1 & 4 \\ 0 & 1+i \end{pmatrix};$$

(c) $$A = (x \quad y \quad z), \quad B = \begin{pmatrix} x \\ y \\ z \end{pmatrix};$$

(d) $$A = \begin{pmatrix} 1 & 0 & 0 & 0 \\ 0 & 1 & 0 & 0 \\ 0 & 0 & 2 & -1 \\ 0 & 0 & 3 & 1 \end{pmatrix}, \quad B = \begin{pmatrix} 1 & 0 & 0 & 0 & 0 \\ 0 & 1 & 0 & 0 & 0 \\ 0 & 0 & 1/5 & 1/5 & 0 \\ 0 & 0 & -3/5 & 2/5 & 0 \end{pmatrix}.$$

Compute the product BA, when it exists, for the matrices given above.

Exercise (3.3). Given the matrices

$$A = \begin{pmatrix} 2 & 3 & 1 & -4 \\ 2 & 1 & 0 & 5 \end{pmatrix}, \quad B = \begin{pmatrix} 2 & 4 \\ 1 & -1 \\ 3 & -1 \end{pmatrix}, \text{ and } C = \begin{pmatrix} 2 & 1 & 3 \\ 4 & -1 & -2 \\ -1 & 0 & 1 \end{pmatrix},$$

compute all possible products of two of these matrices; of three of them. Compute the square of each where possible.

Exercise (3.4). Write out the products in both orders of a general 1 by n matrix by an n by 1 matrix.

Exercise (3.5). Show that the definition of matrix multiplication justifies the notation $x = Ay$ for a linear mapping with matrix A when we write

$$x = \begin{pmatrix} x_1 \\ x_2 \\ \cdot \\ \cdot \\ \cdot \\ x_m \end{pmatrix} \text{ and } y = \begin{pmatrix} y_1 \\ y_2 \\ \cdot \\ \cdot \\ \cdot \\ y_n \end{pmatrix}.$$

Write the mappings of Exercise (3.1) in product form.

Exercise (3.6). Prove that if necessary conformality conditions are satisfied, $AO = O$ for any A.

Exercise (3.7). Prove the distributive laws for the matrix operations

$$A(B + C) = AB + AC, \qquad (A + B)C = AC + BC,$$

discussing the necessary conformality conditions.

Exercise (3.8). Perform the indicated operations in two ways.

(a) $\begin{pmatrix} 2 & 1 \\ 0 & 2 \end{pmatrix} \left[\begin{pmatrix} 1 & 0 & -3 & 2 \\ 1 & 2 & 0 & 1 \end{pmatrix} - \begin{pmatrix} -3 & 0 & 1 & 4 \\ -1 & 2 & 0 & 3 \end{pmatrix} \right]$,

(b) $\begin{pmatrix} -3 & 4 & 0 \\ 7 & -10 & 1 \end{pmatrix} \begin{pmatrix} x \\ y \\ z \end{pmatrix} + \begin{pmatrix} 6 & -5 & 3 \\ 0 & 1 & 2 \end{pmatrix} \begin{pmatrix} x \\ y \\ z \end{pmatrix}$,

(c) $Ax + Ay + Az$, where

$$A = \begin{pmatrix} 1 & 0 & -3 \\ 0 & 1 & 6 \\ 0 & 0 & 5 \end{pmatrix}, \; x = \begin{pmatrix} x_1 \\ x_2 \\ x_3 \end{pmatrix}, \; y = \begin{pmatrix} y_1 \\ y_2 \\ y_3 \end{pmatrix}, \; z = \begin{pmatrix} z_1 \\ z_2 \\ z_3 \end{pmatrix}.$$

Exercise (3.9). Show that A^n is defined for every positive integer n if and only if A is square.

Exercise (3.10). If A is a square matrix, and m and n are positive integers, show that

$$A^m A^n = A^{m+n} \text{ and } (A^m)^n = A^{mn}.$$

Show by example that the third law of exponents $(AB)^n = A^n B^n$ is not always satisfied.

Exercise (3.11). If we define a "product" $AB = (a_{ij})(b_{ij}) = (a_{ij}b_{ij})$, what is the definition of conformality? Is this operation associative? Commutative? Does the cancellation law hold? Similarly discuss the "row-by-row product" $AB = \left(\sum_{k=1}^{n} a_{ik}b_{jk}\right)$.

Section 4. Scalar Multiplication

The elements of the set S from which we form our matrices are sometimes called *scalars*. In this discussion, where S is the set of all complex numbers, scalar and complex number mean the same thing. Let a be any scalar and $A = (a_{ij})$ any m by n matrix.

(4.1) Definition. The left and right *scalar products* of the scalar a and the matrix A are given by $aA = (aa_{ij})$ and $Aa = (a_{ij}a)$.

The matrices aA and Aa are m by n matrices obtained from A by multiplying each element of A by the scalar a. Since the multiplication of scalars is commutative, $aA = Aa$, and scalar multiplication is commutative.

(4.2) Definition. The matrix aI_n is called a *scalar matrix* of order n.

The typical element of a scalar matrix has the form $a\delta_{ij}$ where δ_{ij} is the Kronecker delta defined in the previous section. Since

$$aA = (aa_{ij}) = \left(\sum_{k=1}^{m} a\delta_{ik}a_{kj}\right) = (a\delta_{ij})(a_{ij}) = (aI_m)A,$$

and similarly $Aa = A(aI_n)$, scalar multiplication may be treated as a special case of matrix multiplication where one term of the product is a scalar matrix. If A is m by n, aA may be obtained by premultiplication by a scalar matrix of order m, and Aa by postmultiplication by a scalar matrix of order n.

By the associative law for matrix multiplication, we have for an m by n matrix A, an n by q matrix B, and scalars a and b:

(4.3)
$$a(AB) = (aA)B = A(aB)$$
$$abA = a(bA) = b(aA).$$

For m by n matrices A and B and scalars a and b, the distributive laws for the matrix operations yield:

(4.4)
$$a(A + B) = aA + aB$$
$$(a + b)A = aA + bA.$$

Alternately, the identities (4.3) and (4.4) may be proved directly from Definition (4.1).

EXAMPLE.

$$\left[4\begin{pmatrix}1 & 0 & 2\\ 3 & -2 & 1\end{pmatrix} - 5\begin{pmatrix}2 & 1 & -6\\ 1 & 3 & 0\end{pmatrix}\right]\left[2\begin{pmatrix}1 & 0 & 0\\ 2 & -3 & 1\\ 0 & 4 & 3\end{pmatrix}\right]$$

$$= \left[\begin{pmatrix}4 & 0 & 8\\ 12 & -8 & 4\end{pmatrix} - \begin{pmatrix}10 & 5 & -30\\ 5 & 15 & 0\end{pmatrix}\right]\begin{pmatrix}2 & 0 & 0\\ 4 & -6 & 2\\ 0 & 8 & 6\end{pmatrix}$$

$$= \begin{pmatrix}-6 & -5 & 38\\ 7 & -23 & 4\end{pmatrix}\begin{pmatrix}2 & 0 & 0\\ 4 & -6 & 2\\ 0 & 8 & 6\end{pmatrix} = \begin{pmatrix}-32 & 334 & 218\\ -78 & 170 & -22\end{pmatrix}.$$

Exercise (4.1). Evaluate the following expressions:

(a) $3\begin{pmatrix}4 & 2\\ 1 & -1\\ 5 & 2\end{pmatrix} - 5\begin{pmatrix}2 & 4 & 4\\ 7 & 0 & -4\\ 2 & -1 & 2\end{pmatrix}\begin{pmatrix}2 & 0\\ 0 & 4\\ 1 & 0\end{pmatrix},$

(b) $\left[-3\begin{pmatrix}5 & 2 & 3 & 4\\ 2 & 4 & -1 & 0\\ 6 & 1 & 1 & 2\end{pmatrix} + 2\begin{pmatrix}2 & 0 & 1 & 1\\ 1 & 2 & 0 & -2\\ 0 & 1 & 2 & 2\end{pmatrix}\right]\begin{pmatrix}3\\ 1\\ 5\\ 2\end{pmatrix}.$

Exercise (4.2). Prove the identities (4.3) and (4.4) directly from Definition (4.1).

Exercise (4.3). Prove that $aA = O$ if and only if $a = 0$ or $A = O$.

Exercise (4.4). Show that $A + A + \cdots + A$, with n summands, is the scalar product nA.

Exercise (4.5). Show that $(aI_n)(bI_n) = abI_n$ and $aI_n + bI_n = (a + b)I_n$.

Section 5. Special Matrices. Transposition

It was mentioned in Section 1 that the elements a_{ii} of an m by n matrix A are called principal diagonal elements. If $a_{ij} = 0$ for $i \neq j$, then A is called a *diagonal matrix*. Scalar matrices are square diagonal matrices with equal diagonal elements. A matrix operation which is performed on a single matrix and which may be thought of as a reflection of its elements through the principal diagonal is the operation of *transposition*.

(5.1) Definition. If $A = (a_{ij})$ is an m by n matrix, then A', the *transpose* of A, is the matrix $B = (b_{ij})$ with $b_{ij} = a_{ji}$ for $i = 1, 2, \cdots, n$; $j = 1, 2, \cdots, m$.

Thus A' is an n by m matrix which has as its ith row the ith column of A, and as its jth column the jth row of A. The principal diagonal elements are unchanged by transposition.

EXAMPLE. If $A = \begin{pmatrix} 2 & i \\ \sqrt{5} & -3 \\ 0 & 1 \\ 1/2 & 9 \end{pmatrix}$, then $A' = \begin{pmatrix} 2 & \sqrt{5} & 0 & 1/2 \\ i & -3 & 1 & 9 \end{pmatrix}$.

The principal diagonal elements of both A and A' are $2, -3$.

(5.2) Theorem. If B is conformable with respect to A, then A' is conformable with respect to B' and $(AB)' = B'A'$.

PROOF. Let $A = (a_{ij})$ be an m by n matrix and $B = (b_{ij})$ be an n by p matrix. Then B' is p by n and A' is n by m, so that $B'A'$ is defined and is a p by m matrix. Since AB is an m by p matrix, $(AB)'$ is also a p by m matrix. The typical element of $(AB)'$, that is, the element in the i,j position, is $\sum_{k=1}^{n} a_{jk}b_{ki}$, which is the element in the j,i position of AB. And if $B' = (c_{ij})$ and $A' = (d_{ij})$, then $B'A' = \left(\sum_{k=1}^{n} c_{ik}d_{kj}\right)$. But $c_{ij} = b_{ji}$ and $d_{ij} = a_{ji}$ for all pairs i,j, so that the typical element of $B'A'$ is $\sum_{k=1}^{n} c_{ik}d_{kj} = \sum_{k=1}^{n} b_{ki}a_{jk} = \sum_{k=1}^{n} a_{jk}b_{ki}$.

(5.3) Definition. A matrix A is *symmetric* if $A' = A$.

A symmetric matrix is unaltered by transposition, and $a_{ij} = a_{ji}$ for all pairs i,j. Such a matrix is necessarily square. Since the principal diagonal elements are unchanged by transposition, any square diagonal matrix is symmetric.

A matrix with a single row, that is, a 1 by n matrix, is called a *row matrix*. Similarly, an m by 1 matrix is called a *column matrix*. The transpose of a row matrix is a column matrix, and conversely. Any m by n matrix $A = (a_{ij})$ may be thought of as an m by 1 column matrix with elements which are 1 by n row matrices. If we denote the ith row of A by R_i, we may write

$$A = \begin{pmatrix} R_1 \\ R_2 \\ \cdot \\ \cdot \\ \cdot \\ R_m \end{pmatrix} \quad \text{where } R_i = (a_{i1} \quad a_{i2} \quad \cdots \quad a_{in}).$$

In the same way, if we denote the jth column of A by C_j, we may write

$$A = (C_1 \quad C_2 \quad \cdots \quad C_n) \text{ where } C_j = \begin{pmatrix} a_{1j} \\ a_{2j} \\ \cdot \\ \cdot \\ \cdot \\ a_{mj} \end{pmatrix}.$$

Exercise (5.1). What is the typical element of the product AB, where $A = (a_{ij})$ is any m by n matrix and $B = (b_i\delta_{ij})$ is an n by p diagonal matrix?

Exercise (5.2). Compute AB, $(AB)'$, and $B'A'$ if

$$A = \begin{pmatrix} 4 & 3 & 5 \\ 0 & 1 & 2 \end{pmatrix} \quad \text{and} \quad B = \begin{pmatrix} 3 & 2 & -1 & 2 \\ 1 & 4 & 0 & -2 \\ 6 & 2 & 1 & 3 \end{pmatrix}.$$

Exercise (5.3). Compute in two ways the transpose of ABC if

$$A = \begin{pmatrix} -2 & 3 & 1 \\ 0 & 4 & 2 \end{pmatrix}, B = \begin{pmatrix} 4 & 1 \\ 2 & 5 \\ 3 & 4 \end{pmatrix}, C = \begin{pmatrix} 2 & -1 \\ 4 & 2 \end{pmatrix}.$$

Exercise (5.4). Prove that $(A')' = A$, and that $(aA + bB)' = aA' + bB'$ if A and B are the same size.

Exercise (5.5). Prove that AA' and $A'A$ are both defined and are symmetric matrices.

Exercise (5.6). Prove that if A is square, $A + A'$ is symmetric.

Exercise (5.7). A matrix A is *skew-symmetric* if $-A' = A$. Show that a skew-symmetric matrix is square and that its diagonal elements are zero. Show that if A is square, $A - A'$ is skew-symmetric.

Exercise (5.8). Show that every square matrix can be written as a sum of a symmetric matrix and a skew-symmetric matrix.

Exercise (5.9). Give the formula for the coordinates of the mid-point of a line segment in 3-dimensional space as a matrix identity.

Section 6. Submatrices and Partitioning

A matrix obtained from a given m by n matrix A by deleting any number of rows and any number of columns of A is called a *submatrix* of A. For example if

$$A = \begin{pmatrix} 2 & 4 & -1 & -6 & 3 \\ -1 & 5 & 0 & 2 & 1 \\ 6 & -6 & 10 & 11 & 3 \\ 1 & 2 & 1 & 0 & 5 \end{pmatrix},$$

then $B = \begin{pmatrix} 2 & 4 & -6 \\ 1 & 2 & 0 \end{pmatrix}$ is obtained by deleting the second and third rows and the third and fifth columns of A, while

$$C = \begin{pmatrix} 2 & 4 & -1 & -6 & 3 \\ 6 & -6 & 10 & 11 & 3 \end{pmatrix}$$

is obtained by deleting the second and fourth rows of A.

Each row of A is a 1 by n submatrix obtained by deleting the remaining rows and no columns. Similarly each column is an m by 1 submatrix. An element of A may be thought of as a 1 by 1 submatrix.

If B is an r by s submatrix of the m by n matrix A where $r < m$ and $s < n$, then the submatrix of A obtained by deleting the rows and columns of A which appear in B is called the *complementary submatrix of B in A*. This complementary submatrix is an $(m - r)$ by $(n - s)$ matrix. In the example above, $\begin{pmatrix} 0 & 1 \\ 10 & 3 \end{pmatrix}$ is the complement of B in A. Since C is formed by deleting rows only, C does not have a complement in A. Clearly if B_1 is the complement of B_2 in A, then B_2 is the complement of B_1 in A, so that we may say that B_1 and B_2 are complements in A.

We have already noticed that A can be thought of as a column matrix with elements which are 1 by n submatrices. This is a special case of a more general procedure called *partitioning*, in which we write an m by n matrix $A = (a_{ij})$ as an r by s matrix $A = (A_{ij})$. Each A_{ij} is an m_i by n_j submatrix of A, formed by deleting all but m_i consecutive rows and n_j consecutive columns of A, where $\sum_{i=1}^{r} m_i = m$ and $\sum_{j=1}^{s} n_j = n$. For a fixed i, all A_{ij} for $j = 1, 2, \cdots, s$ are formed from the same m_i rows. For a fixed j, all A_{ij} for $i = 1, 2, \cdots, r$ are formed from the same n_j columns. For example, the submatrices A_{11}, A_{12},

$\cdots$, A_{1s} are formed from the first m_1 rows of A, the submatrices $A_{21}, A_{22}, \cdots, A_{2s}$ are formed from the next m_2 rows, and so forth.

A partition of A is indicated by drawing lines between certain rows and certain columns of A and naming the resulting blocks A_{ij} in proper order.

EXAMPLE 1. $A = \left(\begin{array}{rr|rr|r} 5 & 0 & -2 & 3 & 6 \\ \hline -1 & 2 & 0 & 4 & -10 \\ 7 & 1 & 2 & -6 & 1 \end{array}\right) = \begin{pmatrix} A_{11} & A_{12} & A_{13} \\ A_{21} & A_{22} & A_{23} \end{pmatrix},$

where the submatrices of this partition of A are $A_{11} = (5\ 0)$, $A_{12} = (-2\ 3)$, $A_{13} = (6)$, $A_{21} = \begin{pmatrix} -1 & 2 \\ 7 & 1 \end{pmatrix}$, $A_{22} = \begin{pmatrix} 0 & 4 \\ 2 & -6 \end{pmatrix}$, and $A_{23} = \begin{pmatrix} -10 \\ 1 \end{pmatrix}$.

EXAMPLE 2. $A = \begin{pmatrix} 3 & 0 & 6 \\ -1 & 2 & 1 \\ 2 & 1 & -1 \end{pmatrix}$ may be partitioned into four blocks in (only) the following ways:

$$\left(\begin{array}{r|rr} 3 & 0 & 6 \\ \hline -1 & 2 & 1 \\ 2 & 1 & -1 \end{array}\right), \left(\begin{array}{rr|r} 3 & 0 & 6 \\ \hline -1 & 2 & 1 \\ 2 & 1 & -1 \end{array}\right), \left(\begin{array}{r|rr} 3 & 0 & 6 \\ -1 & 2 & 1 \\ \hline 2 & 1 & -1 \end{array}\right), \text{ and } \left(\begin{array}{rr|r} 3 & 0 & 6 \\ -1 & 2 & 1 \\ \hline 2 & 1 & -1 \end{array}\right).$$

Let A be an arbitrarily partitioned m by n matrix. If B is an m by n matrix partitioned in the same way, we say that A and B are *similarly partitioned.*

(6.1) Theorem. If A and B are similarly partitioned m by n matrices, then the sum $A + B$ may be obtained by adding the correspondingly placed submatrices of A and B.

PROOF. If A and B are similarly partitioned, $A = (A_{pq})$ and $B = (B_{pq})$ where A_{pq} and B_{pq} are correspondingly placed m_p by n_q submatrices of A and B. The sum $A_{pq} + B_{pq} = C_{pq}$ exists and is an m_p by n_q matrix for all pairs p, q. Therefore $C = (C_{pq})$ is an m by n matrix, partitioned similarly to A and B. Considering C in terms of its elements, any element c_{ij} will be in the e,f position of some submatrix C_{pq}. Thus c_{ij} is the sum of the element in position e, f of A_{pq} and the element in position e,f of B_{pq}. But these elements must be the elements a_{ij} and b_{ij} of A and B, since A, B, and C are similarly partitioned. We have $c_{ij} = a_{ij} + b_{ij}$ for all pairs i,j, so that $C = A + B$.

EXAMPLE 3. If

$$A = \left(\begin{array}{ccc|cc} 1 & 0 & 0 & 2 & -3 \\ 0 & 1 & 0 & 1 & 6 \\ 0 & 0 & 1 & 5 & -1 \\ \hline 9 & -5 & 6 & 0 & 0 \\ 2 & 0 & 1 & 0 & 0 \end{array}\right) \text{ and } B = \left(\begin{array}{ccc|cc} 1 & 0 & 0 & -2 & 3 \\ 0 & 1 & 0 & -1 & -6 \\ 0 & 0 & 1 & -5 & 1 \\ \hline 4 & -2 & 1 & 0 & 0 \\ 6 & 3 & -2 & 0 & 0 \end{array}\right),$$

then $A = \begin{pmatrix} I_3 & A_{12} \\ A_{21} & O \end{pmatrix}$ and $B = \begin{pmatrix} I_3 & B_{12} \\ B_{21} & O \end{pmatrix}$ are similarly partitioned so that

$$A + B = \left(\begin{array}{c|c} I_3 + I_3 & A_{12} + B_{12} \\ \hline A_{21} + B_{21} & O + O \end{array}\right) = \left(\begin{array}{ccc|c} & 2I_3 & & O \\ \hline 13 & -7 & 7 & \\ 8 & 3 & -1 & O \end{array}\right)$$

$$= \left(\begin{array}{ccc|cc} 2 & 0 & 0 & 0 & 0 \\ 0 & 2 & 0 & 0 & 0 \\ 0 & 0 & 2 & 0 & 0 \\ \hline 13 & -7 & 7 & 0 & 0 \\ 8 & 3 & -1 & 0 & 0 \end{array}\right).$$

Let $A = (A_{ij})$ be an m by n matrix arbitrarily partitioned into m_i by n_j submatrices A_{ij}. Let B be a matrix conformable with respect to A, say n by q. If $B = (B_{jk})$ is a partition of B into p_j by q_k submatrices B_{jk} such that $n_j = p_j$ for all j, we say that B is *conformably partitioned with respect to A*. Thus the partition of the columns of A must be the same as the partition of the rows of B, but there is no restriction on the partition of the rows of A or the columns of B.

EXAMPLE 4. Let $A = \left(\begin{array}{c|cc} 2 & -3 & 5 \\ \hline 4 & 1 & 6 \\ 0 & -2 & 3 \\ \hline 2 & 1 & -3 \end{array}\right)$ and

$$B = \left(\begin{array}{ccc|cc} 2 & -6 & -1 & 6 & 2 \\ \hline 0 & 2 & 17 & -1 & 0 \\ 1 & 0 & 2 & 7 & 3 \end{array}\right).$$

Since A is 4 by 3 and B is 3 by 5, B is conformable with respect to A. The columns of A have been partitioned between columns 1 and 2, and the rows of B have been partitioned between rows 1 and 2, so that B is conformably partitioned with respect to A.

Writing A and B in partitioned form, $A = \begin{pmatrix} A_{11} & A_{12} \\ A_{21} & A_{22} \\ A_{31} & A_{32} \end{pmatrix}$ and

$B = \begin{pmatrix} B_{11} & B_{12} \\ B_{21} & B_{22} \end{pmatrix}$ are now 3 by 2 and 2 by 2 matrices with elements which are submatrices A_{ij} and B_{jk} respectively. If we multiply A and B formally, using the row-by-column rule, we obtain an indicated product

$$C = \begin{pmatrix} A_{11}B_{11} + A_{12}B_{21} & A_{11}B_{12} + A_{12}B_{22} \\ A_{21}B_{11} + A_{22}B_{21} & A_{21}B_{12} + A_{22}B_{22} \\ A_{31}B_{11} + A_{32}B_{21} & A_{31}B_{12} + A_{32}B_{22} \end{pmatrix}.$$

It follows from the fact that B is conformably partitioned with respect to A that all the indicated matrix operations are possible, and that we obtain a partitioned 4 by 5 matrix. For example, A_{21} is 2 by 1 and B_{11} is 1 by 3 so that $A_{21}B_{11}$ is a 2 by 3 matrix. Similarly $A_{22}B_{21}$ is a 2 by 3 matrix so that the sum $A_{21}B_{11} + A_{22}B_{21}$ exists and is a 2 by 3 matrix.

If we complete the calculations of this example, we find that C is exactly the ordinary matrix product AB. This is an example of the following theorem.

(6.2) Theorem. If A is an arbitrarily partitioned m by n matrix, and if B is an n by q matrix, conformably partitioned with respect to A, then the product AB may be obtained by applying the row-by-column rule to the submatrices of A and B.

PROOF. Let $A = (A_{rs})$ where A_{rs} is an m_r by n_s submatrix. Then since B is conformably partitioned with respect to A, $B = (B_{st})$ where B_{st} is an n_s by q_t submatrix. Let the range of values for s be $1, 2, \cdots, u$. Then for every s, the product $A_{rs}B_{st}$ exists and is an m_r by q_t matrix. Thus the sum $C_{rt} = \sum_{s=1}^{u} A_{rs}B_{st}$ exists for every r and t and is an m_r by q_t matrix. Since for a fixed r all the C_{rt} have m_r rows, and for a fixed t all the C_{rt} have q_t columns, $C = (C_{rt})$ is an m by q matrix in partitioned form. Notice that the partition of the rows of C is the same as that of the rows of A, and that the partition of the columns of C is the same as that of the columns of B.

In terms of the original elements, any element c_{ij} of C is in position e,f of some submatrix $C_{rt} = \sum_{s=1}^{u} A_{rs}B_{st}$. Therefore it is the sum of the elements in position e,f of the products $A_{rs}B_{st}$. The element in position e,f of $A_{rs}B_{st}$ is the sum of the products of the elements in row e of A_{rs} by the elements of column f of B_{st}. But from the fact that the partition of the rows of A is the same as that of the rows of C, the elements of row e of the submatrices A_{rs}, as s takes on the values 1, 2, $\cdots$, u, are the elements a_{ij} of row i of A. Similarly the elements of column f of the B_{st} are the elements b_{ij} of column j of B. Therefore

$$c_{ij} = \sum_{k=1}^{n_1} a_{ik}b_{kj} + \sum_{k=n_1+1}^{n_1+n_2} a_{ik}b_{kj} + \cdots + \sum_{k=n-n_u+1}^{n} a_{ik}b_{kj}$$

$$= \sum_{k=1}^{n} a_{ik}b_{kj}, \text{ and } C = AB \text{ by (3.1).}$$

Exercise (6.1). Compute directly, and by Theorem (6.2), the product AB of the partitioned matrices

$$A = \left(\begin{array}{cc|c|c} 0 & 1 & 0 & 2 \\ 1 & -1 & 0 & 5 \\ \hline 3 & 0 & 1 & 0 \end{array}\right) \text{ and } B = \left(\begin{array}{cc|cc|c} 0 & -1 & 3 & 2 & 0 \\ 0 & 0 & 0 & 4 & 2 \\ \hline 1 & 0 & 1 & 1 & 0 \\ \hline 0 & 0 & 0 & 5 & 0 \end{array}\right).$$

Exercise (6.2). Partition conveniently, and find the product AB for the following pairs of matrices:

(a) $A = \begin{pmatrix} 3 & 0 & 0 & 0 \\ 0 & 3 & 0 & 0 \\ 1 & 1 & 1 & 1 \\ 0 & 1 & 1 & 1 \\ 0 & 0 & 1 & 1 \end{pmatrix}, \quad B = \begin{pmatrix} 3 & 2 & 1 & 0 & 0 & 6 \\ 5 & 3 & 0 & 1 & 0 & 2 \\ 3 & 0 & 0 & 0 & 0 & 4 \\ 0 & 0 & 0 & 0 & 0 & 5 \end{pmatrix};$

(b) $A = \begin{pmatrix} 2 & -1 & 4 & 0 & 7 \\ 6 & 0 & -3 & 0 & -1 \\ 1 & 2 & -1 & 2 & 0 \\ -2 & 0 & 0 & -1 & -1 \\ 0 & 0 & -2 & -2 & 3 \end{pmatrix},$

$B = \begin{pmatrix} 3 & 0 & 0 & 0 & 0 \\ 0 & 3 & 0 & 0 & 0 \\ 0 & 0 & 3 & 0 & 0 \\ 1 & 0 & 0 & -1 & 0 \\ 0 & 1 & 0 & 0 & -1 \end{pmatrix};$

(c) $A = \begin{pmatrix} 1 & 0 & 0 & 0 & 0 \\ 0 & 1 & 0 & 0 & 0 \\ 0 & 0 & 1 & 0 & 0 \\ 0 & 0 & 0 & 5 & 4 \\ 0 & 0 & 0 & 1 & 3 \end{pmatrix},$

$$B = \begin{pmatrix} 2 & 1 & 1 & 5 & 6 & -2 \\ -1 & 2 & 3 & -1 & 4 & -2 \\ 3 & 4 & 5 & 2 & 0 & -2 \\ -6 & 8 & 1 & 1 & 0 & 3 \\ 2 & 3 & 1 & 0 & 1 & 3 \end{pmatrix}.$$

Exercise (6.3). A square matrix is symmetrically partitioned if the submatrices on the diagonal are square. Show that if A and B are similarly partitioned square matrices of order n, and if A is symmetrically partitioned, then B is conformably partitioned with respect to A.

Exercise (6.4). Show that if $A = (A_{ij})$ is a partition of A, then $A' = (B_{ij})$, where $B_{ij} = A_{ji}'$, is a partition of A'.

Exercise (6.5). Show that any m by n matrix A with $m \neq n$ may be partitioned into two blocks such that A_{11} is square. Discuss A' in the cases which arise. This exercise clarifies the characterization of transposition as a reflection through the principal diagonal.

Exercise (6.6). If $\sum_{i=1}^{p-1} m_i = M$ and $\sum_{j=1}^{q-1} n_j = N$ with $p - 1 < r$ and $q - 1 < s$ in a partition of A as an r by s matrix (A_{ij}), write out explicitly the submatrix A_{pq} of the partition.

Exercise (6.7). A relationship R between two objects a and b, indicated as aRb and read "a has relation R to b," is called *symmetric* if aRb implies bRa. Examine each of the following relationships for symmetry.

(a) a is the brother of b, where a and b are males.
(b) a is the brother of b, where a and b are people.
(c) matrix A is equal to matrix B.
(d) A_1 is the complementary submatrix of A_2 in A.
(e) matrix A is the transpose of matrix B.
(f) matrix A is conformable with respect to matrix B.
(g) matrix A is similarly partitioned to matrix B.
(h) matrix A is conformably partitioned with respect to matrix B.

Section 7. Square Matrices

For any positive integer n let $\mathfrak{A}_n$ be the set of all square matrices of order n with complex number elements. Then for every pair of matrices in $\mathfrak{A}_n$, the restrictions of equal size for addition and conformality for multiplication are satisfied. Therefore the matrix operations of addition and multiplication are defined for every pair of matrices A, B in $\mathfrak{A}_n$, and furthermore the matrices $C = A + B = B + A$, $D = AB$, and $E = BA$ are in $\mathfrak{A}_n$. We express these facts by saying that $\mathfrak{A}_n$ is *closed* with respect to matrix addition and multiplication.

In the same way, $\mathfrak{A}_n$ is closed with respect to the matrix operations of scalar multiplication and transposition, since if A is in $\mathfrak{A}_n$, then aA and A' are in $\mathfrak{A}_n$.

Exercise (7.1). Show that for A in $\mathfrak{A}_n$, the equations $A + X = A$ and $AX = A$ have solutions in $\mathfrak{A}_n$.

Exercise (7.2). Prove that $\mathfrak{A}_n$ is closed with respect to subtraction.

Exercise (7.3). Denote the set of all m by n matrices by ${}_m\mathfrak{A}_n$. With respect to which matrix operations is ${}_m\mathfrak{A}_n$ closed?

Section 8. Determinants of Order n

In the following sections we will restrict our attention to square matrices of order n. It has been emphasized in Section 1, that the definition of a matrix does not assign a value to the matrix, although this can be done in many ways (for example, the sum of the elements of A, the product of the diagonal elements of A). We now define a function of the elements of A, called the determinant of A, which had its origin in the solution of systems of linear equations.

The reader is familiar with determinants of order 2, which enter into the solution of the system of equations

$$\begin{aligned} a_{11}x + a_{12}y &= b_1 \\ a_{21}x + a_{22}y &= b_2. \end{aligned}$$

Successive elimination of the unknowns y and x in this system yields the simpler system

$$\begin{aligned} (a_{11}a_{22} - a_{12}a_{21})x &= b_1a_{22} - a_{12}b_2 \\ (a_{11}a_{22} - a_{12}a_{21})y &= a_{11}b_2 - b_1a_{21}. \end{aligned}$$

The function of the elements of the 2 by 2 matrices,

$$\begin{pmatrix} a_{11} & a_{12} \\ a_{21} & a_{22} \end{pmatrix}, \begin{pmatrix} b_1 & a_{12} \\ b_2 & a_{22} \end{pmatrix}, \text{ and } \begin{pmatrix} a_{11} & b_1 \\ a_{21} & b_2 \end{pmatrix},$$

which appears in these latter equations is called a determinant of order 2. It is clear that the values of these determinants determine the nature of the solution.

Similarly, the elimination of the unknowns y and z from the system

$$\begin{aligned} a_{11}x + a_{12}y + a_{13}z &= b_1 \\ a_{21}x + a_{22}y + a_{23}z &= b_2 \\ a_{31}x + a_{32}y + a_{33}z &= b_3, \end{aligned}$$

yields the equation

$$\begin{aligned} &(a_{11}a_{22}a_{33} + a_{12}a_{23}a_{31} + a_{13}a_{21}a_{32} - a_{13}a_{22}a_{31} - a_{12}a_{21}a_{33} - a_{11}a_{23}a_{32})x \\ &\quad = (b_1a_{22}a_{33} + a_{12}a_{23}b_3 + a_{13}b_2a_{32} - a_{13}a_{22}b_3 - a_{12}b_2a_{33} - b_1a_{23}a_{32}). \end{aligned}$$

The function of the elements of the 3 by 3 matrices

$$\begin{pmatrix} a_{11} & a_{12} & a_{13} \\ a_{21} & a_{22} & a_{23} \\ a_{31} & a_{32} & a_{33} \end{pmatrix} \text{ and } \begin{pmatrix} b_1 & a_{12} & a_{13} \\ b_2 & a_{22} & a_{23} \\ b_3 & a_{32} & a_{33} \end{pmatrix}$$

which appear in this equation is called a determinant of order 3.

As in the above examples, the solution of a system of m linear equations in n unknowns involves a certain function of the elements of square submatrices of the matrix of the system. We shall give a general definition of this function, the determinant of a square matrix of order n, and see that it is the function of the above examples in the cases $n = 2$ and $n = 3$. The concept of the determinant of a square matrix has important applications, not only in the solution of systems on linear equations, but in virtually all branches of mathematics.

(8.1) Definition. The *determinant* of a square matrix $A = (a_{ij})$ of order n is the number

$$|A| = \sum_{\text{col}} (-1)^j a_{1j_1}a_{2j_2} \cdots a_{nj_n},$$

where the symbol* $\sum_{\text{col}}$ indicates the sum of all terms of the form $(-1)^j a_{1j_1}a_{2j_2} \cdots a_{nj_n}$ for all possible orderings $j_1, j_2, \cdots, j_n$ of the column subscripts $1, 2, \cdots, n$, and the integer j is the number of interchanges of two digits required to carry the ordering $j_1, j_2, \cdots, j_n$ of a given term into the natural ordering $1, 2, \cdots, n$.

The determinant of $A = (a_{ij})$ is denoted variously by the symbols

$$|A|, \ |a_{ij}|, \text{ and } \begin{vmatrix} a_{11} & \cdots & a_{1n} \\ \cdot & & \cdot \\ \cdot & & \cdot \\ \cdot & & \cdot \\ a_{n1} & \cdots & a_{nn} \end{vmatrix}.$$

* The symbol $\sum_{\text{col}}$ is read "the sum over the column subscripts."

When we analyze Definition (8.1), we find that $|A|$ is a sum of signed products of n elements of A, one from each row and each column, since the row subscripts of the elements in any product are 1, 2, $\cdots$, n, and the column subscripts $j_1, j_2, \cdots, j_n$ are these same numbers in some order. Every product of n elements of A with one element from each row and each column can be written in the form $a_{1j_1}a_{2j_2} \cdots a_{nj_n}$ where $j_1, j_2, \cdots, j_n$ is some ordering of $1, 2, \cdots, n$. Since the sum is taken over all orderings of the column subscripts, $|A|$ is a sum of *all* products of n elements, one from each row and each column, with a certain sign affixed to each product. There are $n!$ orderings of the numbers $1, 2, \cdots, n$ and hence $n!$ terms in the sum.

In order to prove that $|A|$ is a uniquely defined function of the elements a_{ij} of A, we must show that the sign $(-1)^j$ which is affixed to each term of the sum is uniquely determined. The integer j is not unique, for there is more than one way to carry a given ordering $j_1, j_2, \cdots, j_n$ into the natural ordering $1, 2, \cdots, n$ by successively interchanging two digits of the ordering $j_1, j_2, \cdots, j_n$. For example, the ordering 3 2 1 5 4 may be carried into 1 2 3 4 5 in the following ways:

By two interchanges, $3\,2\,1\,5\,4 \rightarrow 1\,2\,3\,5\,4 \rightarrow 1\,2\,3\,4\,5$.
By four interchanges, $3\,2\,1\,5\,4 \rightarrow 2\,3\,1\,5\,4 \rightarrow 2\,1\,3\,5\,4 \rightarrow$
$1\,2\,3\,5\,4 \rightarrow 1\,2\,3\,4\,5$.

We now show that the sign $(-1)^j$ of any given term is uniquely determined, by showing that for a given term, j is always even or always odd.

(8.2) Lemma. Any interchange of two digits in the ordering $j_1, j_2, \cdots, j_n$ may be accomplished by an odd number of interchanges of adjacent digits.

PROOF. Let $j_1, j_2, \cdots, j_r, \cdots, j_s, \cdots, j_n$ be the given ordering where there are m digits between j_r and j_s. We obtain the ordering $j_1, j_2, \cdots, j_{r-1}, j_{r+1}, \cdots, j_s, j_r, \cdots, j_n$ by $m + 1$ interchanges of adjacent digits. We then obtain the ordering $j_1, j_2, \cdots, j_{r-1}, j_s, j_{r+1}, \cdots, j_r, \cdots, j_n$ by m additional adjacent interchanges. Thus we have interchanged j_r and j_s in the ordering by $(m + 1) + m = 2m + 1$ adjacent interchanges.

(8.3) Theorem. The number of interchanges carrying $j_1, j_2, \cdots, j_n$ into $1, 2, \cdots, n$ is always even or always odd.

PROOF. Assume that the theorem is false. This means that it is possible to carry a given ordering $j_1, j_2, \cdots, j_n$ into $1, 2, \cdots, n$ by an odd number of interchanges as well as by an even number of interchanges. By Lemma (8.2), these two sequences of interchanges may be replaced respectively by an odd number and an even number of adjacent interchanges. Therefore our assumptions lead to the following conclusions:

(1) $j_1, j_2, \cdots, j_n \to 1, 2, \cdots, n$ by an odd number, $2r + 1$, of adjacent interchanges.
(2) $j_1, j_2, \cdots, j_n \to 1, 2, \cdots, n$ by an even number, $2s$, of adjacent interchanges.

Applying the interchanges in (2) in reverse order,

(3) $1, 2, \cdots, n \to j_1, j_2, \cdots, j_n$ by $2s$ adjacent interchanges.

Combining (1) and (3),

(4) $j_1, j_2, \cdots, j_n \to 1, 2, \cdots, n \to j_1, j_2, \cdots, j_n$ by $2r + 1 + 2s$ adjacent interchanges.

Thus the ordering $j_1, j_2, \cdots, j_n$ is carried into itself by an odd number of adjacent interchanges. But for every interchange of adjacent digits j_k and j_{k+1}, there must be a subsequent interchange of j_{k+1} and j_k if the original ordering is to be finally obtained. Hence every interchange must be paired with a like interchange. Since there is an odd number of interchanges, this is impossible, and the assumption that the theorem is false has led to a contradiction.

EXAMPLES:

$$\begin{vmatrix} a_{11} & a_{12} \\ a_{21} & a_{22} \end{vmatrix} = \sum\nolimits_{\text{col}} (-1)^j a_{1j_1} a_{2j_2} = (-1)^0 a_{11}a_{22} + (-1)^1 a_{12}a_{21}.$$

$$\begin{vmatrix} a_{11} & a_{12} & a_{13} \\ a_{21} & a_{22} & a_{23} \\ a_{31} & a_{32} & a_{33} \end{vmatrix} = \sum\nolimits_{\text{col}} (-1)^j a_{1j_1} a_{2j_2} a_{3j_3} = a_{11}a_{22}a_{33} + a_{12}a_{23}a_{31} + a_{13}a_{21}a_{32} - a_{13}a_{22}a_{31} - a_{12}a_{21}a_{33} - a_{11}a_{23}a_{32}.$$

$$\begin{vmatrix} -5 & 2 & -3 \\ 0 & 1 & 6 \\ -1 & 2 & -1 \end{vmatrix} = (-5)(1)(-1) + (2)(6)(-1) + (-3)(0)(2) - (-3)(1)(-1) - (2)(0)(-1) - (-5)(6)(2) = 50.$$

Having shown that the determinant of A is unique, we now prove the following identity which we will use in the next section to derive some of the properties of determinants.

(8.4) Theorem. If $A = (a_{ij})$, and if $i_1, i_2, \cdots, i_n$ is a fixed ordering of the integers $1, 2, \cdots, n$ where i is the number of interchanges required to carry $i_1, i_2, \cdots, i_n$ into $1, 2, \cdots, n$, then

$$\sum\nolimits_{\text{col}} (-1)^j a_{i_1j_1} a_{i_2j_2} \cdots a_{i_nj_n} = (-1)^i |A|,$$

where the sum $\sum_{\text{col}}$ is taken over all orderings $j_1, j_2, \cdots, j_n$ of the column subscripts $1, 2, \cdots, n$ and j is the number of interchanges from $j_1, j_2, \cdots, j_n$ to $1, 2, \cdots, n$.

PROOF. Given the fixed ordering $i_1, i_2, \cdots, i_n$ of the row subscripts, every product of n elements of A with one element from each row and each column can be written in the form $a_{i_1j_1}a_{i_2j_2} \cdots a_{i_nj_n}$ for some ordering $j_1, j_2, \cdots, j_n$ of $1, 2, \cdots, n$. Since the sum $S = \sum_{\text{col}} (-1)^j a_{i_1j_1}a_{i_2j_2} \cdots a_{i_nj_n}$ is taken over all orderings of the column subscripts $j_1, j_2, \cdots, j_n$, S is a sum of all products of n elements of A, one from each row and each column, with a certain sign affixed to each product. Thus the terms of S are the terms of $|A|$, except possibly for their signs.

If we reorder the factors $a_{i_kj_k}$ of each term of S as $a_{1l_1}a_{2l_2} \cdots a_{nl_n}$ with the row subscripts in natural order, then $\sum_{\text{col}} (-1)^j a_{i_1j_1}a_{i_2j_2} \cdots a_{i_nj_n} = \sum_{\text{col}} (-1)^j a_{1l_1}a_{2l_2} \cdots a_{nl_n}$ where the latter sum is taken over all orderings $l_1, l_2, \cdots, l_n$ of $1, 2, \cdots, n$. Since the ordering $i_1, i_2, \cdots, i_n$ is fixed, this reordering of the factors can be done in every term by i interchanges of two factors and these interchanges of the factors induce i interchanges of the column subscripts. Thus each new ordering $l_1, l_2, \cdots, l_n$ can be carried into its original ordering $j_1, j_2, \cdots, j_n$ by i interchanges, and hence into the natural ordering $1, 2, \cdots, n$ by $i + j$ interchanges. Therefore

$$|A| = \sum_{\text{col}} (-1)^{i+j} a_{1l_1}a_{2l_2} \cdots a_{nl_n}$$

by Definition (8.1), and

$$\begin{aligned}\sum_{\text{col}} (-1)^j a_{i_1j_1}a_{i_2j_2} \cdots a_{i_nj_n} &= \sum_{\text{col}} (-1)^j a_{1l_1}a_{2l_2} \cdots a_{nl_n} \\ &= (-1)^{2i} \sum_{\text{col}} (-1)^j a_{1l_1}a_{2l_2} \cdots a_{nl_n} \\ &= (-1)^i \sum_{\text{col}} (-1)^{i+j} a_{1l_1}a_{2l_2} \cdots a_{nl_n} \\ &= (-1)^i |A|.\end{aligned}$$

Exercise (8.1). Prove that $|I_n| = 1$ and that $|kA| = k^n|A|$.

Exercise (8.2). Find the signs of the terms $a_{13}a_{24}a_{32}a_{45}a_{51}$ and $a_{45}a_{21}a_{33}a_{12}a_{54}$ in the expansion of a fifth-order determinant. Write out all terms, with proper signs, which contain a_{25} and a_{42}.

Exercise (8.3). The number of *inversions* of the ordering $j_1, j_2, \cdots, j_n$ is the sum $k = \sum_{l=1}^{n} k_l$ where k_l is the number of digits less than l which follow l in the ordering. Prove that if $(-1)^j a_{1j_1} a_{2j_2} \cdots a_{nj_n}$ is any term of a determinant of order n, then $(-1)^j = (-1)^k$.

Exercise (8.4). Prove that the sign of $a_{i_1j_1} a_{i_2j_2} \cdots a_{i_nj_n}$ is $(-1)^{i+j}$ where i is the number of inversions of $i_1, i_2, \cdots, i_n$ and j is the number of inversions of $j_1, j_2, \cdots, j_n$.

Exercise (8.5). Prove that $\sum_{\text{row}} (-1)^i a_{i_1j_1} a_{i_2j_2} \cdots a_{i_nj_n} = (-1)^j |A|$ where the sum $\sum_{\text{row}}$ is taken over all the orderings $i_1, i_2, \cdots, i_n$ of the row subscripts $1, 2, \cdots, n$, where i is the number of interchanges required to carry $i_1, i_2, \cdots, i_n$ into $1, 2, \cdots, n$, and where j is the number of interchanges required to carry the fixed ordering $j_1, j_2, \cdots, j_n$ into $1, 2, \cdots, n$. In particular, obtain the "row definition" of $|A|$

$$\sum_{\text{row}} (-1)^i a_{i_11} a_{i_22} \cdots a_{i_nn} = |A|.$$

Section 9. Properties of Determinants

Let $A = (a_{ij})$ be a square matrix of order n.

(9.1) Theorem. $|A'| = |A|$.

PROOF. If we write $A' = (b_{ij})$, then $b_{ij} = a_{ji}$ for all i,j. By Definition (8.1)

$$|A'| = \sum_{\text{col}} (-1)^j b_{1j_1} b_{2j_2} \cdots b_{nj_n} = \sum_{\text{row}} (-1)^j a_{j_11} a_{j_22} \cdots a_{j_nn}.$$

Now by Exercise (8.5) of the preceding section, the latter sum is the "row definition" of $|A|$, so that $|A'| = |A|$.

This theorem enables us to replace the word "row" by "column" in the statements of the following properties of determinants. Thus, the matrix operation of transposition plays an important role in the theory of determinants.

(9.2) Theorem. If B is a matrix obtained from A by interchanging two rows (columns) of A, then $|B| = -|A|$.

PROOF. By hypothesis, $B = (b_{ij})$, where for all j, $b_{ij} = a_{ij}$ if $i \neq k$ or l, $b_{kj} = a_{lj}$, and $b_{lj} = a_{kj}$. Assume that $k < l$. Then

$$|B| = \sum_{\text{col}} (-1)^j b_{1j_1} b_{2j_2} \cdots b_{kj_k} \cdots b_{lj_l} \cdots b_{nj_n}$$
$$= \sum_{\text{col}} (-1)^j a_{1j_1} a_{2j_2} \cdots a_{lj_k} \cdots a_{kj_l} \cdots a_{nj_n}.$$

Since a single interchange carries the fixed subscripts 1, 2, $\cdots$, l, $\cdots$, k, $\cdots$, n into the natural order 1, 2, $\cdots$, k, $\cdots$, l, $\cdots$, n, it follows from Theorem (8.4) that the latter sum is $(-1)^1|A| = -|A|$.

Now if B is obtained from A by interchanging two columns of A, then B' is obtained from A' by interchanging the corresponding rows of A'. By Theorem (9.1) and by the above proof we have

$$|B| = |B'| = -|A'| = -|A|.$$

(9.3) Theorem. If two rows (columns) of A are identical, then $|A| = 0$.

PROOF. If B is the matrix obtained from A by interchanging these identical rows (columns), then $B = A$ and $|B| = |A|$. However, by Theorem (9.2), $|B| = -|A|$. Thus $|A| = -|A|$, $2|A| = 0$, and $|A| = 0$.

(9.4) Theorem. If B is a matrix obtained from A by multiplying every element of one row (column) of A by the constant m, then $|B| = m|A|$.

PROOF. $B = (b_{ij})$ where for all j, $b_{ij} = a_{ij}$ if $i \neq k$ and $b_{kj} = ma_{kj}$. Then

$$|B| = \sum_{\text{col}} (-1)^j b_{1j_1} b_{2j_2} \cdots b_{kj_k} \cdots b_{nj_n}$$
$$= \sum_{\text{col}} (-1)^j a_{1j_1} a_{2j_2} \cdots (ma_{kj_k}) \cdots a_{nj_n}$$
$$= m \sum_{\text{col}} (-1)^j a_{1j_1} a_{2j_2} \cdots a_{kj_k} \cdots a_{nj_n} = m|A|.$$

As in the proof of Theorem (9.2), Theorem (9.1) can be used to obtain this result for columns. It is left to the reader to supply this part of the proof in the following theorems.

Theorem (9.4) is used to remove common factors from the rows and columns of determinants.

EXAMPLE 1.

$$\begin{vmatrix} 24 & 12 & 6 & -3 \\ 4 & 0 & 1 & 0 \\ -20 & -1 & -5 & 2 \\ 12 & -2 & 3 & 4 \end{vmatrix} = 3 \begin{vmatrix} 8 & 4 & 2 & -1 \\ 4 & 0 & 1 & 0 \\ -20 & -1 & -5 & 2 \\ 12 & -2 & 3 & 4 \end{vmatrix}$$
$$= 12 \begin{vmatrix} 2 & 4 & 2 & -1 \\ 1 & 0 & 1 & 0 \\ -5 & -1 & -5 & 2 \\ 3 & -2 & 3 & 4 \end{vmatrix} = 0.$$

If we write $A = (a_{ij}) = \begin{pmatrix} R_1 \\ \cdot \\ \cdot \\ \cdot \\ R_k \\ \cdot \\ \cdot \\ \cdot \\ R_r \\ \cdot \\ \cdot \\ \cdot \\ R_n \end{pmatrix}$ where $R_i = (a_{i1}\ a_{i2}\ \cdots\ a_{in})$, and

if $B = \begin{pmatrix} R_1 \\ \cdot \\ \cdot \\ \cdot \\ R_k \\ \cdot \\ \cdot \\ \cdot \\ R_r + mR_k \\ \cdot \\ \cdot \\ \cdot \\ R_n \end{pmatrix}$ where m is a scalar, then row r of B is

$$\begin{aligned} R_r + mR_k &= (a_{r1}\ a_{r2}\ \cdots\ a_{rn}) + m(a_{k1}\ a_{k2}\ \cdots\ a_{kn}) \\ &= (a_{r1} + ma_{k1}\ a_{r2} + ma_{k2}\ \cdots\ a_{rn} + ma_{kn}). \end{aligned}$$

The following theorem shows that $|B| = |A|$.

(9.5) Theorem. If B is a matrix obtained from A by adding to each element of a row (column) of A a constant multiple of the corresponding element of another row (column), then $|B| = |A|$.

PROOF. $B = (b_{ij})$ where for all j, $b_{ij} = a_{ij}$ if $i \neq r$ and $b_{rj} = a_{rj} + ma_{kj}$ $(k \neq r)$. Then

$$\begin{aligned} |B| &= \sum_{\text{col}} (-1)^j b_{1j_1} b_{2j_2} \cdots b_{kj_k} \cdots b_{rj_r} \cdots b_{nj_n} \\ &= \sum_{\text{col}} (-1)^j a_{1j_1} a_{2j_2} \cdots a_{kj_k} \cdots (a_{rj_r} + ma_{kj_r}) \cdots a_{nj_n} \\ &= \sum_{\text{col}} (-1)^j a_{1j_1} a_{2j_2} \cdots a_{kj_k} \cdots a_{rj_r} \cdots a_{nj_n} \\ &\quad + \sum_{\text{col}} (-1)^j a_{1j_1} a_{2j_2} \cdots a_{kj_k} \cdots (ma_{kj_r}) \cdots a_{nj_n} \end{aligned}$$

$$= |A| + m \sum_{\text{col}} (-1)^j a_{1j_1} a_{2j_2} \cdots a_{kj_k} \cdots a_{kj_r} \cdots a_{nj_n}$$
$$= |A| + m \cdot 0 = |A|,$$

since the last sum is the expansion of a determinant with two identical rows.

Consider now the three matrices

$$A = \begin{pmatrix} R_1 \\ \cdot \\ \cdot \\ \cdot \\ R_k \\ \cdot \\ \cdot \\ \cdot \\ R_n \end{pmatrix}, \quad B = \begin{pmatrix} R_1 \\ \cdot \\ \cdot \\ \cdot \\ S_k \\ \cdot \\ \cdot \\ \cdot \\ R_n \end{pmatrix}, \quad \text{and } C = \begin{pmatrix} R_1 \\ \cdot \\ \cdot \\ \cdot \\ R_k + S_k \\ \cdot \\ \cdot \\ \cdot \\ R_n \end{pmatrix}.$$

The matrices A, B, and C are identical except possibly for their kth rows, and the kth row of C is the matrix sum of the kth rows of A and B.

(9.6) Theorem. If A, B, and C are defined as above, then $|C| = |A| + |B|$.

PROOF. If $A = (a_{ij})$, $B = (b_{ij})$, and $C = (c_{ij})$, we have for all j, $c_{ij} = a_{ij} = b_{ij}$ if $i \neq k$ and $c_{kj} = a_{kj} + b_{kj}$. Therefore

$$\begin{aligned} |C| &= \sum_{\text{col}} (-1)^j c_{1j_1} c_{2j_2} \cdots c_{kj_k} \cdots c_{nj_n} \\ &= \sum_{\text{col}} (-1)^j c_{1j_1} c_{2j_2} \cdots (a_{kj_k} + b_{kj_k}) \cdots c_{nj_n} \\ &= \sum_{\text{col}} (-1)^j a_{1j_1} \cdots a_{kj_k} \cdots a_{nj_n} \\ &\qquad + \sum_{\text{col}} (-1)^j b_{1j_1} \cdots b_{kj_k} \cdots b_{nj_n} \\ &= |A| + |B|. \end{aligned}$$

EXAMPLE 2.

$$\begin{vmatrix} a+b & c+d \\ e+f & g+h \end{vmatrix} = \begin{vmatrix} a & c+d \\ e & g+h \end{vmatrix} + \begin{vmatrix} b & c+d \\ f & g+h \end{vmatrix}$$
$$= \begin{vmatrix} a & c \\ e & g \end{vmatrix} + \begin{vmatrix} a & d \\ e & h \end{vmatrix} + \begin{vmatrix} b & c \\ f & g \end{vmatrix} + \begin{vmatrix} b & d \\ f & h \end{vmatrix}.$$

Much of the effectiveness of the definition of matrix multiplication lies in the following result.

(9.7) Theorem. If A and B are square matrices of order n, then $|AB| = |A| \cdot |B|$.

PROOF. Let $AB = C$ where $A = (a_{ij})$, $B = (b_{ij})$, and $C = (c_{ij})$. Then $c_{ij} = \sum_{k=1}^{n} a_{ik}b_{kj}$, and we have

$$
\begin{aligned}
|C| &= \sum\nolimits_{\text{col}} (-1)^j c_{1j_1}c_{2j_2} \cdots c_{nj_n} \\
&= \sum\nolimits_{\text{col}} (-1)^j \Big[\sum_{k_1=1}^{n} a_{1k_1}b_{k_1j_1}\Big]\Big[\sum_{k_2=1}^{n} a_{2k_2}b_{k_2j_2}\Big] \cdots \Big[\sum_{k_n=1}^{n} a_{nk_n}b_{k_nj_n}\Big].
\end{aligned}
$$

This product of bracketed sums is equal to a sum of products

$$
|C| = \sum\nolimits_{\text{col}} (-1)^j \Big[\sum_{k_1=1}^{n}\sum_{k_2=1}^{n} \cdots \sum_{k_n=1}^{n} (a_{1k_1}b_{k_1j_1})(a_{2k_2}b_{k_2j_2}) \cdots (a_{nk_n}b_{k_nj_n})\Big].
$$

Since the first summation is over all orderings $j_1, j_2, \cdots, j_n$ of $1, 2, \cdots, n$, it applies only to the $b_{k_ij_i}$, and the order of summation may be interchanged. Thus $|C|$ is equal to

$$
\sum_{k_1=1}^{n}\sum_{k_2=1}^{n} \cdots \sum_{k_n=1}^{n} \Big\{a_{1k_1}a_{2k_2} \cdots a_{nk_n} \Big[\sum\nolimits_{\text{col}} (-1)^j b_{k_1j_1}b_{k_2j_2} \cdots b_{k_nj_n}\Big]\Big\}.
$$

Now for any fixed set of values $k_1, k_2, \cdots, k_n$,

$$
\sum\nolimits_{\text{col}} (-1)^j b_{k_1j_1}b_{k_2j_2} \cdots b_{k_nj_n}
$$

is the determinant of a matrix which has row k_1 of B as its first row, row k_2 of B as its second row, and so on. If any $k_i = k_j$, this determinant is zero by Theorem (9.3). Therefore the only non-zero terms of the sum $\sum_{k_1=1}^{n}\sum_{k_2=1}^{n} \cdots \sum_{k_n=1}^{n}$ are those for which the set of values $k_1, k_2, \cdots, k_n$ is some ordering of the numbers $1, 2, \cdots, n$. In these non-zero terms, $\sum_{\text{col}} (-1)^j b_{k_1j_1}b_{k_2j_2} \cdots b_{k_nj_n} = (-1)^k|B|$ where k is the number of interchanges required to carry the ordering $k_1, k_2, \cdots, k_n$ into $1, 2, \cdots, n$. This follows from Theorem (8.4). We may now write

$$
|C| = \sum\nolimits_{\text{col}} \{a_{1k_1}a_{2k_2} \cdots a_{nk_n} [(-1)^k|B|]\},
$$

where the sum is over all orderings $k_1, k_2, \cdots, k_n$ of $1, 2, \cdots, n$. The proof is now complete, for we have

$$
|C| = \Big\{\sum\nolimits_{\text{col}} (-1)^k a_{1k_1}a_{2k_2} \cdots a_{nk_n}\Big\} |B| = |A| \cdot |B|.
$$

Exercise (9.1). Show that each step is valid.

$$\begin{vmatrix} 3 & 4 & 5 & 7 \\ 2 & 4 & 6 & -3 \\ -1 & 2 & 3 & 1 \\ 2 & -1 & 4 & -1 \end{vmatrix} = \begin{vmatrix} 2 & 6 & 8 & 8 \\ 2 & 4 & 6 & -3 \\ -1 & 2 & 3 & 1 \\ 2 & -1 & 4 & -1 \end{vmatrix}$$

$$= 2\begin{vmatrix} 1 & 3 & 4 & 4 \\ 2 & 4 & 6 & -3 \\ -1 & 2 & 3 & 1 \\ 2 & -1 & 4 & -1 \end{vmatrix} = 2\begin{vmatrix} 1 & 3 & 0 & 4 \\ 2 & 4 & 9 & -3 \\ -1 & 2 & 2 & 1 \\ 2 & -1 & 5 & -1 \end{vmatrix}$$

$$= 2\begin{vmatrix} 1 & 0 & 0 & 4 \\ 2 & -2 & 9 & -3 \\ -1 & 5 & 2 & 1 \\ 2 & -7 & 5 & -1 \end{vmatrix} = -4\begin{vmatrix} 1 & 0 & 0 & 4 \\ 2 & 1 & 9 & -3 \\ -1 & -5/2 & 2 & 1 \\ 2 & 7/2 & 5 & -1 \end{vmatrix}$$

$$= -4\begin{vmatrix} 1 & 0 & 0 & 4 \\ 2 & 1 & 9 & -3 \\ -1/3 & -4/3 & 11/3 & 2/3 \\ 2 & 7/2 & 5 & -1 \end{vmatrix}.$$

Which of these determinants is easiest to expand?

Exercise (9.2). Evaluate the following determinants:

(a) $\begin{vmatrix} 2 & -6 & 4 & 8 \\ 6 & -5 & 4 & 2 \\ -1 & 5 & -2 & -4 \\ 0 & 7 & 14 & 35 \end{vmatrix}$, (b) $\begin{vmatrix} 0 & i & 2i & 3i & 4i \\ -i & 0 & 1 & 2 & 3 \\ -2i & -1 & 0 & 1 & 2 \\ -3i & -2 & -1 & 0 & 1 \\ -4i & -3 & -2 & -1 & 0 \end{vmatrix}$,

(c) $\begin{vmatrix} 2 & 0 & 1 & -3 & 0 \\ 5 & 0 & 2 & 1/4 & -1/3 \\ 1 & 2 & -3 & 1 & 1/3 \\ 1 & 2 & 1/2 & 1/8 & 1/3 \\ -1 & 0 & 2 & 1 & 1 \end{vmatrix}$, (d) $\begin{vmatrix} 1 & 3 & -5 & 7 \\ 0 & 1 & 1 & 6 \\ 0 & 0 & 1 & 2 \\ 0 & 0 & 0 & 1 \end{vmatrix}$.

Exercise (9.3). For the following matrices A, compute $|A^3|$, $|-A|$, $|3A|$, $|-1/2\, A'|$, and $|AA'|$:

(a) $\begin{pmatrix} -3 & 1 & 0 \\ 2 & -5 & 6 \\ 1 & 2 & 1 \end{pmatrix}$, (b) $\begin{bmatrix} 4 & -3 & 1 & 0 \\ 2 & 3 & 6 & 7 \\ 6 & -5 & 4 & 5 \\ -2 & 1 & 2 & 4 \end{bmatrix}$,

(c) $\begin{pmatrix} abc & a^2b & ac^2 \\ b & ab & bc \\ bc & ac & c^2 \end{pmatrix}$, (d) $\begin{bmatrix} 1 & a & a^2 & a^3 \\ 1 & b & b^2 & b^3 \\ 1 & c & c^2 & c^3 \\ 1 & d & d^2 & d^3 \end{bmatrix}$.

Exercise (9.4). Show that if (x_1,y_1) and (x_2,y_2) are distinct points in the plane,

$$\begin{vmatrix} 1 & x & y \\ 1 & x_1 & y_1 \\ 1 & x_2 & y_2 \end{vmatrix} = 0$$

is the equation of the line joining the points.

Exercise (9.5). If A and B are n-rowed square matrices, prove that $|AB| = |BA|$.

Exercise (9.6). What is wrong with the following calculation?

$$\begin{vmatrix} a & b & c \\ d & e & f \\ g & h & i \end{vmatrix} = \begin{vmatrix} a+d & b+e & c+f \\ d+a & e+b & f+c \\ g & h & i \end{vmatrix}$$ by Theorem (9.5); that is,

row 2 has been added to row 1 and row 1 to row 2. [This determinant is zero, and by this method we could "prove" every determinant is zero.]

Exercise (9.7). Show that

$$\begin{vmatrix} a\alpha + b\beta + c\gamma & d\alpha + e\beta + f\gamma \\ a\delta + b\epsilon + c\mu & d\delta + e\epsilon + f\mu \end{vmatrix}$$
$$= \begin{vmatrix} a & b \\ d & e \end{vmatrix} \cdot \begin{vmatrix} \alpha & \beta \\ \delta & \epsilon \end{vmatrix} + \begin{vmatrix} b & c \\ e & f \end{vmatrix} \cdot \begin{vmatrix} \beta & \gamma \\ \epsilon & \mu \end{vmatrix} + \begin{vmatrix} c & a \\ f & d \end{vmatrix} \cdot \begin{vmatrix} \gamma & \alpha \\ \mu & \delta \end{vmatrix}.$$

Exercise (9.8). Show that

$$\begin{vmatrix} 1 & a & bc \\ 1 & b & ca \\ 1 & c & ab \end{vmatrix} = (a-b)(b-c)(c-a) = \begin{vmatrix} 1 & a & a^2 \\ 1 & b & b^2 \\ 1 & c & c^2 \end{vmatrix}.$$

Exercise (9.9). Show that

$$\begin{vmatrix} x & 0 & 0 & a_3 \\ -1 & x & 0 & a_2 \\ 0 & -1 & x & a_1 \\ 0 & 0 & -1 & a_0 \end{vmatrix} = a_0x^3 + a_1x^2 + a_2x + a_3.$$

Exercise (9.10). Show that

$$\begin{vmatrix} x & a & b \\ -a & x & c \\ -b & -c & x \end{vmatrix} = x(x^2 + a^2 + b^2 + c^2).$$

Exercise (9.11). For what value of λ is x a factor of

$$\begin{vmatrix} x-2 & 2 & 2 \\ 1 & 1 & x+2 \\ -1 & 5 & x+\lambda \end{vmatrix}?$$

Exercise (9.12). Find all values of x for which

$$\begin{vmatrix} x+1 & -1 & 3 \\ 2 & x & -2 \\ -2 & 1 & x-4 \end{vmatrix} = 0.$$

Exercise (9.13). Prove directly Theorem (9.5) for columns.

Exercise (9.14). Prove that $|A| = 0$ if one row (column) of A is entirely composed of zeros.

Exercise (9.15). If $A = (C_1 \quad C_2 \quad C_3 \quad C_4)$ where each C_i is a column matrix, prove that $|(C_2 \quad C_4 \quad C_1 \quad C_3)| = -|A|$.

Exercise (9.16). Prove $\begin{vmatrix} a+b & b+c & c+a \\ b+c & c+a & a+b \\ c+a & a+b & b+c \end{vmatrix} = 2\begin{vmatrix} a & b & c \\ b & c & a \\ c & a & b \end{vmatrix}.$

Section 10. Minors. Cofactors. The Laplace Expansion of a Determinant

There are various equivalent ways of defining the determinant of a square matrix. Definition (8.1) was chosen for ease in proving the theorems of the preceding section, but is inconvenient for numerical computation. Such computation is simpler if we use these theorems and the Laplace expansion which we now develop.

(10.1) Definition. The determinant of a square submatrix of order r of a matrix A is called a *minor of order* r, or an *r-rowed minor*, of A.

Although at present we are concerned only with square matrices, Definition (10.1) applies as well to any m by n matrix A. In a square matrix of order n, the complementary submatrix of a square submatrix of order r is square and of order $n - r$. The determinants of these complementary submatrices are called *complementary minors.* In particular, each element a_{ij} of the matrix is a 1-rowed minor which has an $(n - 1)$-rowed complementary minor.

(10.2) Definition. The *cofactor* of the element a_{ij} is $A_{ij} = (-1)^{i+j}\Delta_{ij}$, where Δ_{ij} is the complementary minor of a_{ij}.

The following theorem is an important special case of the Laplace expansion of a determinant.

(10.3) Theorem. For any i, $|A| = \sum_{j=1}^{n} a_{ij}A_{ij}$; and for any j,

$$|A| = \sum_{i=1}^{n} a_{ij}A_{ij}.$$

This is usually referred to as the rule for expanding a determinant according to the ith row (or jth column). Thus

$$|A| = a_{i1}A_{i1} + a_{i2}A_{i2} + \cdots + a_{in}A_{in} \qquad \text{for any } i$$

and

$$|A| = a_{1j}A_{1j} + a_{2j}A_{2j} + \cdots + a_{nj}A_{nj} \qquad \text{for any } j.$$

A determinant of order 3 or more is usually expanded using this theorem together with those of Section 9. The second-order determinant $|a_{ij}| = a_{11}a_{22} - a_{12}a_{21}$ can be expanded directly.

EXAMPLE 1.

$$\begin{vmatrix} -5 & -2 & 0 & -2 \\ 2 & -6 & 1 & 0 \\ 4 & 2 & 3 & 1 \\ -1 & 0 & 2 & 7 \end{vmatrix} = \begin{vmatrix} -1 & 0 & 3 & -1 \\ 14 & 0 & 10 & 3 \\ 4 & 2 & 3 & 1 \\ -1 & 0 & 2 & 7 \end{vmatrix} \quad \text{by Theorem (9.5)}$$

$$= 2 \cdot (-1)^{3+2} \begin{vmatrix} -1 & 3 & -1 \\ 14 & 10 & 3 \\ -1 & 2 & 7 \end{vmatrix} \quad \text{by Theorem (10.3) with } j = 2 \text{ (we have made } a_{12} = a_{22} = a_{42} = 0)$$

$$= -2 \begin{vmatrix} -1 & 0 & 0 \\ 14 & 52 & -11 \\ -1 & -1 & 8 \end{vmatrix} \quad \text{by Theorem (9.5)}$$

$$= -2 \left\{ (-1) \cdot (-1)^{1+1} \begin{vmatrix} 52 & -11 \\ -1 & 8 \end{vmatrix} \right\} \quad \text{by Theorem (10.3) with } i = 1$$

$$= 2(52 \cdot 8 - 11) = 810.$$

Instead of proving this special theorem, we shall prove the general rule for expanding a determinant according to an arbitrary number of rows (or columns).

Let us fix a set $i_1, i_2, \cdots, i_u$ of u rows of A where $i_1 < i_2 < \cdots < i_u$, and let the remaining $v = n - u$ rows be $k_1 < k_2 < \cdots < k_v$. If I is the number of interchanges required to carry the ordering i_1,

$\cdots, i_u, k_1, \cdots, k_v$ into $1, 2, \cdots, n$, then by Theorem (8.4)

$$(-1)^I|A| = \sum\nolimits_{\text{col}} (-1)^j a_{i_1j_1} \cdots a_{i_uj_u}a_{k_1j_{u+1}} \cdots a_{k_vj_n},$$

or

$$|A| = \sum\nolimits_{\text{col}} (-1)^{I+j} a_{i_1j_1} \cdots a_{i_uj_u}a_{k_1j_{u+1}} \cdots a_{k_vj_n},$$

where the sum is taken over all orderings $j_1, j_2, \cdots, j_n$ of $1, 2, \cdots, n$ and where j is the number of interchanges from $j_1, j_2, \cdots, j_n$ to $1, 2, \cdots, n$.

Let j' be the number of interchanges from $j_1, \cdots, j_u, j_{u+1}, \cdots, j_n$ to $r_1, \cdots, r_u, j_{u+1}, \cdots, j_n$ where $r_1 < r_2 < \cdots < r_u$ are the digits $j_1, j_2, \cdots, j_u$ in order; let j'' be the number of interchanges from $r_1, \cdots, r_u, j_{u+1}, \cdots, j_n$ to $r_1, \cdots, r_u, s_1, \cdots, s_v$ where $s_1 < s_2 < \cdots < s_v$ are the digits $j_{u+1}, j_{u+2}, \cdots, j_n$ in order; and let J be the number of interchanges from $r_1, \cdots, r_u, s_1, \cdots, s_v$ to $1, 2, \cdots, n$. Then $(-1)^j = (-1)^{j'+j''+J}$ and

$$|A| = \sum\nolimits_{\text{col}} (-1)^{I+j'+j''+J} a_{i_1j_1} \cdots a_{i_uj_u}a_{k_1j_{u+1}} \cdots a_{k_vj_n}$$
$$= \sum\nolimits_{\text{col}} (-1)^{I+J}[(-1)^{j'} a_{i_1j_1} \cdots a_{i_uj_u} \cdot (-1)^{j''} a_{k_1j_{u+1}} \cdots a_{k_vj_n}].$$

The terms of this sum over the $n!$ orderings $j_1, \cdots, j_u, j_{u+1}, \cdots, j_n$ of $1, 2, \cdots, n$ may be grouped as

(10.4) $$|A| = \Sigma(-1)^{I+J}\{\Sigma(-1)^{j'} a_{i_1j_1} \cdots a_{i_uj_u}(-1)^{j''} a_{k_1j_{u+1}} \cdots a_{k_vj_n}]\},$$

where the first sum is taken over all the $C(n,u) = (n!/u!v!)$ ways of choosing u digits $r_1 < r_2 < \cdots < r_u$ from $1, 2, \cdots, n$. Every separation of the digits $1, 2, \cdots, n$ into two sets $r_1 < r_2 < \cdots < r_u$ and $s_1 < s_2 < \cdots < s_v$ gives one term of this first summation, and this term is itself a sum

$$\Sigma[(-1)^{j'} a_{i_1j_1} \cdots a_{i_uj_u}(-1)^{j''} a_{k_1j_{u+1}} \cdots a_{k_vj_n}]$$

taken over all orderings $j_1, j_2, \cdots, j_u$ of $r_1, r_2, \cdots, r_u$ and all orderings $j_{u+1}, j_{u+2}, \cdots, j_n$ of $s_1, s_2, \cdots, s_v$. Since the arrangement of the r_i is independent of that of the s_j, this sum is equal to a product of two sums

$$\left(\sum\nolimits_{\text{col}} (-1)^{j'} a_{i_1j_1} \cdots a_{i_uj_u}\right)\left(\sum\nolimits_{\text{col}} (-1)^{j''} a_{k_1j_{u+1}} \cdots a_{k_vj_n}\right).$$

Thus

(10.5) $$|A| = \sum (-1)^{I+J}\left\{\left(\sum\nolimits_{\text{col}} (-1)^{j'} a_{i_1j_1} \cdots a_{i_uj_u}\right)\left(\sum\nolimits_{\text{col}} (-1)^{j''} a_{k_1j_{u+1}} \cdots a_{k_vj_n}\right)\right\}.$$

Each sum $\sum_{\text{col}} (-1)^{j'} a_{i_1 j_1} \cdots a_{i_u j_u}$ taken over all orderings $j_1, j_2, \cdots, j_u$ of $r_1, r_2, \cdots, r_u$ where j' is the number of interchanges from $j_1, j_2, \cdots, j_u$ to $r_1, r_2, \cdots, r_u$ is now seen to be the minor of order u of A formed from rows $i_1, i_2, \cdots, i_u$ and columns $r_1, r_2, \cdots, r_u$. A similar analysis shows that $\sum_{\text{col}} (-1)^{j''} a_{k_1 j_{u+1}} \cdots a_{k_v j_n}$ is its complementary minor.

The number $|A|$ has thus been expressed as a sum, with proper signs, of all possible minors formed from a fixed set of rows multiplied by their complementary minors. This is the Laplace expansion by u-rowed minors.

For purposes of computation we may find the sign $(-1)^{I+J}$ by counting inversions as explained in Exercise (8.3).

(10.6) $$(-1)^{I+J} = (-1)^{i_1+\cdots+i_u+r_1+\cdots+r_u}$$

using the notation above. For in the ordering $i_1, \cdots, i_u, k_1, \cdots, k_v$, each k_l has only larger digits following it. And for any i_l, there are $i_l - 1$ smaller digits, of which $l - 1$ of them, $i_1, i_2, \cdots, i_{l-1}$, precede i_l. Thus for each i_l, there are $i_l - l$ smaller digits which follow it. Therefore $(-1)^I = (-1)^{i_1-1+\cdots+i_u-u}$. Similarly $(-1)^J = (-1)^{r_1-1+\cdots+r_u-u}$. Finally

$$(-1)^{I+J} = (-1)^{i_1+\cdots+i_u+r_1+\cdots+r_u-1-1-\cdots-u-u} = (-1)^{i_1+\cdots+i_u+r_1+\cdots+r_u},$$

proving (10.6).

EXAMPLE 2. We may expand the determinant of Example 1 about the second and third rows as

$$\begin{vmatrix} -5 & -2 & 0 & -2 \\ 2 & -6 & 1 & 0 \\ 4 & 2 & 3 & 1 \\ -1 & 0 & 2 & 7 \end{vmatrix} = (-1)^{2+3+1+2} \begin{vmatrix} 2 & -6 \\ 4 & 2 \end{vmatrix} \cdot \begin{vmatrix} 0 & -2 \\ 2 & 7 \end{vmatrix}$$

$$+ (-1)^{2+3+1+3} \begin{vmatrix} 2 & 1 \\ 4 & 3 \end{vmatrix} \cdot \begin{vmatrix} -2 & -2 \\ 0 & 7 \end{vmatrix}$$

$$+ (-1)^{2+3+1+4} \begin{vmatrix} 2 & 0 \\ 4 & 1 \end{vmatrix} \cdot \begin{vmatrix} -2 & 0 \\ 0 & 2 \end{vmatrix}$$

$$+ (-1)^{2+3+2+3} \begin{vmatrix} -6 & 1 \\ 2 & 3 \end{vmatrix} \cdot \begin{vmatrix} -5 & -2 \\ -1 & 7 \end{vmatrix}$$

$$+ (-1)^{2+3+2+4} \begin{vmatrix} -6 & 0 \\ 2 & 1 \end{vmatrix} \cdot \begin{vmatrix} -5 & 0 \\ -1 & 2 \end{vmatrix}$$

$$+ (-1)^{2+3+3+4} \begin{vmatrix} 1 & 0 \\ 3 & 1 \end{vmatrix} \cdot \begin{vmatrix} -5 & -2 \\ -1 & 0 \end{vmatrix}$$

$$= +(28)(4) - (2)(-14) + (2)(-4)$$
$$+ (-20)(-37) - (-6)(-10) + (1)(-2) = 810.$$

In the same way, or using (9.1), if we fix a set of columns $r_1 < r_2 < \cdots < r_u$, we may show that $|A|$ can be obtained as a sum of all possible u-rowed minors from the fixed columns multiplied by their complementary minors, with the sign $(-1)^{i_1+\cdots+i_u+r_1+\cdots+r_u}$ affixed to each product.

In the case $u = 1$, using the row i alone, we get Theorem (10.3), since

$$|A| = \sum_{j=1}^{n} (-1)^{i+j} a_{ij} \cdot \Delta_{ij} = \sum_{j=1}^{n} a_{ij} A_{ij}.$$

It is an important result that

$$\sum_{j=1}^{n} a_{ij} A_{kj} = a_{i1} A_{k1} + a_{i2} A_{k2} + \cdots + a_{in} A_{kn} = 0 \qquad \text{if } i \neq k.$$

For this is the expansion about its kth row of the determinant $|B| = |(b_{rs})|$ with $b_{rs} = a_{rs}$ if $r \neq k$, $b_{ks} = a_{is}$, for all s. But $|B| = 0$ since it has two identical rows, i and k. Combining this equality with Theorem (10.3), we have proved the following theorem.

(10.7) Theorem.

$$\sum_{j=1}^{n} a_{ij} A_{kj} = \delta_{ik} |A| \qquad \text{for all pairs } i,k$$

and

$$\sum_{i=1}^{n} a_{ij} A_{ik} = \delta_{jk} |A| \qquad \text{for all pairs } j,k,$$

where δ_{ij} is the Kronecker delta.

Exercise (10.1). State Theorem (10.7) in words.

Exercise (10.2). Expand in several ways, using the definition, the determinant properties, and the Laplace expansion.

(a) $\begin{vmatrix} 21 & -6 & 37 \\ -81 & 2 & 0 \\ 219 & 1 & 5 \end{vmatrix}$, (b) $\begin{vmatrix} 3 & 2 & -1 & 6 \\ 4 & 0 & 5 & -1 \\ -1 & 1 & -2 & 4 \\ -2 & 7 & -3 & 2 \end{vmatrix}$.

Exercise (10.3). Expand the following determinant
(a) about row 2;
(b) about columns 2 and 4:

$$\begin{vmatrix} -3 & 4 & 3 & 5 & 3 \\ 2 & 0 & 1 & 0 & 2 \\ 0 & 2 & 5 & 0 & 5 \\ 4 & -2 & 2 & 2 & 2 \\ 7 & -6 & 7 & 6 & 6 \end{vmatrix}.$$

Exercise (10.4). Expand the following determinants about a row or column, and also by 2-rowed minors:

(a) $\begin{vmatrix} 2 & 4 & -5 & -1 & -2 \\ 0 & 2 & 3 & 0 & 7 \\ 0 & 2 & 1 & 0 & 1 \\ 3 & -3 & 2 & -5 & 1 \\ 1 & -1 & 4 & 6 & 2 \end{vmatrix}$, (b) $\begin{vmatrix} 1/2 & 2 & -1/2 & 1 \\ 0 & 2 & 1/3 & 0 \\ 4 & -3 & 1/4 & 6 \\ 0 & 3 & 2 & 0 \end{vmatrix}$,

(c) $\begin{vmatrix} 1 & 0 & 0 & 6-7i & 2i \\ 0 & 1 & 0 & 3 & 5+i \\ 0 & 0 & 1 & -3+i & 2+3i \\ 0 & 0 & 0 & 1-i & i \\ 0 & 0 & 0 & -i & 1+i \end{vmatrix}$, (d) $\begin{vmatrix} a_{11} & 0 & 0 & \cdots & 0 \\ a_{21} & a_{22} & 0 & \cdots & 0 \\ \cdot & \cdot & & & \cdot \\ \cdot & \cdot & & & \cdot \\ \cdot & \cdot & & & 0 \\ a_{n1} & a_{n2} & & \cdots & a_{nn} \end{vmatrix}$.

Exercise (10.5). Evaluate the following determinants, making use of the properties of determinants to simplify them before expanding:

(a) $\begin{vmatrix} e^x & e^{2x} & e^{3x} \\ e^x & 2e^{2x} & 3e^{3x} \\ e^x & 4e^{2x} & 9e^{3x} \end{vmatrix}$, (b) $\begin{vmatrix} -1 & b & c \\ -2 & b & 0 \\ 0 & 2a & b \end{vmatrix}$,

(c) $\begin{vmatrix} f_1 & f_2 & f_3 & f_4 & f_5 \\ \dfrac{df_1}{dx} & \dfrac{df_2}{dx} & \dfrac{df_3}{dx} & \dfrac{df_4}{dx} & \dfrac{df_5}{dx} \\ \dfrac{d^2f_1}{dx^2} & \dfrac{d^2f_2}{dx^2} & \dfrac{d^2f_3}{dx^2} & \dfrac{d^2f_4}{dx^2} & \dfrac{d^2f_5}{dx^2} \\ \dfrac{d^3f_1}{dx^3} & \dfrac{d^3f_2}{dx^3} & \dfrac{d^3f_3}{dx^3} & \dfrac{d^3f_4}{dx^3} & \dfrac{d^3f_5}{dx^3} \\ \dfrac{d^4f_1}{dx^4} & \dfrac{d^4f_2}{dx^4} & \dfrac{d^4f_3}{dx^4} & \dfrac{d^4f_4}{dx^4} & \dfrac{d^4f_5}{dx^4} \end{vmatrix}$,

where $f_i = f_i(x) = a_{i0}x^3 + a_{i1}x^2 + a_{i2}x + a_{i3}$.

Exercise (10.6). Write the expansion of the general fourth-order determinant $|a_{ij}|$ in the form of Definition (8.1), and in forms (10.4) and (10.5) for expansion about rows 1 and 3.

Exercise (10.7). Compute all minors of $\begin{pmatrix} 2 & 3 & 0 & 5 \\ -4 & 2 & -7 & 0 \\ -2 & 0 & 0 & 0 \end{pmatrix}$.
How many minors of order u does an m by n matrix have?

Exercise (10.8). Show how we can make all but one element zero of some row or column of the n-rowed square matrix A, and thus reduce the computation of $|A|$ to that of a determinant of order $n - 1$.

Exercise (10.9). Prove Theorem (10.3) directly.

Section 11. Adjoints and Inverses

If $m \neq 0$ is a complex number, the equation $mx = 1$ has a unique complex number solution. We denote this solution by $x = (1/m)$ or $x = m^{-1}$ and call x the *inverse* of m. For example, the inverses of the numbers $9/25$, $\sqrt{3}$, and $1 - i$ are the numbers $25/9$, $1/\sqrt{3}$, and $1/2 + i/2$ respectively. We now define the inverse of a square matrix A of order n similarly.

(11.1) Definition. The matrix X is an *inverse* of the square matrix A if either $AX = I$ or $XA = I$.

We first notice that the inverse of a square matrix of order n is also a square matrix of order n. For if $AX = I$, then X must be n by m for some m in order that AX be defined. Then AX is n by m and $m = n$ since $AX = I$, a square matrix. A similar argument holds if $XA = I$.

In order to find the condition that A have an inverse, we need two definitions.

(11.2) Definition. A is *nonsingular* if $|A| \neq 0$.

(11.3) Definition. The *adjoint* of $A = (a_{ij})$ is the matrix adj $A = (A_{ij})'$ where A_{ij} is the cofactor of a_{ij}.

Thus adj A is an n-rowed square matrix such that the element in position i,j of adj A is the cofactor of the element in position j,i of A. The following property of adj A is a consequence of Theorem (10.7).

(11.4) Theorem. $A(\text{adj } A) = (\text{adj } A)A = |A|I$.

PROOF. $$A(\text{adj } A) = (a_{ij})(A_{ij})' = \left(\sum_{k=1}^{n} a_{ik}A_{jk}\right) = (\delta_{ij}|A|) = |A|I,$$
and similarly for $(\text{adj } A)A$.

(11.5) Theorem. If A is nonsingular, then A has a unique inverse $A^{-1} = \frac{1}{|A|}(\text{adj } A)$ such that $AA^{-1} = A^{-1}A = I$. Conversely, if A has any inverse X, then A is nonsingular and $X = A^{-1}$.

PROOF. If A is nonsingular, then $|A| \neq 0$ and the matrix $A^{-1} = \frac{1}{|A|}(\text{adj } A)$ exists. Then by (11.4), $AA^{-1} = A\left(\frac{1}{|A|} \cdot \text{adj } A\right) = \frac{1}{|A|} \cdot A(\text{adj } A) = I$. Similarly by (11.4) $A^{-1}A = I$. If A has an inverse X such that $AX = I$, we have $X = IX = (A^{-1}A)X = A^{-1}(AX) = A^{-1}I = A^{-1}$. In the same way if $XA = I$, then $X = XI = X(AA^{-1}) = (XA)A^{-1} = IA^{-1} = A^{-1}$. Therefore the only inverse of A is $A^{-1} = \frac{1}{|A|}(\text{adj } A)$.

Conversely, if A has any inverse X, then either $AX = I$ or $XA = I$. By (9.7), $|A| \cdot |X| = |I| = 1$ in each case. Thus $|A| \neq 0$ and A is nonsingular. It follows from the uniqueness proof above that $X = A^{-1}$.

As an application of the above results, we obtain "Cramer's Rule" for the solution of n equations in n unknowns. Such a system of equations can be written as a single matrix equation $Ax = b$ where $A = (a_{ij})$ is a square matrix of order n,

$$x = \begin{pmatrix} x_1 \\ x_2 \\ \cdot \\ \cdot \\ \cdot \\ x_n \end{pmatrix}, \quad \text{and} \quad b = \begin{pmatrix} b_1 \\ b_2 \\ \cdot \\ \cdot \\ \cdot \\ b_n \end{pmatrix}.$$

These are called, respectively, the matrix of coefficients, the column matrix of the unknowns, and the column matrix of the constants on the right-hand side of the equations.

(11.6) Theorem. If A is nonsingular, the system $Ax = b$ of n equations in n unknowns has a unique solution $x = A^{-1}b$.

PROOF. By (11.5), A^{-1} exists, and $x = A^{-1}b$ is a solution, for $A(A^{-1}b) = (AA^{-1})b = Ib = b$. If y is any solution, then $Ay = b$, and $y = Iy = (A^{-1}A)y = A^{-1}(Ay) = A^{-1}b$.

Since $A^{-1} = \frac{1}{|A|} \cdot \text{adj } A = \frac{1}{|A|} \cdot (A_{ij})'$, $A^{-1}b = \frac{1}{|A|} \cdot (A_{ij})'(b_i)$ $= \frac{1}{|A|}\left(\sum_{k=1}^{n} A_{ki}b_k\right) = \left(\sum_{k=1}^{n} A_{ki}b_k \Big/ |A|\right)$, so that the value for x_i in the solution is $x_i = \sum_{k=1}^{n} A_{ki}b_k \Big/ |A| = \Delta_i \Big/ |A|$ where, if $C_1, C_2, \cdots, C_n$ are the columns of A, Δ_i is the determinant of the matrix

$$(C_1 \cdots C_{i-1}\, b\, C_{i+1} \cdots C_n).$$

This is the customary computation of the solution by Cramer's Rule.

Exercise (11.1). Compute $A^{-1} = \frac{1}{|A|}$ adj A for the following matrices:

(a) $A = \begin{pmatrix} 2 & 0 & 2 \\ 0 & 1 & -3 \\ 2 & 1 & 1 \end{pmatrix}$, (b) $A = \begin{bmatrix} 1 & 0 & 3 & -1 \\ 2 & 0 & 1 & 0 \\ 5 & 1 & 2 & 0 \\ 3 & -1 & 0 & 4 \end{bmatrix}$.

Exercise (11.2). Find the inverses of the following matrices by solving the equation $AX = I$:

(a) $A = \begin{bmatrix} 1 & 0 & 0 & 1 & 0 \\ 0 & 1 & 0 & 0 & 0 \\ 0 & 0 & 2 & 0 & i \\ 0 & 0 & 0 & 1 & 0 \\ 0 & 0 & \sqrt{2} & 0 & 3 \end{bmatrix}$, (b) $A = \begin{pmatrix} 3 & 0 & 0 \\ -2 & 1 & 0 \\ 3 & -1 & -5 \end{pmatrix}$,

(c) $A = \begin{bmatrix} 1/2 & 0 & 0 & 0 \\ 0 & 3 & 0 & 0 \\ 0 & 0 & -1 & 0 \\ 0 & 0 & 0 & 2/5 \end{bmatrix}$, (d) $A = (\delta_{ij}a_i)$.

Exercise (11.3). Calling $X = (x_{ij})$ the inverse of a given n-rowed square matrix A, show how the x_{ij} can be determined by solving n sets of n linear equations in n unknowns.

Exercise (11.4). Prove $(A^{-1})^{-1} = A$.

Exercise (11.5). Prove that $(AB)^{-1} = B^{-1}A^{-1}$, and in general that

$$(A_1A_2 \cdots A_k)^{-1} = A_k^{-1} \cdots A_2^{-1}A_1^{-1}.$$

Exercise (11.6). Verify the result of the previous exercise for the special case

$$A = \begin{pmatrix} 2 & 0 & 2 \\ 0 & 1 & 0 \\ -1 & -2 & 2 \end{pmatrix} \quad \text{and} \quad B = \begin{pmatrix} -1 & 2 & 0 \\ 0 & -2 & 1 \\ 1 & 1 & -1 \end{pmatrix}.$$

Exercise (11.7). Note that (11.3) does not define adj A if A is 1 by 1. Supply this definition so that $A^{-1} = \dfrac{1}{|A|}$ adj A for all n.

Exercise (11.8). Prove that if $A = O$, adj $A = O$. Show by example that the converse is not true.

Exercise (11.9). Prove $|\text{adj } A| = |A|^{n-1}$.

Exercise (11.10). Solve the following by the formula of (11.6), and by Cramer's Rule:

(a)
$$\begin{aligned} x + y + z + w &= 1 \\ 2x + y + 3z - w &= 2 \\ x - 4y + 6z + w &= 3 \\ 5x - y - z + 2w &= 4, \end{aligned}$$

(b)
$$\begin{aligned} 3x - 2y + z &= 1 \\ 2x - y + 3z &= -1 \\ x - 2y + z &= 3, \end{aligned}$$

(c)
$$\begin{aligned} 2x - y + z &= 0 \\ x - 3y + 2z &= 0 \\ 5x + 6y - 7z &= 0. \end{aligned}$$

Exercise (11.11). Prove that there exist unique constants A, B, and C such that

$$\frac{ax^2 + bx + c}{(x - r_1)(x - r_2)(x - r_3)} = \frac{A}{x - r_1} + \frac{B}{x - r_2} + \frac{C}{x - r_3},$$

where $ax^2 + bx + c$ is any quadratic and $(x - r_1)(x - r_2)(x - r_3)$ is any cubic with distinct linear factors.

Exercise (11.12). Express the following rational functions as a sum of partial fractions:

(a) $\dfrac{2x^2 - 3x + 4}{x^3 - 2x^2 - 15x}$, (b) $\dfrac{3x^3 - 7x^2 + 2x - 4}{(x + 2)(x + 1)(x - 1)(x - 2)}$.

Exercise (11.13). In the equations

$$\begin{aligned} x &= \rho \sin \phi \cos \theta \\ y &= \rho \sin \phi \sin \theta \\ z &= \rho \cos \phi, \end{aligned}$$

which give the rectangular coordinates of a point in space in terms of the spherical coordinates, solve for the partial derivatives $\frac{\partial \rho}{\partial x}$, $\frac{\partial \phi}{\partial x}$, and $\frac{\partial \theta}{\partial x}$. Similarly, solve for the partial derivatives of ρ, ϕ, and θ with respect to y and z.

Exercise (11.14). The functions $f_1(x), f_2(x), \cdots, f_n(x)$ are said to be linearly independent if the only set of constants $c_1, c_2, \cdots, c_n$ for which $c_1f_1(x) + c_2f_2(x) + \cdots + c_nf_n(x) = 0$ is $0, 0, \cdots, 0$. Repeated differentiation of this relation gives a set of n linear equations in the unknowns $c_1, c_2, \cdots, c_n$. Show that the functions $f_1(x), f_2(x), \cdots, f_n(x)$ are linearly independent if the determinant

$$\begin{vmatrix} f_1 & f_2 & \cdots & f_n \\ \frac{df_1}{dx} & \frac{df_2}{dx} & \cdots & \frac{df_n}{dx} \\ \vdots & \vdots & & \vdots \\ \frac{d^{n-1}f_1}{dx^{n-1}} & \frac{d^{n-1}f_2}{dx^{n-1}} & \cdots & \frac{d^{n-1}f_n}{dx^{n-1}} \end{vmatrix}$$

is not equal to zero for some value of x.

Exercise (11.15). Show that the following sets of functions are linearly independent:

(a) e^x, xe^x, x^2e^x,
(b) $e^{ax} \sin (bx), e^{ax} \cos (bx)$, where $b \neq 0$,
(c) $ax^2 + bx + c, dx + e, f$, where $a \neq 0$, $d \neq 0$, and $f \neq 0$.

II GROUPS OF TRANSFORMATIONS

Section 12. Definition of a Transformation

As we mentioned in Section 1, a system of m linear equations in n unknowns, which can be written as a single matrix equation $Ax = b$, is completely described by the m by $n + 1$ matrix $(A \quad b)$. In the preceding section, we discussed the solution of such a system when A is a nonsingular square matrix. In this chapter, we will be concerned with those matrix operations which lead to a solution in the general case. These operations transform the matrix $(A \quad b)$ into a matrix of an equivalent system of equations for which the solution is evident.

Although our concern at present is with matrix transformations, the idea of a transformation of a set M of objects is of such fundamental importance that we will consider it generally. By so doing, we will develop a concept of wide application and, at the same time, clarify the ideas of our current discussion.

The example of a transformation of a set M which is probably most familiar to the reader, is that of a single-valued real function f, defined by $y = f(x)$, for all real numbers x. Here, M is the set of all real numbers. For every real number x, a unique real number y is determined by the relation $y = f(x)$. Specific examples are $y = \sin x$ and $y = 3x - 5$. On the other hand, $y = \log_e x$ does not define a transformation of the set of all real numbers, since $\log_e x$ is defined only for positive numbers.

We can interpret the equations of a rotation,

$$\begin{aligned} x &= x' \cos \theta - y' \sin \theta \\ y &= x' \sin \theta + y' \cos \theta, \end{aligned}$$

as a rule for mapping a point with coordinates (x',y') onto a new point with coordinates (x,y), where both points are referred to the same coordinate system. These equations then define a transformation of the set M of all points in the plane.

Finally, we consider an example of a transformation of the type with which we will be concerned in this chapter. Let ${}_m\mathfrak{A}_n$ denote the set of all m by n matrices with complex number elements, and let P be a square matrix of order m with elements in this same number system. If* $X \in {}_m\mathfrak{A}_n$, then $PX = Y \in {}_m\mathfrak{A}_n$ is a uniquely defined matrix. Thus each $X \in {}_m\mathfrak{A}_n$ determines a unique matrix $Y \in {}_m\mathfrak{A}_n$ under premultiplication by the given matrix P. This is an example of a transformation of the set ${}_m\mathfrak{A}_n$ of m by n matrices, premultiplication by the fixed matrix P being the rule which defines the transformation.

We now define a transformation of an arbitrary set M.

(12.1) Definition. A *transformation* T of a set M is a rule by which every element $a \in M$ uniquely determines an element $b \in M$. We write $T(a) = b$ and call b the *map* of a by T.

(12.2) Definition. Two transformations T_1 and T_2 of M are *equal* if $T_1(a) = T_2(a)$ for all $a \in M$.

For two transformations of M to be equal, they must have the same effect on every element of the set. If there exists a single element $a \in M$ such that $T_1(a) \neq T_2(a)$, then $T_1 \neq T_2$.

Among the synonyms for "transformation" in common usage are "function," "correspondence," and "mapping." A longer, and more precise, terminology would be "a single-valued transformation (function, and so forth) of M into itself," but by our restrictive Definition (12.1), every transformation is single-valued and sends the set M into itself.†

It should be emphasized that a transformation T of M may map several elements of M onto the same element. For example, $y = \sin x$ maps all real numbers $x = r + 2n\pi$, for n an integer, onto the same real number $\sin r$, since $\sin(r + 2n\pi) = \sin r$ for all integers n. Further, not every element of M need be the map of some element of M. For example, since $|\sin x| \leq 1$, there is no real number x such that $\sin x = y$ if $y > 1$ or $y < -1$.

Let $\mathfrak{I}(M)$ denote the set of all transformations of M. For every $a \in M$, $\mathfrak{I}(M)$ contains the transformation T_a, defined by $T_a(x) = a$ for all $x \in M$, and different elements a and b define unequal transformations T_a and T_b. Thus, the number of transformations in $\mathfrak{I}(M)$ is at least as great as the number of elements in M. In particular, if M is an infinite set, $\mathfrak{I}(M)$ is infinite. The following theorem shows that if M is finite, $\mathfrak{I}(M)$ is finite.

(12.3) Theorem. If $M = \{a_1, a_2, \cdots, a_n\}$, then $\mathfrak{I}(M)$ contains n^n elements.

---

* The notation "$a \in M$" denotes class inclusion and is used to indicate that the element a is a member of the set M. We read $a \in M$ as "a in M," or "a is in M." If a is not a member of M we write $a \notin M$.

† The reader is cautioned that other texts may have slightly different definitions for the term "transformation."

PROOF. A transformation $T \in \mathfrak{T}(M)$ is determined as soon as we know the map of each element. Each element $a_i \in M$ may be mapped onto any one of the n elements $a_1, a_2, \cdots, a_n$. In this way we obtain n^n distinct transformations in $\mathfrak{T}(M)$. But every transformation in $\mathfrak{T}(M)$ is equal to one of these, so that $\mathfrak{T}(M)$ contains exactly n^n elements.

For example, if $M = \{a\}$, then $\mathfrak{T}(M)$ contains only the transformation T defined by $T(a) = a$. If $M = \{a_1,a_2\}$, then $\mathfrak{T}(M)$ consists of the transformations T_1,T_2,T_3, and T_4, defined by

$$T_1(a_1) = a_1,\ T_2(a_1) = a_1,\ T_3(a_1) = a_2,\ T_4(a_1) = a_2$$
$$T_1(a_2) = a_1,\ T_2(a_2) = a_2,\ T_3(a_2) = a_1,\ T_4(a_2) = a_2.$$

(12.4) Definition. T is a *transformation of M onto itself* if T is a transformation of M, and if for every $a \in M$, there exists $b \in M$ such that $T(b) = a$.

A transformation of M onto itself has the additional property that every $a \in M$ is the map of some element of M. We will soon restrict our attention to this special type of transformation. The equation $y = 3x - 5$ defines a transformation of the set of all real numbers onto itself, since for any given real number a, $(a + 5)/3$ is a real number which is mapped onto a. Our previous discussion of the transformation defined by $y = \sin x$ shows that this transformation of the real numbers does not satisfy Definition (12.4).

The simplest transformation which can be defined for a set M is the *identity transformation* which maps every element of M onto itself. It is usually denoted by I, and is defined by $I(a) = a$ for all $a \in M$. It is a transformation of M onto itself.

Exercise (12.1). Write out $\mathfrak{T}(M)$ for $M = \{a_1,a_2,a_3\}$. How many of these transformations are transformations of M onto itself?

Exercise (12.2). Let $M = {}_2\mathfrak{A}_3$ in the matrix example of this section, and let $P = \begin{pmatrix} 3 & 3 \\ 0 & 0 \end{pmatrix}$. Does the transformation T defined by $T(X) = PX$ map different elements of M onto the same element? Does T map ${}_2\mathfrak{A}_3$ onto itself? Answer these same questions for $P = \begin{pmatrix} 2 & 1 \\ 1 & 3 \end{pmatrix}$. Select a matrix P which defines the identity transformation.

Exercise (12.3).

(a) Show that each of the following rules defines a transformation of the set of all real numbers:

$T_1(a) = -a;$
$T_2(a) = [a]$, where $[a]$ is the unique integer such that $[a] \leq a < [a] + 1;$
$T_3(a) = a^6;$
$T_4(a) = a^{3/5};$
$T_5(a) = \text{Arctan } a$, where $-\pi/2 < \text{Arctan } a < \pi/2;$

$$T_6(a) = \begin{cases} 1 \text{ if } a \text{ is rational} \\ 2 \text{ if } a \text{ is not rational.} \end{cases}$$

(b) Which of the above rules define transformations of the set of all real numbers onto itself?
(c) Which rules define transformations of the set of all complex numbers?
(d) Which rules define transformations of the set of all rational numbers? Give a simplified definition for each transformation when possible.
(e) Answer the questions of part (*d*) for the set of all integers.

Section 13. The Multiplication of Transformations

Let S and T be transformations of a set M. If we first apply the transformation S to M, an element $a \in M$ is mapped onto the unique element $S(a) \in M$, and if we then apply the transformation T to M, the element $S(a) \in M$ is mapped onto the unique element $T(S(a)) \in M$. Thus for each $a \in M$, $T(S(a))$ is a uniquely determined element of M, and the result of following S by T is again a transformation of M. This process of following one transformation by another is the most natural way of combining two transformations.

In this chapter, we will be interested in a sequence of transformations which, when applied successively to an m by n matrix A, will yield a matrix of a simple form which exhibits certain characteristic properties of A. Therefore, we must first discuss the nature of this combining operation for transformations.

(13.1) Definition. If S and T are transformations of the set M, then the *product* TS is the transformation defined by $TS(a) = T(S(a))$ for all $a \in M$.

For example, if M is the set of all real numbers, and if f and g are transformations of M defined by $f(x) = \sin x$ and $g(x) = 2x + 5$, then the products fg and gf are defined by $fg(x) = f(g(x)) = \sin(2x + 5)$ and $gf(x) = g(f(x)) = 2 \sin x + 5$. Thus, if transformations are written in ordinary functional notation, the product transformation is a function of a function. Similarly, if $M = {}_m\mathfrak{A}_n$ is the set of all m by n

matrices, if S maps $A \in M$ onto $PA \in M$, and if T maps $A \in M$ onto $QA \in M$, then TS maps A onto QPA, and T^3 maps A onto Q^3A.

Since the product of any two transformations of M is a transformation of M, the set $\mathfrak{I}(M)$, of all transformations of M, is closed with respect to transformation multiplication. This multiplication is not commutative, since in general $TS \neq ST$. In the example above, $fg \neq gf$, since we can find a real number x for which $\sin(2x + 5) \neq 2 \sin x + 5$. In fact, in this example, there is no $x \in M$ for which $fg(x) = gf(x)$.

The following are immediate consequences of Definition (13.1):

(13.2) Theorem. Transformation multiplication is associative.

PROOF. If S, T, and R are any three transformations of M, we use (13.1) to obtain

$$[ST]R(a) = ST(R(a)) = S(T(R(a)))$$
$$S[TR](a) = S(TR(a)) = S(T(R(a)))$$

for all $a \in M$. Thus $(ST)R = S(TR)$ by Definition (12.2).

As in the case of matrix multiplication, the fact that multiplication of transformations is associative allows us to use the symbol STR for either product, $(ST)R$ or $S(TR)$. Moreover, the product of any number of transformations is completely determined by their order of application.

(13.3) Theorem. If S and T are transformations of M onto itself, then TS is a transformation of M onto itself.

PROOF. If $a \in M$, there exists $b \in M$ such that $T(b) = a$; and for $b \in M$, there exists $c \in M$ such that $S(c) = b$. Then by (13.1), $TS(c) = T(S(c)) = T(b) = a$.

We have for all $a \in M$, $IT(a) = I(T(a)) = T(a)$ and $TI(a) = T(I(a)) = T(a)$. Therefore if $T \in \mathfrak{I}(M)$, $IT = TI = T$, so that the identity transformation I is an identity with respect to transformation multiplication.

Exercise (13.1). Write out a multiplication table for the transformations T_1,T_2,T_3,T_4 of $M = \{a_1,a_2\}$, which were defined in Section 12.

Exercise (13.2). The powers of a transformation T are defined by $T^1 = T$, $T^{k+1} = TT^k$. Prove the laws of exponents $T^lT^m = T^{l+m}$ and $(T^l)^m = T^{lm}$.

Exercise (13.3). In the multiplication table of Exercise (13.1) find transformations R and S such that

(i) $RS = SR$ and $(RS)^2 = R^2S^2$;
(ii) $RS \neq SR$ but $(RS)^2 = R^2S^2$;
(iii) $RS \neq SR$ and $(RS)^2 \neq R^2S^2$.

This example shows that the third law of exponents $(ST)^n = S^nT^n$ is not always satisfied for transformation multiplication.

Exercise (13.4). Compute the following products of the transformations defined in Exercise (12.3):

$$T_3T_4,\ T_4T_3,\ T_1T_3,\ T_3T_1,\ T_1T_4,\ T_4T_1,\ T_2T_6,\ T_6T_2,\ T_2^2,\ T_6^2,\ T_1^n.$$

Section 14. One-to-One Transformations

(14.1) Definition. A transformation T of a set M is called *one-to-one* if every $a \in M$ is the map of exactly one $b \in M$.

Thus a one-to-one transformation T is a transformation of M onto itself with the additional property that $T(b) = a$ and $T(c) = a$ imply that $b = c$. If we take the matrix $P \in \mathfrak{A}_m$ to be nonsingular in the example of Section 12, where $T(X) = PX$ for $X \in {}_m\mathfrak{A}_n$, then T is a one-to-one transformation. For given any $Y \in {}_m\mathfrak{A}_n$, the element $P^{-1}Y \in {}_m\mathfrak{A}_n$ is mapped onto Y since $T(P^{-1}Y) = P(P^{-1}Y) = Y$. Furthermore if $T(X) = Y$ for any $X \in {}_m\mathfrak{A}_n$, then $PX = Y$ and $X = P^{-1}Y$. Therefore Y is the map of the single element $P^{-1}Y$. The identity transformation I of any set M is another example of a one-to-one transformation, for every $a \in M$ is the map of the single element a.

If we let $\mathfrak{O}(M)$ denote the set of all one-to-one transformations of M, then $\mathfrak{O}(M)$ is a subset of $\mathfrak{J}(M)$. We have already remarked that $I \in \mathfrak{O}(M)$. We now prove some important properties of $\mathfrak{O}(M)$.

(14.2) Theorem. $\mathfrak{O}(M)$ is closed with respect to transformation multiplication.

PROOF. If S and T are one-to-one transformations, then TS is a transformation of M onto itself by (13.3). Now if $TS(b) = a$ and $TS(c) = a$ for $a,b,c \in M$, then $T(S(b)) = a = T(S(c))$. This implies $S(b) = S(c)$ since T is one-to-one, and $b = c$ since S is one-to-one. Thus the product TS is a one-to-one transformation, and this proves the theorem.

If T is in $\mathfrak{O}(M)$, then for every $a \in M$, there is a unique $b \in M$ such that $T(b) = a$. Thus, if we define S by $S(a) = b$, S is a transformation of M. Moreover, S is a one-to-one transformation. Since a is the unique map of b by T, a is the only element which is mapped onto b by S.

(14.3) Definition. The *inverse* of the one-to-one transformation T is the one-to-one transformation S defined by $S(a) = b$ where $T(b) = a$, for all $a \in M$. We write $S = T^{-1}$.

Our previous discussion shows that T^{-1} exists and is in $\mathfrak{O}(M)$ for every $T \in \mathfrak{O}(M)$. The transformations T and T^{-1} counteract each other when applied to M. This is stated in another form in the following theorem in which we show that T^{-1} is the inverse of T with respect to transformation multiplication.

(14.4) Theorem. If $T \in \mathfrak{O}(M)$, $TT^{-1} = T^{-1}T = I$.

PROOF. If a is any element in M and $T^{-1}(a) = b$, then $TT^{-1}(a) = T(T^{-1}(a)) = T(b) = a$, since $T^{-1}(a) = b$ if and only if $T(b) = a$. Thus $TT^{-1} = I$ by Definition (12.2). The proof that $T^{-1}T = I$ is similar.

The following theorem is often useful in proving that a transformation of M is one-to-one.

(14.5) Theorem. If for $T \in \mathfrak{I}(M)$ there exists an $R \in \mathfrak{I}(M)$ such that $TR = RT = I$, then T is in $\mathfrak{O}(M)$ and $R = T^{-1}$.

PROOF. Since $T \in \mathfrak{I}(M)$, T is a single-valued transformation of M into itself. If a is any element of M, let $R(a) = b$. Then $T(b) = a$ since $a = I(a) = TR(a) = T(R(a)) = T(b)$, so that T is a transformation of M onto itself. If $T(a) = T(b)$, then $R(T(a)) = R(T(b))$, so that $a = I(a) = RT(a) = R(T(a)) = R(T(b)) = RT(b)) = I(b) = b$. Therefore T is a one-to-one transformation of M. Since $T \in \mathfrak{O}(M)$, T^{-1} exists and $R = RI = R(TT^{-1}) = (RT)T^{-1} = IT^{-1} = T^{-1}$.

It is an important consequence of Theorem (14.5) that T^{-1} is the unique inverse with respect to transformation multiplication of a transformation $T \in \mathfrak{O}(M)$.

Exercise (14.1). If $T \in \mathfrak{O}(M)$, and if $R \in \mathfrak{I}(M)$ satisfies either $RT = I$ or $TR = I$, prove that $R = T^{-1}$.

Exercise (14.2). If $S,T \in \mathfrak{O}(M)$, show that $(ST)^{-1} = T^{-1}S^{-1}$.

Exercise (14.3). If we define $T^0 = I$ and $T^{-n} = (T^n)^{-1}$ for $T \in \mathfrak{O}(M)$, prove that $T^mT^n = T^{m+n}$ and $(T^m)^n = T^{mn}$ for all integers m and n.

Exercise (14.4). Which of the transformations of Exercise (12.3) is one-to-one? Find the inverse of each.

Exercise (14.5). Prove that if T is a transformation of a finite set M onto itself, then T is one-to-one. Give an example which shows that this is not true for infinite sets.

Section 15. Groups of Transformations

If M is any set, we have shown in the preceding section that $\mathfrak{O}(M)$ contains the product of any two of its members and the inverse of each of its members. This implies that $\mathfrak{O}(M)$ contains all finite power products like $T_1^2T_3^{-3}T_2^{-1}T_3^4T_1T_2^{-2}$ and a solution $X = S^{-1}T$ of every equation $SX = T$ for S and T in $\mathfrak{O}(M)$. Thus the result of all such calculations performed in $\mathfrak{O}(M)$ is again a transformation in $\mathfrak{O}(M)$. There are certain subsets of $\mathfrak{O}(M)$ which have this same closure property. Any such set of transformations is called a group of transformations.

(15.1) Definition. A set G of transformations in $\mathfrak{O}(M)$ is called a *group of transformations* of M if G satisfies the following three conditions:

(i) if S and T are in G, then ST is in G;
(ii) the identity transformation I is in G;
(iii) if T is in G, then T^{-1} is in G.

The results of the preceding section show that $\mathfrak{O}(M)$ is itself a group of transformations of M. The reader may verify that the set consisting of the identity transformation alone is a group of transformations. If M is a finite set with n elements, a one-to-one transformation of M is called a *permutation*, and the group $\mathfrak{O}(M)$ is called the *symmetric group on n letters*.

EXAMPLE 1. If $M = \{a_1,a_2,a_3,a_4\}$, $\mathfrak{O}(M)$ contains 24 permutations. The subset $G = \{T_1,T_2,T_3,T_4\}$ is a group of transformations, where $T_1 = I$, T_2 interchanges a_1 and a_2 but leaves a_3 and a_4 fixed, T_3 interchanges a_3 and a_4 but leaves a_1 and a_2 fixed, and where $T_4 = T_2T_3 = T_3T_2$. The reader may verify that G is a group of transformations by showing that $T_2^2 = T_3^2 = T_4^2 = I$, $T_2T_4 = T_4T_2 = T_3$, and $T_3T_4 = T_4T_3 = T_2$. Notice that this group has a commutative multiplication.

For purposes of the present chapter and the later chapters on matrices, we will consider groups of transformations defined on an infinite set of matrices. The group in the following example is typical.

EXAMPLE 2. Let $M = {}_m\mathfrak{A}_n$, the set of all m by n matrices. Let G be the set of all transformations T_P of M, defined by $T_P(X) = PX$ for $X \in M$, where P is any nonsingular m-rowed square matrix. Then G is a subset of $\mathfrak{O}(M)$, since we showed in the preceding section that each T_P is a one-to-one transformation of M. We now verify that G is a group of transformations.

If T_P and T_Q are in G, then $|P| \neq 0$ and $|Q| \neq 0$. By (9.7), $|PQ| \neq 0$ and T_{PQ} is in G, where $T_{PQ}(X) = (PQ)X$. But $T_PT_Q(X) = T_P(T_Q(X)) = T_P(QX) = P(QX) = (PQ)X = T_{PQ}(X)$ for all $X \in M$.

Therefore $T_P T_Q = T_{PQ}$. This proves (i) and gives a general product rule.

To prove (ii), we note that $T_{I_m} \epsilon G$ and T_{I_m} is the identity transformation I since $T_{I_m}(X) = I_m X = X$ for all $X \epsilon M$.

Finally, if $T_P \epsilon G$, then $|P| \neq 0$ so that P^{-1} exists. Further, $|P^{-1}| \neq 0$, and $T_{P^{-1}}$ is in G. Since $T_P T_{P^{-1}} = T_{PP^{-1}} = T_{I_m} = I$ by the general product rule, $T_{P^{-1}} = (T_P)^{-1}$, proving (iii).

Exercise (15.1). Show that each of the following sets G is a group of transformations on the designated set M.

(a) M is the set of all real numbers. G is the set of all linear functions f defined by $f(x) = ax + b$, $a \neq 0$.
(b) M is the set of all points in the plane. G is the set of all rotations about a fixed point.
(c) M is the set $\mathfrak{A}_n$ of all n-rowed square matrices. G consists of the two transformations I and T where $T(A) = A'$, the transpose of A.
(d) M is arbitrary. G is the set of all transformations in $\mathfrak{S}(M)$ which leave fixed the element $a \epsilon M$.

Which of these groups is commutative?

Exercise (15.2). Show that if $T \epsilon \mathfrak{S}(M)$, the powers T^i of T form a group of transformations.

Exercise (15.3). If M has n elements, how many elements does $\mathfrak{S}(M)$ have?

Exercise (15.4). Why is $\mathfrak{T}(M)$ not a group of transformations?

Exercise (15.5). Show by constructing an infinite set of transformations in $\mathfrak{S}(M)$, that if M is infinite, $\mathfrak{S}(M)$ is infinite.

Section 16. Equivalence Relations

Let M be any set of elements and let a relation R be defined on M so that for every ordered pair a,b (not necessarily distinct) of elements of M, aRb is either true or false. The whole of mathematics is concerned with the study of relations between mathematical objects, that is, elements of sets. Elementary mathematics is usually restricted to sets of numbers or to the points and lines of the Euclidean plane. In Chapter I we were concerned with relations between matrices, such as A has the same size as B, B is conformable with respect to A, A is the transpose of B, and so on.

We shall see that each group G of transformations of a set M leads in a natural way to a special type of relation on M, called an *equivalence relation*, which separates M into classes of related elements. In order to determine the properties of the elements of M which describe this separation induced by the group G, we now discuss equivalence relations in some detail.

For the groups of matrix transformations, which are our particular interest in this chapter and in Chapter VIII, we will select a representative matrix of a simple form from each class of related matrices which exhibits the essential features of that class. The process of "reducing a matrix A to canonical form" is that of finding a sequence of transformations in the group under consideration which sends A into the matrix which is representative of the class containing A.

(16.1) Definition. The relation R on the set M is an *equivalence relation* on M if, for elements $a, b, c \in M$,

(i) aRa for all $a \in M$,
(ii) if aRb, then bRa,
(iii) if aRb and bRc, then aRc.

We use the symbol $\sim$ to denote an equivalence relation, and if $a \sim b$, we say that *a is equivalent to b*. The reader should observe that the properties (i), (ii), and (iii) are those of the ordinary equality of elements. Indeed, equality is the most familiar equivalence relation, and an equivalence relation can be thought of as a generalization of this fundamental concept.

The three conditions of this definition are known respectively as the reflexive, symmetric, and transitive laws. Of the relations between matrices mentioned above, only the first is an equivalence relation. Indeed, conformality satisfies no one of the three conditions, and transposition is only symmetric. If M is the set of all n-rowed square matrices, the relation $a \sim b$ if and only if $|A| = |B|$, is an equivalence relation. Relations between geometric objects such as parallelism of lines* and similarity and congruence of triangles are examples of equivalence relations.

Let $\sim$ be an equivalence relation defined on M and consider for each $a \in M$ the subset U_a of M consisting of those elements of M which are equivalent to a. These subsets, defined for every $a \in M$, are called *equivalence classes*. Their fundamental property is given by the following theorem.

---

* In order for parallelism of lines to be an equivalence relation, coincident lines must be considered parallel.

(16.2) Theorem. $a \sim b$ if and only if $U_a = U_b$.

PROOF. Assume first that $a \sim b$. If x is any element in U_a, then $x \sim a$ by the definition of the class U_a. Since $x \sim a$ and $a \sim b$, we may use the transitive property of the equivalence relation to obtain $x \sim b$. This means that $x \in U_b$ by the definition of the class U_b. Since x is any element in U_a, we have proved that every element in U_a is in U_b, or that* $U_a \subseteq U_b$. Similarly if $y \in U_b$, then $y \sim b$. But $a \sim b$ implies $b \sim a$ by the symmetric property of the equivalence relation. Since $y \sim b$ and $b \sim a$ imply $y \sim a$ by the transitive property, $y \in U_a$ and $U_b \subseteq U_a$. Thus we have shown that $U_a = U_b$.

Conversely, assume that $U_a = U_b$. By the reflexive law $a \sim a$, so that $a \in U_a$. But $a \in U_a$ implies $a \in U_b$ since the classes are identical. Finally $a \in U_b$ implies $a \sim b$ by the definition of the class U_b.

The meaning of Theorem (16.2) is that an equivalence relation (which is a generalized equality), defined on the elements of the set M, becomes ordinary equality for the corresponding equivalence classes of M. In any discussion concerning an equivalence relation, equivalence of elements may be replaced by equality of classes. This is illustrated by the following example from plane analytic geometry.

EXAMPLE 1. Let M be the set of all linear equations $Ax + By + C = 0$, and let two such equations be equivalent if their coefficients are proportional. Thus $(Ax + By + C = 0) \sim (A'x + B'y + C' = 0)$ if and only if $A' = kA$, $B' = kB$, and $C' = kC$ for a non-zero constant k. This is an equivalence relation. For any equation $L: (Ax + By + C = 0)$ is equivalent to itself since $A = 1 \cdot A$, $B = 1 \cdot B$, $C = 1 \cdot C$. If L is equivalent to equation $L': (A'x + B'y + C' = 0)$, then $A' = kA$, $B' = kB$, $C' = kC$ for $k \neq 0$. But $1/k \neq 0$ and $A = (1/k)A'$, $B = (1/k)B'$, $C = (1/k)C'$, so that $L' \sim L$. Finally if $L \sim L'$ and $L' \sim L'': (A''x + B''y + C'' = 0)$ with $A'' = k_1A'$, $B'' = k_1B'$, $C'' = k_1C'$, $k_1 \neq 0$, then $A'' = k_1A' = k_1(kA) = k_1kA$, $B'' = k_1kB$, and $C'' = k_1kC$. Since $k_1k \neq 0$, $L \sim L''$.

Now any two equations in a given equivalence class are equations of the same line, and conversely any two equations of a given line are in the same equivalence class. Thus there is a one-to-one correspondence between equivalence classes of equations and lines of the plane, and the geometric interpretation of the equations amounts to the replacement of equivalence of equations by equality of classes.

---

* The notation $A \subseteq B$ means that the set A is a subset of the set B, that is, every element in A is in B. If $A \subseteq B$ and $B \subseteq A$, then $A = B$.

(16.3) Theorem. The equivalence classes of an equivalence relation $\sim$ on a set M separate M into mutually disjoint* subsets, where a and b are in the same subset if and only if $a \sim b$.

PROOF. Since $a \sim a$, $a \in U_a$ for all $a \in M$, so that every element of M is in at least one equivalence class and every equivalence class contains at least one element of M. Two equivalence classes are either identical or have no elements in common. For if the classes U_a and U_b have some element c in common, then $c \sim a$ and $c \sim b$, and by symmetry and transitivity, $a \sim b$. Thus $U_a = U_b$ by (16.2). Finally, if a and b are in the same class U_c, then $a \sim c$ and $b \sim c$, so that $a \sim b$; and conversely if $a \sim b$, a and b are in the same class U_b.

Such a separation is called a *partition* of M, or more precisely, the natural partition of M induced by the equivalence relation.

EXAMPLE 2. Let M be the set of all integers, and let $a \sim b$ if $a - b$ is divisible by 3. It is easy to check that this is an equivalence relation. The equivalence class U_0 of all integers x, such that $x - 0 = x$ is divisible by 3, consists of all integers of the form $3k$ for $k = 0, \pm 1, \pm 2, \cdots$. Similarly U_1 consists of all integers x such that $x - 1$ is divisible by 3, that is, all integers of the form $3k + 1$, and U_2 consists of all integers of the form $3k + 2$. Since any integer n has one of these three forms, every equivalence class U_n has the element n in common with one of these three classes U_0, U_1, and U_2, and is therefore identical with that class. Further, since no two of the integers 0, 1, and 2 are equivalent, the classes U_0, U_1, and U_2 are mutually disjoint and form a partition of the set of all integers.

This example may be generalized by replacing 3 by any positive integer n. The classes are then $U_0, U_1, \cdots, U_{n-1}$, where a and b are in the same class if and only if $a - b$ is divisible by n. These classes are called the *residue classes of the integers modulo n*.

We have seen that every equivalence relation leads to a partition. Conversely, if we partition M into mutually disjoint subsets, then an equivalence relation on M may be defined by $a \sim b$ if and only if a and b are in the same subset. If each subset of M consists of a single element, the corresponding equivalence relation is the ordinary equality $a = b$.

Our principal interest in equivalence relations in this and the later chapters on matrices lies in their connection with groups of transformations. This connection is given by the following theorem.

---

* Two sets are *disjoint* if they have no elements in common. Two or more sets are *mutually disjoint* if each pair of them is disjoint.

(16.4) Theorem. Every group G of transformations of M induces an equivalence relation $\sim$ on M defined by

$$a \sim b \text{ if there exists a transformation } T \in G \text{ such that } T(a) = b.$$

PROOF. Since $I \in G$ and $I(a) = a$ for all $a \in M$, we have the reflexive property $a \sim a$. If $a \sim b$, there exists a transformation $T \in G$ such that $T(a) = b$. Since G is a group, $T^{-1} \in G$, and since $T^{-1}(b) = a$, we have that $b \sim a$. Therefore the relation is symmetric. Finally, if $a \sim b$ and $b \sim c$, there exist S and T in G such that $S(a) = b$ and $T(b) = c$. Again, since G is a group, $TS \in G$, and since $TS(a) = T(S(a)) = T(b) = c$, we have that $a \sim c$. Thus the relation is transitive, and is an equivalence relation.

If $a \sim b$ where $\sim$ is the equivalence relation induced by the group G of transformations of M, we say that a is *equivalent to b under the group G*. Thus a is equivalent to b under the group G if there exists a transformation $T \in G$ such that $T(a) = b$.

EXAMPLE 3. Let M be the set of all straight lines $y = mx + b$ and $x = c$. Let G be the set of all translations

$$\begin{aligned} x' &= x \\ y' &= y + k \qquad \text{for } k \text{ a real number.} \end{aligned}$$

This is the set of all translations of the plane through a distance k parallel to the Y-axis, and it is easy to prove that this is a group of transformations of M. Under this group each line $x = c$ is mapped onto itself and is the only element in its equivalence class. The line $y = mx + b$ can be mapped onto the line $y = m'x + b'$ if and only if $m = m'$. Therefore the lines through the origin, $y = mx$, are all in different classes, each class consisting of one line $y = mx$ and all lines parallel to it.

EXAMPLE 4. Let M be the same set as that considered in Example 3, but let G be the group of all rotations about the origin. The distance of a line from the origin remains fixed under all transformations in G. Thus each equivalence class consists of all lines tangent to a circle of radius $d \geq 0$ with center at the origin.

Exercise (16.1). Prove that the relation in Example 2 is an equivalence relation when 3 is replaced by an arbitrary positive integer n.

Exercise (16.2). Prove that the relation R on the subsets of M, defined by ARB if A is a subset of B, is reflexive and transitive but not symmetric.

Exercise (16.3). Show that the relation R is reflexive if it is symmetric and transitive, and if for every $x \in M$ there exists at least one $y \in M$ such that xRy. Why must we make the last hypothesis?

Exercise (16.4). If M is the set of Example 3, discuss the equivalence relation induced by all translations $x' = x + h$, $y' = y + k$, where h and k are real numbers.

Exercise (16.5). If M is the set of all polynomials in x, discuss the equivalence classes of each of the following equivalence relations:

(a) $f(x) \sim g(x)$ if and only if $df(x)/dx = dg(x)/dx$;
(b) $f(x) \sim g(x)$ if and only if degree of $f(x)$ = degree of $g(x)$;
(c) $f(x) \sim g(x)$ if and only if $f(x) - g(x)$ is divisible by x.

Exercise (16.6). What is the relation induced in M by $\mathfrak{S}(M)$? What is that induced by the group consisting of the identity transformation I alone?

Exercise (16.7). If $G_1 \subseteq G_2$ are two groups of transformations of M inducing the equivalence relations $\sim$ and $\wedge$ respectively, prove that $a \sim b$ implies $a \wedge b$. Discuss the induced partitions of M.

Section 17. Representatives and Canonical Forms

Let M be any set of elements and let an equivalence relation $\sim$ be defined on M.

(17.1) Definition. The subset N of M is a *set of representatives* of M for the equivalence relation $\sim$

(i) if every element of M is equivalent to at least one element of N,

and

(ii) if no two distinct elements of N are equivalent.

An alternate form of (ii) is the statement that if $a \sim b$ where $a \in N$ and $b \in N$, then $a = b$.

It follows from the definition that each element of M is equivalent to exactly one element of N. For if $a \sim b$ and $a \sim c$ with b and c in N, then $b \sim c$ and hence $b = c$.

The set $N = 0, 1, 2$ is a set of representatives for the equivalence relation in Example 2 of the Section 16. For every integer has one of the three forms $3k$, $3k + 1$, and $3k + 2$ and hence is equivalent to 0, 1, or 2, while no two of these three integers are equivalent. Similarly in Example 3 of that section, the lines $y = mx$ and $x = c$ for all real numbers m and c form a set of representatives.

A convenient method for choosing a set of representatives is given by the following theorem.

(17.2) Theorem. A subset N of M is a set of representatives for the equivalence relation $\sim$ if and only if N contains exactly one element from each equivalence class of the relation.

PROOF. Let N be a set of representatives, and let a be any element of the equivalence class U. By (i) there exists an element $b \in N$ such that $a \sim b$, and therefore $b \in U$ since U contains all elements equivalent to a. If also the element $c \in N$ is in U, we would have $b \sim c$ and therefore $b = c$ by (ii). Thus N contains exactly one element from each equivalence class. Conversely, let N be formed by choosing exactly one element from each class. If $a \in M$, then $a \in U_a$ and is equivalent to the element of N chosen from U_a, proving (i). Since two elements are equivalent only if they are in the same equivalence class, no two elements of N are equivalent, proving (ii). Therefore N is a set of representatives.

In view of Theorem (17.2) we call each element of a set of representatives N, the representative of the class to which it belongs. The theorem shows that we may choose any element of an equivalence class as a representative of the class. Usually we choose a particular set of representatives with additional properties of simplicity and utility suggested by the equivalence relation under consideration. For example, the numbers 329, -35, and 42 are a set of representatives in Example 2 of Section 16, but we prefer the set 0, 1, 2 since it is easy to describe and the conditions of Definition (17.1) are readily verified for this set. The choice of a best set of representatives for a given equivalence relation will often depend on the problem under consideration.

In our work with matrices we will be dealing exclusively with equivalence relations which are induced by a group of transformations, that is, with equivalence under a group as defined in Section 16. For most such equivalence relations, there exists a special set of representatives which exhibits the properties of the elements which are significant with respect to the given group of transformations. Such a set of representatives is called a *set of canonical forms for the group G*. A set N of canonical forms for a group will satisfy, usually by inspection, the conditions of Definition (17.1), which for equivalence under the group G, take the following form:

(17.3) (i) For every $a \in M$, there exists $T \in G$ such that $T(a) \in N$.

and

(ii) If b and c are distinct elements of N, there is no transformation in G which maps b onto c.

In Example 4 of Section 16, we took M to be the set of all lines in the plane and G to be the group of rotations about the origin. One choice of a set of canonical forms is the set of all lines $x = d$ for $d \geq 0$. An equally good choice would be the set of lines $y = d$ for $d \geq 0$. Each set exhibits clearly that distance from the origin is the only significant property of lines when we subject them to this group of transformations.

Exercise (17.1). In Example 1 of Section 16,

(a) prove that the set of all equations $y = mx + b$ and $x = c$ is a set of representatives;
(b) give a set of representatives in intercept form;
(c) list other sets of representatives.

Exercise (17.2). Give sets of representatives for the equivalence relations in the exercises of Section 16.

Exercise (17.3). Prove that conditions (17.3) for a set of representatives for a group follow from Definition (17.1).

Section 18. The Equivalence of Rectangular Matrices

We are now in a position to consider the particular group of matrix transformations which is associated with the problem of solving m linear equations in n unknowns. The results of the next several sections are applied to this problem at the end of this chapter. In Chapter III, these results have application in the study of vector spaces, which includes the problem of simplifying linear and bilinear mappings.

The customary way to begin the following discussion is with the simple matrix transformations, called elementary transformations, which correspond to the ordinary processes used in solving systems of equations by elimination. However, in order to obtain a precise statement of the problem under consideration in terms of the ideas which we have developed, we define an equivalence transformation directly, and then show that an equivalence transformation is equal to a sequence of these elementary transformations.

Let $M = {}_m\mathfrak{A}_n$ be the set of all m by n matrices with complex number elements. Consider the set of all transformations $T_{P,Q}$ of M defined by

$$T_{P,Q}(A) = PAQ \text{ for all } A \in M,$$

where P is a nonsingular m-rowed square matrix and Q is a nonsingular n-rowed square matrix.

These transformations are one-to-one transformations of M. For given $A \in M$, the matrix $T_{P,Q}(A) = PAQ$ is a uniquely determined matrix in M, so that $T_{P,Q}$ is single-valued. Secondly $T_{P,Q}$ maps M onto itself, for if $A \in M$, then $B = P^{-1}AQ^{-1} \in M$ and $T_{P,Q}(B) = A$. Finally $T_{P,Q}$ is one-to-one, for if also $T_{P,Q}(C) = A$, then $PCQ = A$ and $C = P^{-1}AQ^{-1} = B$.

(18.1) Definition. The one-to-one transformation $T_{P,Q}$ of ${}_m\mathfrak{A}_n$ is called an *equivalence transformation* of ${}_m\mathfrak{A}_n$.

Let $\mathcal{E}({}_m\mathfrak{A}_n)$ be the set of all equivalence transformations of ${}_m\mathfrak{A}_n$. We showed above that $\mathcal{E}({}_m\mathfrak{A}_n) \subseteq \mathcal{O}({}_m\mathfrak{A}_n)$.

(18.2) Lemma. If $T_{P,Q}$ and $T_{R,S}$ are in $\mathcal{E}({}_m\mathfrak{A}_n)$, then $T_{R,S}T_{P,Q} = T_{RP,QS} \in \mathcal{E}({}_m\mathfrak{A}_n)$.

PROOF. Since P and R are both nonsingular m-rowed square matrices, the product RP exists and is a nonsingular m-rowed square matrix. Similarly QS is a nonsingular n-rowed square matrix, so that $T_{RP,QS} \in \mathcal{E}({}_m\mathfrak{A}_n)$. The product rule follows from $T_{RP,QS}(A) = (RP)A(QS) = R(PAQ)S = T_{R,S}T_{P,Q}(A)$ for all $A \in {}_m\mathfrak{A}_n$.

Similarly $T_{P_1,Q_1}T_{P_2,Q_2} \cdots T_{P_n,Q_n} = T_{P,Q}$ where $P = P_1P_2 \cdots P_n$. $Q = Q_n \cdots Q_2Q_1$.

(18.3) Theorem. $\mathcal{E}({}_m\mathfrak{A}_n)$ is a group of transformations.

PROOF. We proved in Lemma (18.2) that $\mathcal{E}({}_m\mathfrak{A}_n)$ is closed with respect to transformation multiplication. Now $T_{I_m,I_n} \in \mathcal{E}({}_m\mathfrak{A}_n)$ and $T_{I_m,I_n} = I$ by the product rule. Finally if $T_{P,Q} \in \mathcal{E}({}_m\mathfrak{A}_n)$, then $T_{P^{-1},Q^{-1}}$ is in $\mathcal{E}({}_m\mathfrak{A}_n)$ and $T_{P^{-1},Q^{-1}} = (T_{P,Q})^{-1}$, again by Lemma (18.2).

(18.4) Definition. The equivalence relation induced in ${}_m\mathfrak{A}_n$ by the group $\mathcal{E}({}_m\mathfrak{A}_n)$ is called the *equivalence of rectangular matrices.*

Thus the matrices A and B in ${}_m\mathfrak{A}_n$ are equivalent if and only if there exist nonsingular matrices P and Q such that $B = PAQ$.

We will characterize this equivalence relation by obtaining a set of canonical matrices for the group $\mathcal{E}({}_m\mathfrak{A}_n)$. As we indicated earlier, our first step is to express each equivalence transformation as a product of simple transformations called elementary transformations.

Exercise (18.1). Show that in the set $\mathfrak{A}_n$ of n-rowed square matrices every nonsingular matrix is equivalent to I_n.

Exercise (18.2). What matrices in ${}_m\mathfrak{A}_n$ are equivalent to the zero matrix?

Exercise (18.3). Prove directly that $A \sim PAQ$ is an equivalence relation.

Exercises (18.4). Prove that the following pairs of matrices are equivalent by finding matrices P and Q such that $B = PAQ$:

(a) $A = (1\ 0)$, $B = (5\ 0)$; **(b)** $A = (1\ 0)$, $B = (0\ 1)$;

(c) $A = (1\ 1)$, $B = (2\ 0)$; **(d)** $A = \begin{pmatrix} 1 & 0 \\ 0 & 1 \end{pmatrix}$, $B = \begin{pmatrix} 3 & -1 \\ 2 & 5 \end{pmatrix}$;

(e) $A = (1\ 2\ 3)$, $B = (2\ 3\ 4)$.

Section 19. Elementary Transformations

There are three types of elementary transformation matrices, which we shall call U, V, and W. For any p, the matrix U is obtained from I_p by interchanging rows r and s $(r \neq s)$; V is obtained from I_p by adding to row r the elements of row s multiplied by the scalar g $(r \neq s)$; and W is obtained from I_p by multiplying row r by the scalar $c \neq 0$. By Section 9, $|U| = -1$, $|V| = +1$, and $|W| = c$. Since $I_p = (\delta_{ij})$, we have

$$\begin{aligned}
U &= (u_{ij}) \text{ where for all } j\colon & u_{ij} &= \delta_{ij} \text{ if } i \neq r \text{ or } s, \\
&& u_{rj} &= \delta_{sj},\ u_{sj} = \delta_{rj}; \\
V &= (v_{ij}) \text{ where for all } j\colon & v_{ij} &= \delta_{ij} \text{ if } i \neq r \\
&& v_{rj} &= \delta_{rj} + g\delta_{sj}; \\
W &= (w_{ij}) \text{ where for all } j\colon & w_{ij} &= \delta_{ij} \text{ if } i \neq r,\ w_{rj} = c\delta_{rj}.
\end{aligned}$$

We may also describe these matrices in terms of their columns: U is obtained from I_p by interchanging columns r and s $(r \neq s)$; V by adding to column s the elements of column r multiplied by the scalar g $(r \neq s)$; and W by multiplying column r by the scalar $c \neq 0$. Only in the description of V is there any change from the row description.

We call U, V, and W *elementary transformation matrices of types* I, II, and III respectively. For each type we define two transformations, $T_{U,I}$, $T_{I,U}$, $T_{V,I}$, $T_{I,V}$, $T_{W,I}$, and $T_{I,W}$. Choosing the U, V, W, and I of proper size, these are six equivalence transformations of the set of all m by n matrices. They are called the *elementary row and column transformations of types* I, II, and III.

We now describe the effect of these elementary transformations on an m by n matrix $A = (a_{ij})$.

(19.1) $$T_{U,I}(A) = UAI = UA = \Big(\sum_{k=1}^{m} u_{ik}a_{kj}\Big).$$

If $i \neq r$ and $i \neq s$, $\sum_{k=1}^{m} u_{ik}a_{kj} = \sum_{k=1}^{m} \delta_{ik}a_{kj} = a_{ij}$, since $\delta_{ik} = 0$ if $k \neq i$, and $\delta_{ii} = 1$. Thus the rows of UA, except for rows r and s, are the same as the rows of A. The elements of row r of UA are given by $\sum_{k=1}^{m} u_{rk}a_{kj} = \sum_{k=1}^{m} \delta_{sk}a_{kj} = a_{sj}$, so that row r of UA is the same as row s of A. Similarly, row s of UA is the same as row r of A, and $T_{U,I}$, called an *elementary row transformation of type* I, has the effect of interchanging rows r and s of A.

Since U is obtained from I_m by interchanging rows r and s, $T_{U,I_m}(U) = UUI_m = UU$ is equal to I_m by the argument in the previous paragraph. Therefore $U^{-1} = U$ and $(T_{U,I})^{-1} = T_{U^{-1},I^{-1}} = T_{U,I}$.

If A is square, $|T_{U,I}(A)| = |UA| = -|A|$.

We may show by a similar discussion that $T_{I,U}$, the *elementary column transformation of type* I, has the effect of interchanging columns r and s of the matrix A. For example, the elements of column r of $T_{I,U}(A) = AU$ are the elements $\sum_{k=1}^{n} a_{ik}u_{kr} = \sum_{k=1}^{n} a_{ik}\delta_{ks} = a_{is}$ of column s of A.

(19.2) $$T_{V,I}(A) = VAI = VA = \left(\sum_{k=1}^{m} v_{ik}a_{kj}\right).$$

If $i \neq r$, $\sum_{k=1}^{m} v_{ik}a_{kj} = \sum_{k=1}^{m} \delta_{ik}a_{kj} = a_{ij}$, so that the rows of VA, except for row r, are the same as the rows of A. The elements of row r of VA are given by $\sum_{k=1}^{m} v_{rk}a_{kj} = \sum_{k=1}^{m} (\delta_{rk} + g\delta_{sk})a_{kj} = \sum_{k=1}^{m} \delta_{rk}a_{kj} + g\sum_{k=1}^{m} \delta_{sk}a_{kj} = a_{rj} + ga_{sj}$. Thus $T_{V,I}$, called an *elementary row transformation of type* II, has the effect of adding to row r of A the elements of row s of A multiplied by the scalar g.

Let $\bar{V}$ be the elementary transformation matrix of type II obtained from I_m by adding to row r the elements of row s multiplied by $-g$. Then $T_{\bar{V},I_m}(V) = \bar{V}VI_m = \bar{V}V = I_m$ by the previous paragraph, so that $\bar{V} = V^{-1}$. Therefore $(T_{V,I})^{-1} = T_{V^{-1},I^{-1}} = T_{\bar{V},I}$ is again an elementary row transformation of type II.

If A is square, $|T_{V,I}(A)| = |VA| = |A|$.

Similarly $T_{I,V}$, the *elementary column transformation of type* II, has the effect on A of adding to column s the elements of column r multiplied by the scalar g.

(19.3) $$T_{W,I}(A) = WAI = WA = \Big(\sum_{k=1}^{m} w_{ik}a_{kj}\Big).$$

If $i \neq r$, $\sum_{k=1}^{m} w_{ik}a_{kj} = \sum_{k=1}^{m} \delta_{ik}a_{kj} = a_{ij}$, and $\sum_{k=1}^{m} w_{rk}a_{kj} = \sum_{k=1}^{m} c\delta_{rk}a_{kj} = ca_{rj}$. Thus $T_{W,I}$, the *elementary row transformation of type* III, has the effect of multiplying each element of row r by the scalar $c \neq 0$. Its inverse, $T_{W^{-1},I}$ where W^{-1} is obtained from I_m by multiplying row r by the scalar $1/c \neq 0$, is again of type III. If A is square, $|T_{W,I}(A)| = |WA| = c|A|$.

Finally $T_{I,W}$, the *elementary column transformation of type* III, has the effect of multiplying each element of column r of A by the scalar $c \neq 0$.

We have described the effect of the elementary transformations in sufficient detail that when we apply such a transformation to a matrix A, we may write down the resulting matrix without carrying out the indicated matrix multiplication. Conversely we may construct the elementary transformation matrix which defines a desired elementary transformation by performing that elementary transformation on the identity matrix.

Since elementary transformations are equivalence transformations, any finite sequence of elementary transformations applied to A will yield a matrix B which is equivalent to A. Our next step is to show that we may choose a sequence of elementary transformations which will transform a given m by n matrix A into a diagonal matrix with only ones and zeros on its principal diagonal. We call this process the reduction of A to diagonal form.

Exercise (19.1). Prove the statements in the text concerning the effect of elementary column transformations on a matrix.

Exercise (19.2). Find the following products without multiplying the matrices:

$$\begin{pmatrix} 1 & 0 & 0 \\ 0 & 0 & 1 \\ 0 & 1 & 0 \end{pmatrix}\begin{pmatrix} 2 & 3 & -1 & 4 \\ 1 & -2 & 3 & 2 \\ 5 & 2 & 1 & -3 \end{pmatrix}, \quad \begin{pmatrix} 3 & 1 & 2 \\ 2 & 1 & 5 \\ 4 & -1 & -3 \end{pmatrix}\begin{pmatrix} 1 & -2 & 0 \\ 0 & 1 & 0 \\ 0 & 0 & 1 \end{pmatrix}.$$

Exercise (19.3). Given the matrices $A = \begin{pmatrix} -2 & 1 & 3 \\ 0 & 1 & 5 \end{pmatrix}$ and $B = \begin{pmatrix} 4 & 1 & 3 \\ 7 & -2 & 0 \\ 2 & -5 & 0 \\ -1 & 0 & 1 \end{pmatrix}$, construct the elementary transformation matrices which by pre- or postmultiplication perform the following transformations of A and B:

(a) interchange columns 1 and 2;
(b) multiply row 2 by -2 and add to row 1;
(c) multiply column 2 by -1.

Exercise (19.4). Show that the identity transformation may be described as an elementary transformation of either type II or III.

Exercise (19.5). Prove that a row transformation of any type commutes with a column transformation of any type. Show by examples that the row transformations do not in general commute with each other.

Exercise (19.6). Show that $U' = U$ and $W' = W$. Show that although $V' \neq V$, V' is an elementary transformation matrix of type II.

Exercise (19.7). Show that if U_π is any product of a finite number of elementary transformation matrices of type I, then $U_\pi^{-1} = U_\pi'$.

Exercise (19.8). Prove that the transformation defined on $\mathfrak{A}_n$ by $T_{E',E}(A) = E'AE$ where E is an elementary transformation matrix of any type has the same effect on the rows as on the columns of A.

Exercise (19.9). Prove that the set of all products of elementary transformations is a group of transformations contained in the group of all equivalence transformations.

Section 20. Reduction of a Matrix by Elementary Transformations

Let $A = (a_{ij})$ be any m by n matrix, and let D_r be the diagonal m by n matrix $\begin{pmatrix} I_r & 0 \\ 0 & 0 \end{pmatrix}$ for each integer r in the range $0 \leq r \leq \min(m, n)$.*

(20.1) Theorem. There exists an equivalence transformation T which is a product of elementary transformations such that $T(A) = D_r$ for some r.

PROOF. If A is the zero matrix, it is already in diagonal form D_r with $r = 0$, and we may take T to be the identity transformation. Otherwise, some element $a_{ij} \neq 0$. Let $T_{U_1,I}$ be the elementary row transformation of type I which interchanges row 1 and row i of A, and let T_{I,U_2} be the column transformation which interchanges column 1 and column j of A. Then $T_{I,U_2}T_{U_1,I}(A) = A^{(1)} = (a_{ij}^{(1)})$ where $a_{11}^{(1)}$

* The number $\min(m,n)$ is the smaller of m and n.

$= a_{ij} \neq 0$. We may omit one or both of these steps if $i = 1$ or $j = 1$. Secondly, if $T_{W,I}$ is the elementary row transformation of type III which multiplies the first row of A by $1/a_{11}^{(1)} \neq 0$, then $T_{W,I}(A^{(1)}) = A^{(2)} = (a_{ij}^{(2)})$ where $a_{11}^{(2)} = 1$. Now if $a_{i1}^{(2)} \neq 0$ for any $i > 1$, then $T_{V,I}(A^{(2)}) = A^{(3)} = (a_{ij}^{(3)})$ with $a_{11}^{(3)} = 1$ and $a_{i1}^{(3)} = 0$, if we choose $T_{V,I}$ to be the elementary row transformation of type II which adds to row i of $A^{(2)}$ the elements of row 1 multiplied by $-a_{i1}^{(2)}$. Therefore, applying at most $m - 1$ transformations of this type to $A^{(2)}$, we obtain a matrix $A^{(4)} = (a_{ij}^{(4)})$, where $a_{11}^{(4)} = 1$ and $a_{i1}^{(4)} = 0$ for $i = 2, 3, \cdots, m$. Similarly, a sequence of at most $n - 1$ column transformations of type II will yield a matrix

$$A^{(5)} = \begin{bmatrix} 1 & 0 & \cdots & 0 \\ 0 & a_{22}^{(5)} & \cdots & a_{2n}^{(5)} \\ \cdot & \cdot & & \cdot \\ \cdot & \cdot & & \cdot \\ \cdot & \cdot & & \cdot \\ 0 & a_{m2}^{(5)} & \cdots & a_{mn}^{(5)} \end{bmatrix}.$$

Now any elementary row transformation which affects only the last $m - 1$ rows of $A^{(5)}$ leaves the first column of $A^{(5)}$ unaltered, and similarly any column transformation affecting only the last $n - 1$ columns leaves the first row of $A^{(5)}$ unaltered. Therefore, we may continue the above process on the $m - 1$ by $n - 1$ submatrix

$$\begin{bmatrix} a_{22}^{(5)} & \cdots & a_{2n}^{(5)} \\ \cdot & & \cdot \\ \cdot & & \cdot \\ \cdot & & \cdot \\ a_{m2}^{(5)} & \cdots & a_{mn}^{(5)} \end{bmatrix}$$

without affecting the first row or column of $A^{(5)}$. Clearly the above process may be continued until the diagonal form D_r is obtained. The equivalence transformation T which we set out to obtain is the product of the elementary transformations needed to carry out this reduction.

The reader should notice that the above proof is constructive, that is, it actually describes how to choose the finite number of elementary transformations which reduce A to a diagonal form D_r. Knowing these transformations, we may construct the matrices P and Q such that $PAQ = D_r$ by the product rule (18.2).

In carrying out the above process, if it is not part of the problem to find the individual elementary transformation matrices, we may find a pair P and Q without matrix multiplication. This is based on the following result.

Elementary transformation	P	Q	PAQ
	I_3	I_4	A
Interchange rows 1 and 2	$\begin{pmatrix} 0 & 1 & 0 \\ 1 & 0 & 0 \\ 0 & 0 & 1 \end{pmatrix}$	*	$\begin{pmatrix} 1 & 5 & 4 & -1 \\ 0 & -3 & -1 & 1 \\ 1 & 2 & 3 & 0 \end{pmatrix}$
Add to row 3 the elements of row 1 multiplied by -1	$\begin{pmatrix} 0 & 1 & 0 \\ 1 & 0 & 0 \\ 0 & -1 & 1 \end{pmatrix}$	*	$\begin{pmatrix} 1 & 5 & 4 & -1 \\ 0 & -3 & -1 & 1 \\ 0 & -3 & -1 & 1 \end{pmatrix}$
Add to column 2 the elements of column 1 multiplied by -5	*	$\begin{pmatrix} 1 & -5 & 0 & 0 \\ 0 & 1 & 0 & 0 \\ 0 & 0 & 1 & 0 \\ 0 & 0 & 0 & 1 \end{pmatrix}$	$\begin{pmatrix} 1 & 0 & 4 & -1 \\ 0 & -3 & -1 & 1 \\ 0 & -3 & -1 & 1 \end{pmatrix}$
Add to column 3 the elements of column 1 multiplied by -4	*	$\begin{pmatrix} 1 & -5 & -4 & 0 \\ 0 & 1 & 0 & 0 \\ 0 & 0 & 1 & 0 \\ 0 & 0 & 0 & 1 \end{pmatrix}$	$\begin{pmatrix} 1 & 0 & 0 & -1 \\ 0 & -3 & -1 & 1 \\ 0 & -3 & -1 & 1 \end{pmatrix}$

Add to column 4 the elements of column 1 multiplied by 1	*	$\begin{pmatrix} 1 & -5 & -4 & 1 \\ 0 & 1 & 0 & 0 \\ 0 & 0 & 1 & 0 \\ 0 & 0 & 0 & 1 \end{pmatrix}$	$\begin{pmatrix} 1 & 0 & 0 & 0 \\ 0 & -3 & -1 & 1 \\ 0 & -3 & -1 & 1 \end{pmatrix}$
Multiply the elements of row 2 by $-1/3$	$\begin{pmatrix} 0 & 1 & 0 \\ -1/3 & 0 & 0 \\ 0 & -1 & 1 \end{pmatrix}$	*	$\begin{pmatrix} 1 & 0 & 0 & 0 \\ 0 & 1 & 1/3 & -1/3 \\ 0 & -3 & -1 & 1 \end{pmatrix}$
Add to row 3 the elements of row 2 multiplied by 3	$\begin{pmatrix} 0 & 1 & 0 \\ -1/3 & 0 & 0 \\ -1 & -1 & 1 \end{pmatrix}$	*	$\begin{pmatrix} 1 & 0 & 0 & 0 \\ 0 & 1 & 1/3 & -1/3 \\ 0 & 0 & 0 & 0 \end{pmatrix}$
Add to column 3 the elements of column 2 multiplied by $-1/3$	*	$\begin{pmatrix} 1 & -5 & -7/3 & 1 \\ 0 & 1 & -1/3 & 0 \\ 0 & 0 & 1 & 0 \\ 0 & 0 & 0 & 1 \end{pmatrix}$	$\begin{pmatrix} 1 & 0 & 0 & 0 \\ 0 & 1 & 0 & -1/3 \\ 0 & 0 & 0 & 0 \end{pmatrix}$
Add to column 4 the elements of column 2 multiplied by $1/3$	*	$\begin{pmatrix} 1 & -5 & -7/3 & -2/3 \\ 0 & 1 & -1/3 & 1/3 \\ 0 & 0 & 1 & 0 \\ 0 & 0 & 0 & 1 \end{pmatrix}$	$\begin{pmatrix} 1 & 0 & 0 & 0 \\ 0 & 1 & 0 & 0 \\ 0 & 0 & 0 & 0 \end{pmatrix} = D_2$

(20.2) If $T_{P,Q}$ is any equivalence transformation,

$$T_{P,Q}(A_1 \cdots A_s) = T_{P,I}(A_1) \cdot A_2 \cdots A_{s-1} \cdot T_{I,Q}(A_s).$$

This follows from the fact that

$$\begin{aligned} T_{P,Q}(A_1 \cdots A_s) &= P(A_1 \cdots A_s)Q = (PA_1I)(A_2 \cdots A_{s-1})(IA_sQ) \\ &= T_{P,I}(A_1) \cdot A_2 \cdots A_{s-1} \cdot T_{I,Q}(A_s). \end{aligned}$$

Specifically, $T(AB) = T(A) \cdot B$ if T is any elementary row transformation, and $T(AB) = A \cdot T(B)$ if T is any elementary column transformation.

We illustrate this by reducing $A = \begin{pmatrix} 0 & -3 & -1 & 1 \\ 1 & 5 & 4 & -1 \\ 1 & 2 & 3 & 0 \end{pmatrix}$. Writing $A = I_3AI_4$, we have that $T(A) = T(I_3) \cdot AI_4$ if T is any row transformation. Choosing the T which interchanges rows 1 and 2, we have $P_1AI_4 = A_1$ where $P_1 = T(I_3) = \begin{pmatrix} 0 & 1 & 0 \\ 1 & 0 & 0 \\ 0 & 0 & 1 \end{pmatrix}$ and $A_1 = T(A)$ $= \begin{pmatrix} 1 & 5 & 4 & -1 \\ 0 & -3 & -1 & 1 \\ 1 & 2 & 3 & 0 \end{pmatrix}$. Similarly $T(A_1) = T(P_1) \cdot AI_4$ for any row transformation T. Choosing the T which subtracts row 1 from row 3, we have $P_2AI_4 = A_2$ where $P_2 = T(P_1) = \begin{pmatrix} 0 & 1 & 0 \\ 1 & 0 & 0 \\ 0 & -1 & 1 \end{pmatrix}$ and A_2 $= T(A_1) = \begin{pmatrix} 1 & 5 & 4 & -1 \\ 0 & -3 & -1 & 1 \\ 0 & -3 & -1 & 1 \end{pmatrix}$. Since $T(A_2) = P_2A \cdot T(I_4)$ for any column transformation, choosing the column transformation T which adds to column 2 the elements of column 1 multiplied by -5, we have $P_2AQ_1 = A_3$ where $Q_1 = T(I_4) = \begin{Vmatrix} 1 & -5 & 0 & 0 \\ 0 & 1 & 0 & 0 \\ 0 & 0 & 1 & 0 \\ 0 & 0 & 0 & 1 \end{Vmatrix}$ and A_3 $= T(A_2) = \begin{pmatrix} 1 & 0 & 4 & -1 \\ 0 & -3 & -1 & 1 \\ 0 & -3 & -1 & 1 \end{pmatrix}$. We continue in this way until we have reduced A to diagonal form. At no time do we have to multiply matrices.

This work is summarized and the problem completed in the table on the preceding pages.

Each new matrix in the table is obtained from the one above by performing the elementary transformation described at the left; an asterisk indicates there is no change in that matrix. This process may be checked at any stage by actual multiplication. The description of the elementary transformation at the left is given only for reference and is not part of the computation. Skillful choice of the elementary transformation at each step will often simplify the work considerably.

The set of all products of elementary transformations is a group of transformations of ${}_m\mathfrak{A}_n$ contained in the group $\mathcal{E}({}_m\mathfrak{A}_n)$ of equivalence transformations [see Exercise (19.9)]. It is a consequence of the following theorem that these groups are identical.

(20.3) Theorem. Every nonsingular matrix is a product of elementary transformation matrices.

PROOF. Let A be a nonsingular m-rowed square matrix. By Theorem (20.1), there exist nonsingular m-rowed square matrices P_1 and Q_1, which are products of elementary transformation matrices, such that $P_1AQ_1 = D_r$ where $0 \leq r \leq m$. Now $|D_r| = |P_1AQ_1| = |P_1| \cdot |A| \cdot |Q_1| \neq 0$, so that $r = m$ and $D_r = I_m$. We have $P_1AQ_1 = I_m$ and $A = P_1^{-1}I_mQ_1^{-1} = P_1^{-1}Q_1^{-1}$. If we write $P_1 = E_1E_2 \cdots E_k$ where the E_i are elementary transformation matrices, then

$$P_1^{-1} = E_k^{-1}E_{k-1}^{-1} \cdots E_2^{-1}E_1^{-1}.$$

But we have shown that the inverse of an elementary transformation matrix is again an elementary transformation matrix of the same type. Therefore P_1^{-1} is a product of elementary transformation matrices. The same is true of Q_1^{-1}, and this completes the proof.

(20.4). Corollary. Every equivalence transformation is a product of elementary transformations.

PROOF. Let $T_{P,Q}$ be an equivalence transformation in $\mathcal{E}({}_m\mathfrak{A}_n)$. Then P and Q are nonsingular matrices of orders m and n respectively. By Theorem (20.3), $P = P_1P_2 \cdots P_r$ and $Q = Q_1Q_2 \cdots Q_s$, where each P_i and Q_j is an elementary transformation matrix. Then

$$T_{P,Q} = T_{P_1P_2\cdots P_r,Q_1Q_2\cdots Q_s} = T_{P_1,I}T_{P_2,I} \cdots T_{P_r,I}T_{I,Q_s} \cdots T_{I,Q_2}T_{I,Q_1}.$$

(20.5) Corollary. The matrices A and B in ${}_m\mathfrak{A}_n$ are equivalent if and only if B can be obtained from A by a finite sequence of elementary transformations.

PROOF. By Corollary (20.4), the group $\mathcal{E}({}_m\mathfrak{A}_n)$ is identical with the group of all products of elementary transformations.

Corollary (20.5) gives us one way of characterizing equivalence. In the next section, we obtain a numerical characterization of this relation and a set of canonical matrices for the group $\mathcal{E}({}_m\mathfrak{A}_n)$.

One interesting application of the process of reducing a matrix to diagonal form is to the problem of finding the inverse of a nonsingular m-rowed square matrix A. The method is based on the fact that if A is nonsingular, A can be reduced to diagonal form I_m by elementary row transformations alone. The proof of this result is left to the reader in Exercise (20.6). Using this, we have

$$E_1E_2 \cdots E_{k-1}E_kA = I_m,$$

where each E_i is an elementary transformation matrix. Then,

$$A = E_k^{-1}E_{k-1}^{-1} \cdots E_2^{-1}E_1^{-1},$$

and

$$\begin{aligned} A^{-1} = (E_k^{-1}E_{k-1}^{-1} \cdots E_2^{-1}E_1^{-1})^{-1} &= E_1E_2 \cdots E_{k-1}E_k \\ &= E_1E_2 \cdots E_{k-1}E_kI_m. \end{aligned}$$

This means that we can compute the inverse of A by applying to the identity matrix I_m the same sequence of elementary row transformations which we use to carry A to diagonal form. This method of computing inverses is usually shorter than the computation using adj A.

Exercise (20.1). What is the maximum number of transformations needed to reduce a 3 by 4 matrix to diagonal form, following the procedure outlined in the proof of Theorem (20.1)?

Exercise (20.2). Complete the example in the text by interchanging the second and fourth columns at the sixth step. Also compute the matrices P and Q, starting with an interchange of the first and fourth columns.

Exercise (20.3). Find $T_{P,Q}$ such that $T_{P,Q}(A) = D_r$ for the following matrices A:

$$\begin{pmatrix} 0 & 2 & 0 & 0 \\ 0 & 1 & 4 & 3 \\ 0 & 3 & 0 & 0 \end{pmatrix}, \begin{pmatrix} 1 & 3 & 4 \\ 2 & 5 & 1 \\ 4 & 1 & 2 \end{pmatrix}, \begin{pmatrix} 1 & 3 & 2 & 7 \\ 1 & 5 & -6 & 4 \end{pmatrix},$$

$$\begin{pmatrix} 2 & 0 & -2 & 1 \\ 0 & 5 & 1 & 7 \\ -2 & 0 & 0 & 1 \\ 4 & -3 & 1 & 0 \end{pmatrix}.$$

Exercise (20.4). Show that an elementary transformation of type I can be obtained as a sequence of transformations of types II and III.

Exercise (20.5). Show that by using row transformations alone, A can be reduced to a matrix B with only zeros below its principal diagonal.

Exercise (20.6). Prove that by using row transformations alone, a nonsingular m-rowed square matrix A can be reduced to diagonal form I_m.

Exercise (20.7). Find the inverses of the following matrices:

(a) $\begin{pmatrix} 2 & 1 & 7 \\ 5 & 3 & -1 \\ -4 & -3 & 2 \end{pmatrix}$, (b) $\begin{bmatrix} 3 & -1 & 0 & 5 \\ 2 & 0 & 5 & 0 \\ 3 & 1 & 5 & 4 \\ 10 & 0 & 5 & 6 \end{bmatrix}$,

(c) $\begin{pmatrix} 3/5 & -2/5 & 1/5 \\ 2 & 1/2 & 1/3 \\ -3 & 2 & -1/4 \end{pmatrix}$, (d) $\begin{bmatrix} 0 & 0 & 2 & -2 \\ 0 & 0 & 5 & 3 \\ 3 & -1 & 0 & 0 \\ 1 & 4 & 0 & 0 \end{bmatrix}$.

Section 21. The Rank of a Matrix

In Section 10 we defined a t-rowed minor of A to be the determinant of a t-rowed square submatrix of A.

(21.1) Definition. The *rank* of A is the largest order r of the nonvanishing minors of A; the rank of a zero matrix is zero.

A nonsingular square matrix of order n has rank n. If r is the rank of $A \in {}_m\mathfrak{A}_n$, then $0 \leq r \leq \min(m,n)$.

(21.2) Lemma. If T is an elementary transformation and $T(A) = B$, then rank $B \leq$ rank A.

PROOF. Let r be the rank of A. If r is one of the dimensions of A, it is a dimension of B, and rank $B \leq r$. Otherwise $r < \min(m,n)$, and $|A_1| = 0$ for every square submatrix A_1 of A with more than r rows.

Let B_1 be any t-rowed square submatrix of B. We will enumerate the various ways in which B_1 can be formed, and prove that in every case $|B_1| = 0$ if $t > r$. We give only the discussion for row transformations since parallel proofs hold for column transformations.

Assume that T is of type I. Since T interchanges two rows of A, the rows and columns of B_1 are the rows and columns of some t-rowed square submatrix A_1 of A, with the rows in possibly a different order. Therefore $|B_1| = \pm|A_1|$ by (9.2), and $|B_1| = \pm|A_1| = 0$ if $t > r$.

Assume that T of type II adds to row i the elements of row j multiplied by the scalar g. Let A_1 be the submatrix of A correspondingly placed to B_1. If row i is not one of the rows of A_1, then $B_1 = A_1$ and $|B_1| = |A_1|$. If row i is a row of A_1, then $|B_1| = |A_1| + g|A_2|$ by (9.6), where A_2 is a square matrix obtained from A_1 by replacing the elements in row i of A by the corresponding ones of row j. If row j is also a row of A_1, then A_2 contains row j of A twice, and $|A_2| = 0$ for all t by (9.3). And if row j is not a row of A_1, then A_2 is a submatrix of A, except possibly that its rows are out of order. Therefore in all cases, $|A_1| = |A_2| = 0$ and $|B_1| = 0$ if $t > r$.

Finally, assume that T of type III multiplies row i by the scalar $c \neq 0$, and again let A_1 be the submatrix of A correspondingly placed to B_1. If row i is not a row of A_1, $B_1 = A_1$ and $|B_1| = |A_1|$; and if row i is a row of A_1, $|B_1| = c|A_1|$ by (9.4). But in either case if $t > r$, $|A_1| = 0$ and therefore $|B_1| = 0$.

Therefore every t-rowed minor of B is zero if $t > r$, so that a non-vanishing minor of B can have an order of at most r, and rank $B \leq r$ = rank A.

(21.3) Theorem. If T is an elementary transformation and $T(A) = B$, then rank A = rank B.

PROOF. By Lemma (21.2), rank $B \leq$ rank A. But T^{-1} is also an elementary transformation and $T^{-1}(B) = A$. Again by (21.2), rank $A \leq$ rank B, and therefore rank A = rank B.

(21.4) Theorem. Every m by n matrix A is equivalent to the diagonal matrix D_r where r is the rank of A.

PROOF. By (20.1), every matrix A is equivalent to a diagonal matrix D_r, for some r, under a finite sequence of elementary transformations. Since each of these elementary transformations preserves the rank of A by Theorem (21.3), we have rank A = rank D_r. But the rank of D_r is r, by inspection, so that r is the rank of A.

Since the rank r of a matrix A is preserved by elementary transformations, we call r a *numerical invariant* of this set of transformations. It is now possible to completely characterize the equivalence of rectangular matrices in terms of the invariant r.

(21.5) Theorem. If A and B are in ${}_m\mathfrak{A}_n$, then A and B are equivalent if and only if they have the same rank.

PROOF. If A is equivalent to B, then by (20.4), B can be obtained from A by a finite sequence of elementary transformations, each of which preserves the rank of A by (21.3). Therefore, rank A = rank B.

Conversely let rank A = rank $B = r$. Then by Theorem (21.4) there exist equivalence transformations T_1 and T_2 such that $T_1(A) = D_r$ and $T_2(B) = D_r$. Therefore $T_2^{-1}T_1(A) = T_2^{-1}[T_1(A)] = T_2^{-1}(D_r) = B$, and A is equivalent to B since $T_2^{-1}T_1$ is an equivalence transformation.

The set of canonical matrices for the group of equivalence transformations $\mathcal{E}({}_m\mathfrak{A}_n)$ is the set $D_0, D_1, D_2, \cdots, D_h$, where $D_r = \begin{pmatrix} I_r & O \\ O & O \end{pmatrix}$ and $h = \min(m,n)$. For by (21.4), every matrix in ${}_m\mathfrak{A}_n$ is equivalent to one of these. Moreover, any two of them have different ranks, and thus are not equivalent by Theorem (21.5). Each equivalence class of matrices for the equivalence relation induced by $\mathcal{E}({}_m\mathfrak{A}_n)$ consists of all the matrices in ${}_m\mathfrak{A}_n$ with a given rank r, and the canonical matrix D_r is a representative of the class.

We will need the following result on the rank of a product of two matrices in the next chapter.

(21.6) Theorem. Let A be an m by n matrix and B an n by p matrix. Then the rank of the product $C = AB$ does not exceed the rank of either factor.

PROOF. If B has rank r, then there exist nonsingular matrices P and Q of appropriate sizes such that $PBQ = \begin{pmatrix} I_r & O \\ O & O \end{pmatrix}$. We may then write

$$CQ = ABQ = A(P^{-1}P)BQ = AP^{-1}(PBQ) = AP^{-1}\begin{pmatrix} I_r & O \\ O & O \end{pmatrix}.$$

Partitioning AP^{-1} into two submatrices A_1 and A_2 which are respectively m by r and m by $n - r$, we obtain by multiplying in blocks

$$CQ = AP^{-1}\begin{pmatrix} I_r & O \\ O & O \end{pmatrix} = (A_1\ A_2)\begin{pmatrix} I_r & O \\ O & O \end{pmatrix} = (A_1\ O).$$

Therefore, the rank of CQ is equal to the rank of A_1, which is less than or equal to r since r is one of the dimensions of A_1. But since Q is a product of elementary transformation matrices, the rank of CQ is equal to the rank of C by (21.3). Therefore, the rank of C is less than or equal to r, the rank of B. A similar calculation

$$PC = PAQQ^{-1}B = \begin{pmatrix} I_s & O \\ O & O \end{pmatrix} Q^{-1}B = \begin{pmatrix} I_s & O \\ O & O \end{pmatrix}\begin{pmatrix} B_1 \\ B_2 \end{pmatrix} = \begin{pmatrix} B_1 \\ O \end{pmatrix},$$

where s is the rank of A, shows that the rank of C is less than or equal to the rank of A.

Exercise (21.1). Find the rank of each of the following matrices by reducing to some obvious stage:

$$\begin{pmatrix} 2 & -2 & 2 & 5 & 1 \\ 1 & 1 & 1 & 3 & -1 \\ 3 & 5 & 4 & 2 & 4 \end{pmatrix}, \quad \begin{pmatrix} 3 & 2 & 1 & 0 & 0 \\ 0 & 1 & 2 & 0 & 0 \\ 1 & 4 & 7 & 2 & 3 \\ 5 & 3 & -1 & 1 & 2 \\ 6 & 1 & -2 & 3 & 6 \end{pmatrix},$$

$$\begin{pmatrix} 2 & 6 & -5 & 8 \\ 4 & 3 & -1 & 7 \\ -1 & 1 & 6 & 0 \\ 5 & 2 & 4 & 7 \end{pmatrix}.$$

Exercise (21.2). List other sets of matrices which might be used as a set of representatives of ${}_m\mathfrak{A}_n$ for the group $\mathcal{E}({}_m\mathfrak{A}_n)$.

Exercise (21.3). Prove that A and A' have the same rank for any m by n matrix. Give the condition that A and A' be equivalent.

Section 22. Rational Equivalence of Matrices

In the foregoing sections we have assumed that the elements of our matrices and the scalars are complex numbers. This set C of all complex numbers is closed with respect to the rational operations of addition, subtraction, multiplication, and division by a non-zero number. The operations of addition and multiplication satisfy the associative and commutative laws, and these two operations are connected by the distributive law.

Certain subsets of C have the property of being closed with respect to the rational operations defined in C. When such a subset does not consist of the number zero alone, we call it a *number field*. The most important number fields are, in order of increasing size, the field R of all rational numbers, the field $R^{\#}$ of all real numbers, and the field C itself. These three number fields will be of particular interest in our work with matrices.

Let F be any number field. There is a non-zero element $a \in F$ so that $a - a = 0 \in F$ and $a/a = 1 \in F$. Thus every number field contains 0 and 1. Also $-a = 0 - a$ and $a^{-1} = 1/a$ are in F. If a and b are in F, there is a solution $x = b - a \in F$ to the equation $a + x = b$ and a solution $y = b/a \in F$ to the equation $ay = b$ if $a \neq 0$. Finally if a and b are in F and $ab = 0$, then $a = 0$ or $b = 0$. For if $a \neq 0$, then $a^{-1} \in F$ and $b = (a^{-1}a)b = a^{-1}(ab) = a^{-1}0 = 0$. These simple facts, together with the operational rules for addition and multiplication, are the only properties of the complex numbers which we have used until now.

It follows from this discussion of the properties of a number field that every number field contains the set of all rational numbers, that is, R is the smallest number field. Given any set S of complex numbers, there always exists a smallest number field which contains S. It is the set of all complex numbers generated by performing the four rational operations on the numbers in S. For example, the smallest number field F containing the numbers $\sqrt{7}$ and $2 - 3i$ is the set of all complex numbers of the form $a + b\sqrt{7} + ci + di\sqrt{7}$, where a, b, c, and d are rational numbers. Since every number field contains all rational numbers, a number field containing $\sqrt{7}$ and $2 - 3i$ contains $1/3[2 - (2 - 3i)] = i$, and therefore all numbers of the specified form. It is left as an exercise for the reader to show that the set of all numbers of this form is closed with respect to the four rational operations, that is, is a number field F.

Since the properties of the complex numbers which we have used are valid in every number field, the results previously obtained for matrices with complex number elements can be extended to other number fields. We say that a matrix $A = (a_{ij})$ is *in the number field* F if every $a_{ij} \in F$. The following statements concerning matrices in F are then immediate:

(i) If A is in F, then $-A$ and A' are in F.

(ii) If A and B are in F, then $A + B$ and AB are in F whenever these operations are defined. For example if the m by n matrices $A = (a_{ij})$ and $B = (b_{ij})$ are in F, then each sum $a_{ij} + b_{ij} \in F$, so that $A + B$ is in F.

(iii) If A is in F and $a \in F$, then aA is in F.

(iv) If the square matrix A is in F, then $|A| \in F$. For $|A|$ is a rational function of the elements of A.

(v) If A is a nonsingular square matrix in F, then A^{-1} is in F. For adj A is in F, $|A| \in F$, and $1/|A| \in F$, so that $A^{-1} = 1/|A|$ adj A is in F.

We have not considered number fields until now because, as the above statements indicate, our previous results are independent of the number field. But in our future work with matrices, the results we obtain will depend on the number field in which we are working. We will now see how the concept of a number field enters into the discussion of the equivalence of rectangular matrices.

(22.1) Definition. Let F be the smallest number field which contains the elements of a matrix A. Then the equivalence transformation $T_{P,Q}$ is a *rational transformation* of A if P and Q are in F.

Let $A = \begin{pmatrix} -3 & \sqrt[5]{2} \\ 1 & 1 + \sqrt{3} \end{pmatrix}$. Then if F is the smallest number field containing the elements of A, we have $R \subseteq F \subseteq R^{\#}$. If $B = T_{P,Q}(A)$ where $T_{P,Q}$ is a rational transformation of A, then P,Q, and $B = PAQ$ have elements in $F \subseteq R^{\#}$.

(22.2) Theorem. If A is any matrix of rank r, there exists a rational equivalence transformation $T_{P,Q}$ of A such that $T_{P,Q}(A) = D_r$.

PROOF. The transformation constructed in Theorem (20.1) is a rational transformation of A. To show this, let A have elements in the number field F and let $T_sT_{s-1} \cdots T_1(A) = T_{P,Q}(A) = D_r$ indicate the sequence of elementary transformations defined in this proof. If k is any integer, assume that $T_kT_{k-1} \cdots T_1(A) = T_{P_k,Q_k}(A) = A_k$ where P_k and Q_k, and therefore A_k, have elements in F. Then the elementary transformation matrix belonging to the $(k + 1)$st elementary transformation T_{k+1} is constructed using only the numbers 0 and 1, and possibly $\pm a_{ij}$ or $1/a_{ij}$ (if $a_{ij} \neq 0$) where a_{ij} is an element of A_k. Therefore the elementary transformation matrix defining T_{k+1} has elements in F, and $T_{k+1}T_k \cdots T_1(A) = T_{P_{k+1},Q_{k+1}}(A)$, where P_{k+1} and Q_{k+1} have elements in F. This proves by induction on k that $P = P_s$ and $Q = Q_s$ have elements in F. The reader should notice that this argument includes implicitly the case $k = 1$. This can be made explicit by starting with $k = 0$, $P_0 = I_m$, $Q_0 = I_n$, and $A_0 = A$.

(22.3) Definition. Let F be the smallest number field which contains the elements of the m by n matrices A and B. Then A and B are *rationally equivalent* if there exists an equivalence transformation $T_{P,Q}$ with P and Q in F such that $T_{P,Q}(A) = B$.

(22.4) Theorem. Two m by n matrices are rationally equivalent if and only if they are equivalent.

PROOF. Let A and B be equivalent m by n matrices, so that A and B have the same rank r by (21.5). Let F be the smallest number field containing the elements of A and B. Then by Theorem (22.2) there exist $T_{P,Q}$ and $T_{R,S}$ with P, Q, R, and S in F such that $T_{P,Q}(A) = D_r$ and $T_{R,S}(B) = D_r$. Therefore $T_{R^{-1},S^{-1}}T_{P,Q}(A) = T_{R^{-1}P,QS^{-1}}(A) = B$, and A and B are rationally equivalent since $R^{-1}P$ and QS^{-1} are matrices in F. Conversely, if A and B are rationally equivalent, then by Definition (22.3) they are equivalent.

(22.5) Corollary. Two m by n matrices are rationally equivalent if and only if they have the same rank.

This theorem means that we may restrict ourselves to the four rational operations when working with equivalence, or that the concept of rational equivalence is sufficient to characterize matrices under the full equivalence group. Thus if a matrix contains only real numbers, we may reduce it to diagonal form using only real transformations. Because of this result, we call the matrices D_r *rational canonical forms.*

Another interpretation of Theorem (22.4) can be given. If we denote by ${}_m\mathfrak{A}_n(F)$ the set of all m by n matrices with elements in the number field F, then ${}_m\mathfrak{A}_n(F)$ is a subset of ${}_m\mathfrak{A}_n = {}_m\mathfrak{A}_n(C)$. An *equivalence transformation of* ${}_m\mathfrak{A}_n(F)$ is defined to be an equivalence transformation $T_{P,Q}$ where P and Q have elements in F. Then the set of all equivalence transformations of ${}_m\mathfrak{A}_n(F)$ is a group of transformations denoted by $\mathcal{E}({}_m\mathfrak{A}_n(F))$, and the equivalence relation induced in ${}_m\mathfrak{A}_n(F)$ by this group is called *equivalence over* F. If $F = C$, the group $\mathcal{E}({}_m\mathfrak{A}_n(F))$ is the group $\mathcal{E}({}_m\mathfrak{A}_n)$ which we have discussed in the foregoing sections, but if F is properly contained in C, $\mathcal{E}({}_m\mathfrak{A}_n(F))$ is properly contained in $\mathcal{E}({}_m\mathfrak{A}_n) = \mathcal{E}({}_m\mathfrak{A}_n(C))$. Nevertheless, the equivalence relations induced in ${}_m\mathfrak{A}_n(F)$ by these two groups are the same. For it follows from Theorem (22.4) that the matrices A and B with elements in F are equivalent over F if and only if they are equivalent (over C).

Exercise (22.1). Which of the following sets of numbers are number fields?

(a) The set $\{a + b\sqrt{5}\}$, where a and b are in R.
(b) The set $\{a + b\sqrt{5}\}$, where a and b are integers.
(c) The set $\{a + b\sqrt[3]{3}\}$, where a and b are in R.
(d) The set $\{a + bi + c\sqrt{7} + d\sqrt{7}\,i\}$, where a, b, c, and d are in R.
(e) The set $\{a - b\sqrt{5}\,i\}$, where a and b are in R.
(f) The set $\{a + b\sqrt{2}\}$, where a and b are in a number field F.

Exercise (22.2). Show that every number field contains the rational numbers, that is, R is the smallest number field.

Exercise (22.3). Complete the proofs of (i) through (v).

Exercise (22.4). What is the smallest number field which contains the elements of the following matrices?

(a) $\begin{pmatrix} 2 & -1 & 3 & 5 \\ 0 & 1 & 2 & 7 \\ -3 & 4 & 1 & 8 \end{pmatrix}$, (b) $\begin{pmatrix} 1+i & 2i \\ 1/2 - i & 0 \end{pmatrix}$,

(c) $\begin{pmatrix} \sqrt{2} & -\sqrt{5} \\ 0 & 1/2 + \sqrt{2} \\ 7/16 & 1 \end{pmatrix}$, (d) $\begin{pmatrix} 3 & 0 & 0 \\ 0 & 3 & 0 \\ 0 & 0 & 3 \end{pmatrix}$.

Exercise (22.5). What is the smallest number field which contains the number π?

Exercise (22.6). Reduce $A = \begin{pmatrix} 2 & 3 \\ 4 & 5 \end{pmatrix}$ to D_2 by a rational transformation. Also find an equivalence transformation $T_{P,Q}$ which reduces this matrix to D_2 and which is not a rational transformation of A.

Exercise (22.7). Which of the following 3 by 4 matrices are equivalent over R? Over $R^{\#}$? Over C?

(a) $\begin{pmatrix} \sqrt{2} & -1 & 4 & 3 \\ i & 1/2 & 0 & 1 \\ 0 & 2 & 1/3 & 5 \end{pmatrix}$, (b) $\begin{pmatrix} 1 & 0 & -2 & 3 \\ 4 & 1 & -5 & 2 \\ 1 & 0 & 0 & 1 \end{pmatrix}$,

(c) $\begin{pmatrix} 1/2 & -3 & 6/15 & 2 \\ 3 & 1 & 4/9 & 1 \\ 1 & 1/2 & 3 & 4 \end{pmatrix}$, (d) $\begin{pmatrix} \sqrt{3} & 0 & 0 & 1 \\ 2 & -1 & 0 & \sqrt{3} \\ 1 & 3 & -2 & 0 \end{pmatrix}$,

(e) $\begin{pmatrix} 7 & -1 & 3 & 0 \\ 5 & 3 & 3 & 2 \\ -1 & 2 & 0 & 1 \end{pmatrix}$.

Exercise (22.8). Prove that $\mathcal{E}({}_m\mathfrak{A}_n(F))$ is a group of transformations of ${}_m\mathfrak{A}_n(F)$.

Exercise (22.9). Prove that rational equivalence is an equivalence relation on ${}_m\mathfrak{A}_n = {}_m\mathfrak{A}_n(C)$.

Section 23. Systems of Linear Equations

As we have indicated throughout the first two chapters, one of the principal applications of the foregoing material is to the problem of solving m linear equations in n unknowns. The solution of this classical algebraic problem is useful throughout mathematics.

We consider a system of equations

$$\sum_{j=1}^{n} a_{ij}x_j = b_i \qquad \text{for } i = 1, 2, \cdots, m, \tag{23.1}$$

where the coefficients a_{ij} and the b_i are numbers in some number field F, and we wish to find a set of numbers $c_1, c_2, \cdots, c_n$ in C such that $\sum_{j=1}^{n} a_{ij}c_j = b_i$ for $i = 1, 2, \cdots, m$. Such a set of complex numbers c_i is called a *solution* of the given system of equations.

The system of equations (23.1) can be conveniently written as a single matrix equation

$$AX = b \tag{23.2}$$

where $x = \begin{pmatrix} x_1 \\ x_2 \\ \cdot \\ \cdot \\ \cdot \\ x_n \end{pmatrix}$ and $b = \begin{pmatrix} b_1 \\ b_2 \\ \cdot \\ \cdot \\ \cdot \\ b_m \end{pmatrix}$ are column matrices and $A = (a_{ij})$ is an m by n matrix called the *matrix of the coefficients.* In matrix form, a solution is a column matrix $c = \begin{pmatrix} c_1 \\ c_2 \\ \cdot \\ \cdot \\ \cdot \\ c_n \end{pmatrix} \in {}_n\mathfrak{A}_1$, such that $Ac = b$.

If P is any nonsingular m-rowed square matrix in $\mathfrak{A}_m$, then the new system of equations, $PAx = Pb$, is equivalent to the system (23.2). By this we mean that c is a solution of $PAx = Pb$ if and only if c is a solution of $Ax = b$. For if $Ac = b$, then $PAc = Pb$, and conversely, if $PAc = Pb$, then $P^{-1}(PAc) = P^{-1}(Pb)$ and $Ac = b$. Since P is nonsingular, P is a product of elementary transformation matrices by (20.3). If E is any elementary transformation matrix, the system $EAx = Eb$ is obtained from (23.2) by interchanging two equations, by adding to one equation another equation multiplied by a constant, or by multiplying an equation by a non-zero constant. Therefore the equivalent system $PAx = Pb$ is obtained from $Ax = b$ by a finite sequence of these operations, which are the ones used in elementary algebra.

By row transformations alone we can reduce A to a matrix $A^* = (a_{ij}^*)$ which can be described as follows [see Exercise (20.5)]:

There exist integers $1 \leq n_1 < n_2 < \cdots < n_r \leq n$, where r is the rank of A, such that $a_{in_i}^* = 1$ for $i = 1, 2, \cdots, r$ and $a_{ij}^* = 0$ if $j < n_i$ or if $i > r$.

Further, the above reduction can be accomplished by row transformations which are rational in the elements of A so that there exists a nonsingular matrix P with elements in F such that $PA = A^*$.

EXAMPLE 1. Let $A = \begin{pmatrix} 1/2 & -3 & 2 & 1 \\ 0 & 1/3 & 5 & -3 \\ 4 & 6 & 0 & -2 \end{pmatrix}$. Then, using elementary row transformations,

$$A^{(1)} = \begin{pmatrix} 1 & -6 & 4 & 2 \\ 0 & 1/3 & 5 & -3 \\ 4 & 6 & 0 & -2 \end{pmatrix}, \quad A^{(2)} = \begin{pmatrix} 1 & -6 & 4 & 2 \\ 0 & 1/3 & 5 & -3 \\ 0 & 30 & -16 & -10 \end{pmatrix},$$

$$A^{(3)} = \begin{pmatrix} 1 & -6 & 4 & 2 \\ 0 & 1 & 15 & -9 \\ 0 & 30 & -16 & -10 \end{pmatrix}, \quad A^{(4)} = \begin{pmatrix} 1 & -6 & 4 & 2 \\ 0 & 1 & 15 & -9 \\ 0 & 0 & -466 & 260 \end{pmatrix},$$

$$A^* = \begin{pmatrix} 1 & -6 & 4 & 2 \\ 0 & 1 & 15 & 9 \\ 0 & 0 & 1 & -130/233 \end{pmatrix}.$$

Thus $n_1 = 1$, $n_2 = 2$, $n_3 = 3$, and $r = 3$.

EXAMPLE 2. The matrix

$$A^* = \begin{pmatrix} 1 & 3 & 0 & 5 & -2 & 4 & 0 & 0 \\ 0 & 0 & 0 & 1 & 2 & 0 & 3 & -2 \\ 0 & 0 & 0 & 0 & 0 & 0 & 1 & -3 \\ 0 & 0 & 0 & 0 & 0 & 0 & 0 & 0 \end{pmatrix}$$

is in triangular form with $n_1 = 1$, $n_2 = 4$, $n_3 = 7$, and $r = 3$.

The equivalent system of equations $PAx = A^*x = Pb$ is obtained from $Ax = b$ by performing the same row transformations on the column matrix b of constants as on the matrix of coefficients A. Letting

$$Pb = b^* = \begin{pmatrix} b_1^* \\ b_2^* \\ \cdot \\ \cdot \\ \cdot \\ b_m^* \end{pmatrix},$$ the equations now have the form

$$
\begin{aligned}
x_{n_1} + a_{1,n_1+1}{}^*x_{n_1+1} + a_{1,n_1+2}{}^*x_{n_1+2} + \cdots + a_{1,n}{}^*x_n &= b_1{}^* \\
x_{n_2} + a_{2,n_2+1}{}^*x_{n_2+1} + \cdots + a_{2,n}{}^*x_n &= b_2{}^* \\
\cdots \\
x_{n_r} + \cdots + a_{r,n}{}^*x_n &= b_r{}^* \\
0 &= b_{r+1}{}^* \\
\cdots \\
0 &= b_m{}^*
\end{aligned}
\tag{23.3}
$$

If $b_{r+1}{}^* = b_{r+2}{}^* = \cdots = b_m{}^* = 0$, we obtain a solution for the equations by choosing arbitrary values in F for the variables other than $x_{n_1}, x_{n_2}, \cdots, x_{n_r}$ and solving the equations in turn for $x_{n_r}, x_{n_{r-1}}, \cdots, x_{n_2}, x_{n_1}$. Since the matrix P has elements in F, the matrices A^* and b^* have elements in F, and therefore the solution matrix c will have elements in F. Thus we say that the equations have a rational solution.

If any one of $b_{r+1}{}^*, b_{r+2}{}^*, \cdots, b_m{}^*$ is not zero, then the equations do not have a solution and are called *inconsistent*. The following theorem gives the condition for the consistency of a system of equations in terms of the coefficients of the original form of the equations $Ax = b$. The m by $n + 1$ matrix $(A\ b)$ is called the *augmented matrix* of the equations. It is clear that rank $A \leq$ rank $(A\ b)$.

(23.4) Theorem. The equations $Ax = b$ have a solution c in F if and only if rank A = rank $(A\ b)$.

PROOF. The equations $Ax = b$ have a solution c in F if and only if the equations (23.3) $A^*x = b^*$ have the solution c, and $A^*x = b^*$ have a solution if and only if $b_{r+1}{}^* = b_{r+2}{}^* = \cdots = b_m{}^* = 0$. But this is just the condition that rank $(A^*\ b^*)$ = rank $A^* = r$. Since P is nonsingular, $(A^*\ b^*) = (PA\ Pb) = P(A\ b)$ has the same rank as $(A\ b)$ and $A^* = PA$ has the same rank as A, completing the proof.

In particular, if $m = n$ and A is nonsingular, then A has rank n. Since the augmented matrix $(A\ b)$ is n by $n + 1$, $(A\ b)$ also has rank n, and the equations are consistent by Theorem (23.4). In this case, the (unique) solution c can be found by Cramer's Rule following Theorem (11.6).

EXAMPLE 3. Consider the system

$$
\begin{aligned}
2x_1 - x_2 \qquad\quad - x_4 + 2x_5 &= 2 \\
x_1 + 3x_2 + 4x_3 - 3x_4 - x_5 &= 4 \\
3x_1 + 2x_2 + 4x_3 + 2x_4 + 3x_5 &= 2.
\end{aligned}
$$

The augmented matrix $(A\ b) = \begin{pmatrix} 2 & -1 & 0 & -1 & 2 & 2 \\ 1 & 3 & 4 & -3 & -1 & 4 \\ 3 & 2 & 4 & 2 & 3 & 2 \end{pmatrix}$ can be reduced by row transformations to triangular form $(A^* b^*) = \begin{pmatrix} 1 & 3 & 4 & -3 & -1 & 4 \\ 0 & 1 & 8/7 & -5/7 & -4/7 & 6/7 \\ 0 & 0 & 0 & 1 & 1/3 & -2/3 \end{pmatrix}$, and the equations have the equivalent form

$$\begin{aligned} x_1 + 3x_2 + \quad 4x_3 - \quad 3x_4 \quad - x_5 &= 4 \\ x_2 + 8/7\, x_3 - 5/7\, x_4 - 4/7\, x_5 &= 6/7 \\ x_4 + 1/3\, x_5 &= -2/3. \end{aligned}$$

We can select arbitrary values for x_3 and x_5 and solve successively for the other unknowns x_4, x_2, and x_1. If we select x_3 and x_5 in R, the solution will be in R.

EXAMPLE 4. The augmented matrix $(A\ b)$ of the system

$$\begin{aligned} x_1 + 3x_2 - x_3 \qquad\quad + 2x_5 &= 2 \\ 2x_1 + 6x_2 + x_3 + 6x_4 + 4x_5 &= 13 \\ -x_1 - 3x_2 \qquad - 2x_4 - 2x_5 &= -6 \end{aligned}$$

is $\begin{pmatrix} 1 & 3 & -1 & 0 & 2 & 2 \\ 2 & 6 & 1 & 6 & 4 & 13 \\ -1 & -3 & 0 & -2 & -2 & -6 \end{pmatrix}$ and can be reduced to $(A^* b^*)$ $= \begin{pmatrix} 1 & 3 & -1 & 0 & 2 & 2 \\ 0 & 0 & 1 & 2 & 0 & 3 \\ 0 & 0 & 0 & 0 & 0 & -1 \end{pmatrix}$ which has rank 3 while A^* has rank 2. Thus the system has no solution.

The system $Ax = b$ is called *homogeneous* if the matrix of constants $b = O$. Since $(A\ b) = (A\ O)$ has the same rank as A, a homogeneous system is consistent, having the obvious solution $c = O$. The condition that a homogeneous system have a solution other than the trivial $c = O$ solution is given by the following theorem.

(23.5) Theorem. The homogeneous system $Ax = O$ of m linear equations in n unknowns has a nontrivial solution if and only if rank $A < n$.

PROOF. Since A is m by n, rank $A \leq n$. If rank $A = r < n$, then the variables $x_{n_1}, x_{n_2}, \cdots, x_{n_r}$ in (23.3) do not include all variables $x_1, x_2, \cdots, x_n$, so that there is at least one variable which can be chosen arbitrarily when we solve the equations. If we choose a nonzero value for this variable, the resulting solution will be nontrivial. Conversely, if rank $A = n$, each x_i appears as the first variable in an equation of (23.3). Therefore if c is a solution, each $c_i = 0$.

EXAMPLE 5.

$$\begin{aligned} x_1 + 2x_2 + 5x_3 \qquad\quad &= 0\\ 4x_1 + 12x_2 + 21x_3 + 2x_4 &= 0\\ -3x_1 - 6x_2 - 15x_3 + 3x_4 &= 0. \end{aligned}$$

Since $A = \begin{pmatrix} 1 & 2 & 5 & 0 \\ 4 & 12 & 21 & 2 \\ -3 & -6 & -15 & 3 \end{pmatrix}$ can be transformed by row transformations to $\begin{pmatrix} 1 & 2 & 5 & 0 \\ 0 & 4 & 1 & 2 \\ 0 & 0 & 0 & 3 \end{pmatrix}$, the original system is equivalent to

$$\begin{aligned} x_1 + 2x_2 + 5x_3 \qquad &= 0\\ 4x_2 + x_3 + 2x_4 &= 0\\ 3x_4 &= 0, \end{aligned}$$

and has a nontrivial solution. A value for x_3 can be chosen arbitrarily.

Exercise (23.1). Solve the equations whenever possible.

(a) $\begin{aligned} 12x_1 - 7x_2 + 5x_3 &= 4\\ x_1 - 2x_2 + 3x_3 &= 6; \end{aligned}$

(b) $\begin{aligned} 2x_1 - 4x_2 + 5x_3 &= 10\\ 2x_1 - 11x_2 + 10x_3 &= 36\\ 4x_1 - x_2 + 5x_3 &= -6; \end{aligned}$

(c) $\begin{aligned} 4x_1 - 7x_2 &= 6\\ 8x_1 - 14x_2 &= 8; \end{aligned}$

(d) $\begin{aligned} 2x_1 - x_2 + x_3 &= 4\\ 3x_1 - x_2 + x_3 &= 6\\ 4x_1 - x_2 + 2x_3 &= 7\\ -x_1 + x_2 - x_3 &= 9; \end{aligned}$

(e) $\begin{aligned} 2x_1 - 7x_2 + 5x_3 - 8x_4 &= 7\\ 4x_1 - 14x_2 + 10x_3 - 5x_4 &= 2; \end{aligned}$

(f) $\begin{aligned} 3x_1 - 7x_2 + 2x_4 &= 5\\ x_2 - 7x_3 + x_4 &= 6\\ 2x_1 + 3x_3 - x_4 &= 2. \end{aligned}$

Exercise (23.2). Find nontrivial solutions whenever possible.

(a) $\begin{aligned} 3x_1 - 7x_2 + 2x_3 &= 0\\ 2x_1 - 7x_2 - x_3 &= 0; \end{aligned}$

(b) $\begin{aligned} 2x_1 - 7x_2 - x_3 &= 0\\ 4x_1 + x_2 + 2x_3 &= 0\\ 5x_1 - x_2 - x_3 &= 0; \end{aligned}$

(c) $\begin{aligned} 2x_1 - x_2 + 3x_3 &= 0\\ 4x_1 - x_2 + 5x_3 &= 0\\ 2x_1 + x_2 + x_3 &= 0; \end{aligned}$

(d) $\begin{aligned} 2x_1 - x_2 + x_3 &= 0\\ x_1 + x_2 - 2x_3 &= 0\\ 4x_1 - 3x_2 + 4x_3 &= 0\\ 2x_1 - x_2 - 4x_3 &= 0; \end{aligned}$

(e) $\begin{aligned} 3x_1 + 4x_2 - 2x_3 &= 0\\ -2x_1 + 3x_2 - 4x_3 &= 0\\ 5x_1 + x_2 + 2x_3 &= 0\\ -9x_1 + 5x_2 - 10x_3 &= 0. \end{aligned}$

Exercise (23.3). Show that if there are fewer equations than unknowns, a homogeneous system $Ax = O$, has a nontrivial solution.

Exercise (23.4). Show that the system of equations $PAQy = Pb$, where P and Q are nonsingular matrices, is equivalent to the system $Ax = b$, by showing that $c = \begin{pmatrix} c_1 \\ c_2 \\ \cdot \\ \cdot \\ \cdot \\ c_n \end{pmatrix}$ is a solution of $Ax = b$ if and only if $\xi = \begin{pmatrix} \xi_1 \\ \xi_2 \\ \cdot \\ \cdot \\ \cdot \\ \xi_n \end{pmatrix} = Q^{-1} \begin{pmatrix} c_1 \\ c_2 \\ \cdot \\ \cdot \\ \cdot \\ c_n \end{pmatrix}$ is a solution of $PAQy = Pb$. Show that the equations $Ax = b$ have an equivalent form

$$\begin{pmatrix} y_1 \\ y_2 \\ \cdot \\ \cdot \\ \cdot \\ y_r \\ 0 \\ \cdot \\ \cdot \\ \cdot \\ 0 \end{pmatrix} = \begin{pmatrix} b_1{}^* \\ b_2{}^* \\ \cdot \\ \cdot \\ \cdot \\ b_r{}^* \\ b_{r+1}{}^* \\ \cdot \\ \cdot \\ \cdot \\ b_m{}^* \end{pmatrix}.$$

Exercise (23.5). Find the matrices P and Q which reduce the systems of equations of Exercise (23.1) (a) and (b) to the form discussed in Exercise (23.4).

III VECTOR SPACES

Section 24. Sequence Spaces

In the plane with rectangular coordinates, the complex number $\alpha = a + bi$, where a and b are real, can be represented as the point with coordinates (a,b), as shown in Figure 2. A non-zero complex number $\alpha = a + bi$ can then be identified with the directed line segment from the origin to the point (a,b). In this identification, the sum $\alpha + \beta = (a + c) + (b + d)i$ of the complex numbers $\alpha = a + bi$ and β

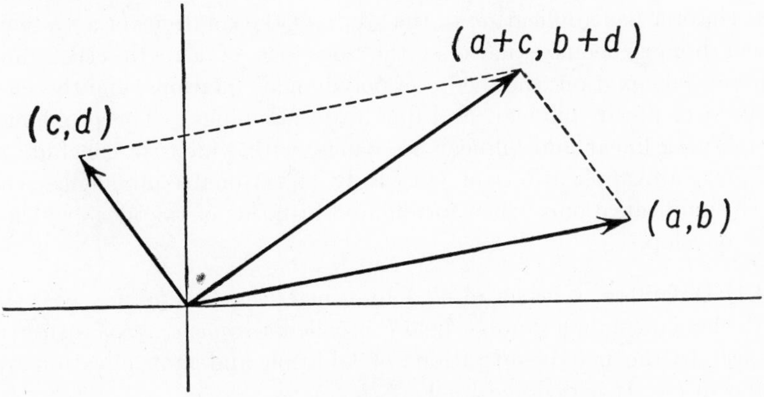

Fig. 2

$= c + di$ is the directed line segment from the origin to the fourth vertex $(a + c,\ b + d)$ of a parallelogram determined by the three points $(0,0)$, (a,b), and (c,d). The product $r\alpha = ra + rbi$ of $\alpha = a + bi$ and the non-zero real number r is the directed line segment from the origin to the point (ra,rb) on the same line and r times as far from the origin as the point (a,b).

The set of all directed line segments in the plane with initial point at the origin, together with two laws of combination, namely, the "parallelogram rule" for addition and multiplication by a real scalar as described above, is known as the set of vectors in the plane. The study of this system (vector analysis) is important in many physical applications of mathematics, since vectors may be used to represent such quantities as forces, velocities, and accelerations which have magnitude and direction and which are combined by the parallelogram rule. The real numbers a and b are called the components of the vector.

If we treat the coordinates (a,b) of a point as a matrix, we see that the composition of vectors and multiplication by a scalar become just matrix addition and scalar multiplication. Thus, all matrix results depending on these operations apply to vectors and, as in the study of matrices, we may generalize the above example in two ways. In the first place, we may consider vectors with more than two components, and secondly, we may choose the components from other algebraic systems. We will consider vectors with n components in a number field F, where n is any positive integer. This set of vectors exhibits the algebraic features of many systems which occur in mathematics, and the following study of vector spaces unifies ideas which are important in diverse mathematical discussions. Specifically, the material of this chapter has application in the study of the solutions of a system of linear homogeneous equations; the solutions of an nth order linear differential equation; the theory of polynomial equations; and the classification of linear, bilinear, and quadratic mappings. The problems of simplifying linear and bilinear mappings, with which we conclude this chapter, are applications of our study of rational equivalence which have significance only when formulated in terms of the ideas which we now develop.

(24.1) Definition. The set of all 1 by n matrices $\alpha = (a_1, a_2, \cdots, a_n)$ with elements a_i in a number field F is called a *sequence vector space* with respect to the matrix operations of addition and multiplication by a scalar in F. It is denoted by $V_n(F)$.

The members of $V_n(F)$ are called *vectors;* the elements a_i of a vector $\alpha = (a_1, a_2, \cdots, a_n)$ are called the *components* of α; and the elements of the number field F are called *scalars*. The following properties of $V_n(F)$, listed here for reference, are consequences of our earlier study of matrices.

(24.2) If $\alpha = (a_1, a_2, \cdots, a_n)$, $\beta = (b_1, b_2, \cdots, b_n)$, and $\gamma = (c_1, c_2, \cdots, c_n)$ are vectors in $V_n(F)$ and c and d are scalars in F, then:

(i) $\alpha = \beta$ if and only if $a_i = b_i$ for $i = 1, 2, \cdots, n$;
(ii) $\alpha \pm \beta = (a_1 \pm b_1, a_2 \pm b_2, \cdots, a_n \pm b_n) \in V_n(F)$;
(iii) $(\alpha + \beta) + \gamma = \alpha + (\beta + \gamma)$ and $\alpha + \beta = \beta + \alpha$;
(iv) $\alpha + O = \alpha$ where $O = (0, 0, \cdots, 0) \in V_n(F)$;
(v) $c\alpha = (ca_1, ca_2, \cdots, ca_n) \in V_n(F)$;
(vi) $c(d\alpha) = d(c\alpha) = (cd)\alpha$;

(vii) $(c + d)\alpha = c\alpha + d\alpha$;
(viii) $c(\alpha + \beta) = c\alpha + c\beta$;
(ix) $1 \cdot \alpha = \alpha$.

(24.3) Definition. A non-empty subset S of $V_n(F)$ which is closed with respect to addition and scalar multiplication is called a *subspace* of $V_n(F)$.

If $\alpha,\beta \in S$, then by Definition (24.3), $\alpha + (-1)\beta = \alpha - \beta \in S$. Since S is non-empty, S contains some vector α, and therefore S contains $\alpha - \alpha = O$ and $O - \alpha = -\alpha$. The whole space $V_n(F)$ as well as the zero vector $O = (0, 0, \cdots, 0)$ alone are subspaces. The latter subspace is referred to as the zero subspace. The following theorem gives a simple characterization of a subspace.

(24.4) Theorem. A subset S of $V_n(F)$ is a subspace if and only if S is non-empty and $c\alpha + d\beta \in S$ for all $\alpha,\beta \in S$ and $c,d \in F$.

PROOF. If S is a subspace, then by (24.3), S is non-empty and contains $c\alpha + d\beta$ for $\alpha,\beta \in S$ and $c,d \in F$. Conversely, if $c\alpha + d\beta \in S$ for all $\alpha,\beta \in S$ and all $c,d \in F$, then S contains $1 \cdot \alpha + 1 \cdot \beta = \alpha + \beta$ and $c\alpha + 0\beta = c\alpha$ for every $\alpha,\beta \in S$ and $c \in F$. Thus S is closed with respect to the two operations.

The plane vectors (a,b) discussed at the beginning of this section form a $V_2(R^\#)$. Those vectors which lie on a line through the origin form a subspace of $V_2(R^\#)$. For if the vectors $\alpha = (a_1,a_2)$ and $\beta = (b_1,b_2)$ lie on the line $y = mx$, then $a_2 = ma_1$ and $b_2 = mb_1$. Therefore, for all $c,d \in R^\#$, the vector $c\alpha + d\beta = (ca_1,cma_1) + (db_1,dmb_1) = (ca_1 + db_1, m(ca_1 + db_1)) = (f_1,mf_1)$ lies on the line $y = mx$, and by Theorem (24.4), these vectors form a subspace.

The vector space $V_3(R^\#)$ can be thought of as the set of all directed line segments with initial point at the origin of a three-dimensional Cartesian coordinate system. A subspace of $V_3(R^\#)$, other than the whole space or the zero subspace, consists either of those vectors which lie in a plane through the origin, or those which lie on a line through the origin. In the former case, the subspace is composed of all vectors in $V_3(R^\#)$ with coordinates which satisfy an equation of the form $ax + by + cz = 0$; and in the latter case, the coordinates of the vectors in the subspace satisfy equations of the form $x/a = y/b = z/c$.

Exercise (24.1). Construct the plane vectors $-\alpha$, 4β, $2\alpha - 3\beta$, and $3(-\alpha + 5\beta)$ if $\alpha = (3,1)$ and $\beta = (-1,2)$.

Exercise (24.2). Find $2\alpha + \beta$, $5\alpha - 1/2\,\beta$, and $2(\alpha - \beta)$ for the following pairs of vectors in $V_4(R)$:

(a) $\alpha = (2,-1,3,5)$, $\beta = (-1,0,1,4)$;
(b) $\alpha = (1/3,\ 1/2,\ -2,\ 0)$, $\beta = (1/2,\ 2/3,\ -4,\ 1)$.

Exercise (24.3). Show that the subspaces of $V_2(R^\#)$ mentioned in the text are the only ones besides the zero subspace and the whole space.

Exercise (24.4). Prove that the set of all vectors in $V_3(R^\#)$ which have coordinates satisfying the equation $ax + by + cz = 0$, is a subspace of $V_3(R^\#)$.

Exercise (24.5). Show that the set of all vectors with first component zero is a subspace of $V_n(F)$, but that the set of those with first component 1 is not.

Exercise (24.6). Which of the following are subspaces of $V_3(R)$?
(a) all vectors with $a_1 = 5a_2$;
(b) all vectors with $a_1{}^2 = a_2a_3$;
(c) all vectors with $a_1 + a_2 = a_3$;
(d) all vectors with $a_1 + a_2 = a_3 - 1$.

Exercise (24.7). Give a general form for the vectors in the smallest subspace of $V_4(R^\#)$ which contains the vector $\alpha = (2,1,-3,4)$. Do the same for the smallest subspace which contains the two vectors α and $\beta = (1,2,-6,8)$. Find a vector in this latter subspace which has $a_1 = 4$ and $a_2 = 5$. Why can you not find a vector with $a_2 = 4$ and $a_3 = 5$?

Exercise (24.8). Show that $V_n(R^\#)$ is not a subspace of $V_n(C)$.

Exercise (24.9). Prove that the set of all solutions in F of the homogeneous system, $Ax = O$, of m equations in n unknowns with coefficients in the number field F, is a subspace of $V_n(F)$.

Exercise (24.10). If we define $V_n(F)$ to be the set of sequences $(a_1, a_2, \cdots, a_n)$, and use (i), (ii), and (v) of (24.2) to define equality, addition, and multiplication by a scalar in F, verify that (iii), (iv), (vi), (vii), (viii), and (ix) of (24.2) are true.

Section 25. Linear Dependence

If $\alpha_1, \alpha_2, \cdots, \alpha_k$ is any set of vectors in $V_n(F)$, then the set S of all linear combinations $c_1\alpha_1 + c_2\alpha_2 + \cdots + c_k\alpha_k$ of the α_i with coefficients $c_1, c_2, \cdots, c_k$ in F is a subspace of $V_n(F)$. The proof of this fact, which is an immediate consequence of Theorem (24.4), is left for the reader as an exercise. We call S the space *spanned* by the vectors $\alpha_1, \alpha_2, \cdots, \alpha_k$.

For example, in $V_2(R^\#)$ the single vector $\alpha = (3,3)$ spans the subspace S of all vectors on the line $y = x$; while in $V_3(R^\#)$, the vectors $\alpha_1 = (1,2,0)$, $\alpha_2 = (-2,-1,1)$, and $\alpha_3 = (0,3,1)$ span the plane $2x - y + 3z = 0$, since any vector $\alpha = c_1\alpha_1 + c_2\alpha_2 + c_3\alpha_3$ has components which satisfy the equation of this plane.

If there are linear relations between the α_i of the form $d_1\alpha_1 + d_2\alpha_2 + \cdots + d_k\alpha_k = O \in V_n(F)$ where the numbers $d_i \in F$ are not all zero, then a vector in S can be written in many ways as a linear combination of the α_i. In the second example above, the α_i satisfy the relation $2\alpha_1 + \alpha_2 - \alpha_3 = O$. The vector $\beta = (1,-1,-1)$ is in the plane $2x - y + 3z = 0$, which is the subspace spanned by α_1, α_2, and α_3, and β can be expressed in various ways, such as

$$\begin{aligned}\beta &= 1 \cdot \alpha_1 + 0 \cdot \alpha_2 - 1 \cdot \alpha_3 = -1 \cdot \alpha_1 - 1 \cdot \alpha_2 + 0 \cdot \alpha_3 \\ &= 0 \cdot \alpha_1 - 1/2 \cdot \alpha_2 - 1/2 \cdot \alpha_3 = 3 \cdot \alpha_1 + 1 \cdot \alpha_2 - 2 \cdot \alpha_3.\end{aligned}$$

We will prove that if S is any subspace of $V_n(F)$, there exists at least one set of vectors $\alpha_1, \alpha_2, \cdots, \alpha_k$ which span S, such that each vector in S is uniquely expressible as a linear combination of $\alpha_1, \alpha_2, \cdots, \alpha_k$. The integer k, which will be called the dimension of S, is uniquely determined by S. These proofs are based on the concept of a linearly dependent set of vectors.

(25.1) Definition. The vectors $\alpha_1, \alpha_2, \cdots, \alpha_k$ in $V_n(F)$ form a *linearly dependent set* (over F) if there exist scalars $c_1, c_2, \cdots, c_k$ in F, which are not all zero, such that $c_1\alpha_1 + c_2\alpha_2 + \cdots + c_k\alpha_k = O \in V_n(F)$. Otherwise, the set is said to form a *linearly independent set.*

In the above example, the set α_1, α_2, α_3 of vectors in $V_3(R^\#)$ is linearly dependent since $2\alpha_1 + \alpha_2 - \alpha_3 = O$. The vectors α_1 and α_2 form a linearly independent set. For if $c_1\alpha_1 + c_2\alpha_2 = O$, then

$$c_1(1,2,0) + c_2(-2,-1,1) = (c_1 - 2c_2, 2c_1 - c_2, c_2) = (0,0,0).$$

This vector equation is the same as a system of three homogeneous equations in two unknowns with only the trivial solution $c_1 = c_2 = 0$. The two vectors α_1 and α_2 span the same plane $2x - y + 3z = 0$ as that spanned by all three vectors, α_1, α_2, and α_3.

The zero vector alone, and consequently any set of vectors which contains it, is a linearly dependent set since $1 \cdot O = O$. On the other hand, any non-zero vector is a linearly independent set with one element.

(25.2) Theorem. The vectors $\alpha_1, \alpha_2, \cdots, \alpha_k \in V_n(F)$ form a linearly dependent set if and only if some α_i is in the subspace S spanned by the remaining vectors.

PROOF. If $\alpha_1, \alpha_2, \cdots, \alpha_k$ form a linearly dependent set, then there is a relation

$$c_1\alpha_1 + c_2\alpha_2 + \cdots + c_k\alpha_k = O$$

with at least one coefficient not zero. For any $c_i \neq 0$,

$$c_i\alpha_i = -c_1\alpha_1 - \cdots - c_{i-1}\alpha_{i-1} - c_{i+1}\alpha_{i+1} - \cdots - c_k\alpha_k$$

and

$$\alpha_i = -c_i^{-1}c_1\alpha_1 - \cdots - c_i^{-1}c_{i-1}\alpha_{i-1} - c_i^{-1}c_{i+1}\alpha_{i+1} - \cdots - c_i^{-1}c_k\alpha_k.$$

Conversely, if

$$\alpha_i = d_1\alpha_1 + \cdots + d_{i-1}\alpha_{i-1} + d_{i+1}\alpha_{i+1} + \cdots + d_k\alpha_k,$$

then

$$d_1\alpha_1 + \cdots + d_{i-1}\alpha_{i-1} + (-1)\alpha_i + d_{i+1}\alpha_{i+1} + \cdots + d_k\alpha_k = O,$$

and $\alpha_1, \alpha_2, \cdots, \alpha_k$ form a linearly dependent set.

The following theorem gives a useful matrix criterion for finding whether or not a given set of vectors is a linearly dependent set. Let

$$\alpha_i = (a_{i1}, a_{i2}, \cdots, a_{in}) \qquad \text{for } i = 1, 2, \cdots, k.$$

(25.3) Theorem. The vectors $\alpha_1, \alpha_2, \cdots, \alpha_k$ in $V_n(F)$ form a linearly dependent set if and only if the rank of $A = \begin{pmatrix} \alpha_1 \\ \alpha_2 \\ \cdot \\ \cdot \\ \cdot \\ \alpha_k \end{pmatrix}$ is less than k.

PROOF. The vectors $\alpha_1, \alpha_2, \cdots, \alpha_k$ are linearly dependent if and only if the vector equation $x_1\alpha_1 + x_2\alpha_2 + \cdots + x_k\alpha_k = O$ has a solution $(x_1, x_2, \cdots, x_k) = (c_1, c_2, \cdots, c_k)$ with not every $c_i = 0$. This vector equation can be written in the form

$$(x_1, x_2, \cdots, x_k)\begin{pmatrix} a_{11} & a_{12} & \cdots & a_{1n} \\ a_{21} & a_{22} & \cdots & a_{2n} \\ \cdot & \cdot & & \cdot \\ \cdot & \cdot & & \cdot \\ \cdot & \cdot & & \cdot \\ a_{k1} & a_{k2} & \cdots & a_{kn} \end{pmatrix} = (0, 0, \cdots, 0),$$

or $XA = O$. When transposed, this equation assumes the form $A'X' = O$ of Theorem (23.5) which has a nontrivial solution if and only if the rank of A' is less than k. Since rank A = rank A', $XA = O$ has a solution $(x_1, x_2, \cdots, x_k) = (c_1, c_2, \cdots, c_k)$ with not every $c_i = 0$ if and only if the rank of A is less than k.

This theorem is, of course, equivalent to the statement that $\alpha_1, \alpha_2, \cdots, \alpha_k$ is a linearly independent set if and only if the rank of A is equal to k.

(25.4) Corollary. Any set of $n + 1$ vectors in $V_n(F)$ is linearly dependent.

PROOF. The matrix A of the theorem is $n + 1$ by n, and therefore has rank less than $n + 1$.

EXAMPLE 1. The vectors $\alpha_1 = (1,0,3,4)$, $\alpha_2 = (2,1,-1,0)$, $\alpha_3 = (1,0,0,1)$, and $\alpha_4 = (1,0,-1,0)$ in $V_4(R)$ are linearly dependent since the matrix $A = \begin{pmatrix} 1 & 0 & 3 & 4 \\ 2 & 1 & -1 & 0 \\ 1 & 0 & 0 & 1 \\ 1 & 0 & -1 & 0 \end{pmatrix}$ has rank 3. To find scalars $c_i \in R$ such that $c_1\alpha_1 + c_2\alpha_2 + c_3\alpha_3 + c_4\alpha_4 = O$, we solve the matrix equation $(x_1,x_2,x_3,x_4)A = (0,0,0,0)$. This can be done by transposing the equation and solving as in Section 23, or by applying column transformations to A directly. By column transformations alone, the equation can be reduced to

$$(x_1,x_2,x_3,x_4)\begin{pmatrix} 1 & 0 & 0 & 0 \\ 2 & 1 & 0 & 0 \\ 1 & 0 & -3 & 0 \\ 1 & 0 & -4 & 0 \end{pmatrix} = (0,0,0,0),$$

which has solutions with x_4 arbitrary, $x_3 = -4/3\, x_4$, $x_2 = 0$, and $x_1 = -x_3 - x_4$. Thus with $x_4 = 3$, $\alpha_1 - 4\alpha_3 + 3\alpha_4 = O$.

Exercise (25.1). Prove that the set of all linear combinations of any set of vectors in $V_n(F)$ is a subspace of $V_n(F)$.

Exercise (25.2). Show that any two plane vectors in $V_2(R^\#)$ which do not lie on the same line through the origin are linearly independent and span $V_2(R^\#)$.

Exercise (25.3). Give the equations of the subspace of $V_3(R^\#)$ spanned by each of the following sets of vectors:

(a) $\alpha = (2,1,1)$;
(b) $\alpha_1 = (2,3,2)$, $\alpha_2 = (5,-1,3)$;
(c) $\alpha_1 = (6,0,-2)$, $\alpha_2 = (-9,0,3)$;
(d) $\alpha_1 = (1,4,0)$, $\alpha_2 = (2,1,3)$, $\alpha_3 = (-1,3,2)$;
(e) $\alpha_1 = (3,0,1)$, $\alpha_2 = (3,3,0)$, $\alpha_3 = (-1,2,-1)$.

Exercise (25.4). Show that $\alpha_1 = (1,2,3,4)$, $\alpha_2 = (2,3,1,5)$, $\alpha_3 = (3,1,2,7)$, and $\alpha_4 = (1,1,-2,1)$ form a linearly dependent set. Which of these vectors is not in the subspace spanned by the other three?

Exercise (25.5). Test each set for linear dependence, and find a relation of dependence when one exists.

(a) $\alpha_1 = (2,3,1,4)$, $\alpha_2 = (2,8,4,-2)$, $\alpha_3 = (-2,3,-2,-4)$, $\alpha_4 = (0,-7,5,-6)$;
(b) $\alpha_1 = (-3,1,0,7)$, $\alpha_2 = (-2,2,3,0)$, $\alpha_3 = (0,4,-1,-5)$, $\alpha_4 = (2,0,6,-3)$;
(c) $\alpha_1 = (3,2,1,1)$, $\alpha_2 = (1,1,1,0)$, $\alpha_3 = (-3,2,-1,0)$, $\alpha_4 = (-2,2,0,2)$, $\alpha_5 = (-4,1,2,2)$.

Exercise (25.6). Prove that $\alpha_1, \alpha_2, \cdots, \alpha_k$ form a linearly independent set if and only if any relation $c_1\alpha_1 + c_2\alpha_2 + \cdots + c_k\alpha_k = O$ requires that $c_1 = c_2 = \cdots = c_k = 0$.

Exercise (25.7). Show that $\epsilon_1, \epsilon_2, \cdots, \epsilon_n$ is a linearly independent set which spans $V_n(F)$, where $\epsilon_i = (\delta_{i1}, \delta_{i2}, \cdots, \delta_{in})$ and δ_{ij} is the Kronecker delta.

Exercise (25.8). Show that the set $\alpha_1, \alpha_2, \cdots, \alpha_k$ of vectors in $V_n(F)$ is linearly dependent if any one of the following statements is true:

(a) some α_i is zero;
(b) some $\alpha_i = \alpha_j$ for $i \neq j$;
(c) some subset, $\alpha_{i_1}, \alpha_{i_2}, \cdots, \alpha_{i_j}$, is linearly dependent;
(d) some α_i is in the space spanned by the preceding ones, $\alpha_1, \alpha_2, \cdots, \alpha_{i-1}$;
(e) there are more than n vectors in the set.

Exercise (25.9). Show that if $\alpha_1, \alpha_2, \cdots, \alpha_k$ is a linearly dependent set where $\alpha_1 \neq O$, there exists a smallest integer j such that the set $\alpha_1, \alpha_2, \cdots, \alpha_{j-1}$ is linearly independent, but the set $\alpha_1, \alpha_2, \cdots, \alpha_{j-1}, \alpha_j$ is linearly dependent.

Section 26. The Dimension of a Subspace

In the example $V_2(R^\#)$, the vectors $\epsilon_1 = (1,0)$ and $\epsilon_2 = (0,1)$ are linearly independent, and any vector $\gamma = (a,b) \in V_2(R^\#)$ can be written as a linear combination, $\gamma = a \cdot \epsilon_1 + b \cdot \epsilon_2$, of ϵ_1 and ϵ_2. This property of the "unit vectors," ϵ_1 and ϵ_2, is shared by any two plane vectors α and β which do not lie on the same line through the origin (see Figure 3). This is true since α and β are linearly independent, and $\gamma = c_1\alpha + c_2\beta$.

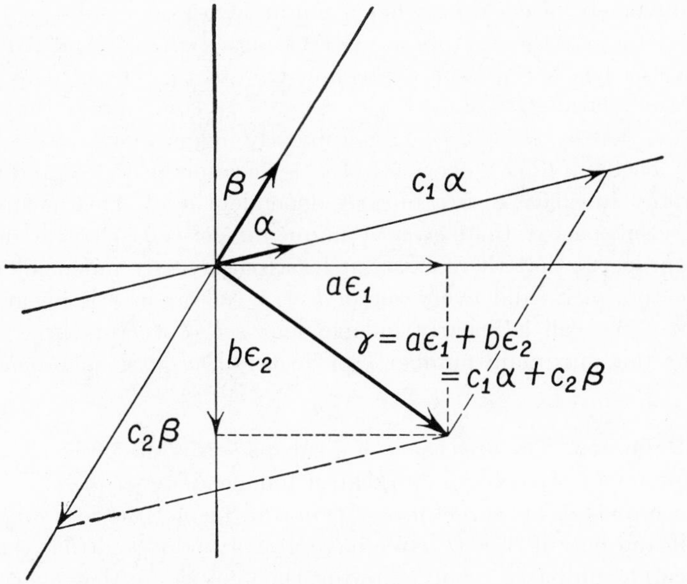

Fig. 3

These ideas lead to the notions of basis and dimension for the subspaces of $V_n(F)$.

(26.1) Definition. The vectors $\alpha_1, \alpha_2, \cdots, \alpha_m$ are a *basis* of the subspace S of $V_n(F)$ if they form a linearly independent set which spans S.

The vectors $\epsilon_1, \epsilon_2, \cdots, \epsilon_n$, where $\epsilon_i = (\delta_{i1}, \delta_{i2}, \cdots, \delta_{in})$, are a basis of $V_n(F)$ by Exercise (25.7). If $\alpha = (a_1, a_2, \cdots, a_n)$ is any vector in $V_n(F)$, $\alpha = a_1 \cdot \epsilon_1 + a_2 \cdot \epsilon_2 + \cdots + a_n \cdot \epsilon_n$. The zero subspace does not have a basis since the zero vector alone is a linearly dependent set. The following theorem characterizes a basis of a subspace.

(26.2) Theorem. The vectors $\alpha_1, \alpha_2, \cdots, \alpha_m \in S$ are a basis of the subspace $S \neq O$ if and only if for each $\beta \in S$ there exist unique scalars $c_i \in F$ such that $\beta = c_1\alpha_1 + c_2\alpha_2 + \cdots + c_m\alpha_m$.

PROOF. If $\alpha_1, \alpha_2, \cdots, \alpha_m$ are a basis of S, then for each $\beta \in S$, there exist scalars $c_i \in F$ such that $\beta = c_1\alpha_1 + c_2\alpha_2 + \cdots + c_m\alpha_m$. Now if $\beta = d_1\alpha_1 + d_2\alpha_2 + \cdots + d_m\alpha_m$ is any expression for β with scalars $d_i \in F$, then

$$O = \beta - \beta = (c_1 - d_1)\alpha_1 + (c_2 - d_2)\alpha_2 + \cdots + (c_m - d_m)\alpha_m.$$

But since $\alpha_1, \alpha_2, \cdots, \alpha_m$ are linearly independent, this requires that $c_i - d_i = 0$, or that $c_i = d_i$ for all i. Therefore, the c_i are unique.

Conversely, if each $\beta \in S$ has a unique expression $\beta = c_1\alpha_1 + c_2\alpha_2 + \cdots + c_m\alpha_m$, the vectors $\alpha_i \in S$ certainly span S. And since the zero vector has the unique expression $O = 0 \cdot \alpha_1 + 0 \cdot \alpha_2 + \cdots + 0 \cdot \alpha_m$, any relation $O = d_1\alpha_1 + d_2\alpha_2 + \cdots + d_m\alpha_m$ implies that every $d_i = 0$, so that $\alpha_1, \alpha_2, \cdots, \alpha_m$ is a linearly independent set.

By Theorem (25.3), every set of $n + 1$ vectors in $V_n(F)$, and therefore in any subspace S, is a linearly dependent set. This means that for every subspace S, there exists a unique integer k, $0 \leq k \leq n$, defined by the property that there exists at least one linearly independent set of k vectors in S, and every set of $k + 1$ vectors in S is linearly dependent. We call a linearly independent set of vectors in S which contains this maximum number k of vectors a *greatest independent set* in S.

(26.3) Definition. The *dimension* of a subspace S is the integer k where k is the number of vectors in a greatest independent set in S.

Since there exists a vector $\alpha \neq O$ in S if S is not the zero subspace, $k = 0$ if and only if $S = O$. We have already remarked that the zero subspace has no basis. The following theorem shows that every subspace $S \neq O$ has a basis and that all bases of S have the same number of elements, the number being the dimension k of S.

(26.4) Theorem. A subspace $S \neq O$ of $V_n(F)$ has dimension k if and only if S has a basis of k vectors, $(k \geq 1)$.

PROOF. Assume first that $S \neq O$ has dimension k. Then S contains at least one greatest independent set M of vectors, $\alpha_1, \alpha_2, \cdots, \alpha_k$, with $k \geq 1$. If β is any vector in S, the set $\beta, \alpha_1, \alpha_2, \cdots, \alpha_k$ is linearly dependent by the definition of a greatest independent set. Thus there is a relation $c\beta + c_1\alpha_1 + c_2\alpha_2 + \cdots + c_k\alpha_k = O$ in S with not all of the coefficients zero. If $c = 0$, then some $c_i \neq 0$, and $\alpha_1, \alpha_2, \cdots, \alpha_k$ would be a dependent set, contrary to the choice of M. Therefore $c \neq 0$, and $\beta = (-c^{-1}c_1)\alpha_1 + (-c^{-1}c_2)\alpha_2 + \cdots + (-c^{-1}c_k)\alpha_k$. Hence M spans S, and since the vectors of M are linearly independent, M is a basis of S containing $k \geq 1$ vectors.

Conversely, let S be a subspace of $V_n(F)$ which has a basis, $\alpha_1, \alpha_2, \cdots, \alpha_k$, of $k \geq 1$ vectors, and let S have dimension h. Then since $\alpha_1, \alpha_2, \cdots, \alpha_k$ are linearly independent, $h \geq k$ by the definition of h, and in particular, $S \neq O$. By the first part of the proof, S has a basis $\beta_1, \beta_2, \cdots, \beta_h$ of h vectors. Writing the vectors β_j in terms of the basis $\alpha_1, \alpha_2, \cdots, \alpha_k$, we have that

$$\beta_j = c_{j1}\alpha_1 + c_{j2}\alpha_2 + \cdots + c_{jk}\alpha_k, \qquad \text{for } j = 1, 2, \cdots, h.$$

These h vector equations can be written as the single matrix equation,

$$\begin{pmatrix} \beta_1 \\ \beta_2 \\ \cdot \\ \cdot \\ \cdot \\ \beta_h \end{pmatrix} = \begin{pmatrix} c_{11} & c_{12} & \cdots & c_{1k} \\ c_{21} & c_{22} & \cdots & c_{2k} \\ \cdot & \cdot & & \cdot \\ \cdot & \cdot & & \cdot \\ \cdot & \cdot & & \cdot \\ c_{h1} & c_{h2} & \cdots & c_{hk} \end{pmatrix} \cdot \begin{pmatrix} \alpha_1 \\ \alpha_2 \\ \cdot \\ \cdot \\ \cdot \\ \alpha_k \end{pmatrix},$$

where the matrices of the β's and the α's have ranks h and k respectively, since both sets are linearly independent sets. This matrix equation shows that $h \leq k$, since the rank of the product of two matrices does not exceed the rank of either factor by (21.6). Therefore $h = k$, proving the second half of the theorem.

(26.5) Corollary. Every set of k linearly independent vectors in a subspace S of dimension k is a basis of S.

PROOF. Any set of k linearly independent vectors is a greatest independent set in a subspace of dimension k, and is a basis by the proof of Theorem (26.4).

(26.6) Corollary. Any two bases of a subspace S have the same number of elements.

PROOF. If S had bases of h and k elements with $h \neq k$, then by Theorem (26.4), the dimension of S would be both h and k. But by Definition (26.3) a subspace can have only one dimension.

(26.7) Corollary. If the set M of vectors $\alpha_1, \alpha_2, \cdots, \alpha_m$ spans the subspace $S \neq O$ of dimension k, then there exists a subset of k elements of M which is a basis of S. In particular, $k \leq m$.

PROOF. Let $\alpha_{i_1}, \alpha_{i_2}, \cdots, \alpha_{i_j}$ be any greatest linearly independent subset M' of M. Then $1 \leq j \leq m$. If $j = m$, then M itself is a basis and $m = k$ by Corollary (26.6). If $j < m$, then every set of $j + 1$ vectors of M is linearly dependent, and as in the proof of Theorem (25.2), every $\alpha_i \in M$ can be written as a linear combination of the vectors in M'. Now since each $\beta \in S$ can be written as a linear combination of the vectors in M, each $\beta \in S$ can be written as a linear combination of the vectors in M'. Therefore the set M' is a basis of S, and $j = k$ by (26.6).

Exercise (26.1). Given a basis $\alpha = (a_1,a_2)$ and $\beta = (b_1,b_2)$ of $V_2(R^\#)$, solve for constants d_1 and d_2 such that $\gamma = d_1 \cdot \alpha + d_2 \cdot \beta$ where $\gamma = (c_1,c_2)$.

Exercise (26.2). Prove that $(4,-1,2)$, $(3,1,5)$, and $(6,2,-1)$ are a basis of $V_3(R^\#)$, and find the expression for the vector $(3,\sqrt{2},1)$ in terms of this basis.

Exercise (26.3). Find two subsets of the set M of vectors, $\alpha_1 = (2,1,5,3)$, $\alpha_2 = (4,-1,2,7)$, $\alpha_3 = (4,2,10,6)$, $\alpha_4 = (6,-3,-1,11)$, $\alpha_5 = (-1,1-1,1)$, which are bases of the subspace S spanned by M. Write each vector in M as a linear combination of the vectors in one of the bases.

Exercise (26.4). Prove that if β can be written as a linear combination of the vectors $\alpha_1, \alpha_2, \cdots, \alpha_m$, but not of $\alpha_1, \alpha_2, \cdots, \alpha_{m-1}$, then α_m can be written as a linear combination of the vectors $\alpha_1, \alpha_2, \cdots, \alpha_{m-1}, \beta$. Give an example to show why the second hypothesis is necessary.

Exercise (26.5). Show that if M is a linearly independent set of vectors in a subspace S, M is contained in a basis of S.

Exercise (26.6). Let the vectors $\alpha_1, \alpha_2, \cdots, \alpha_m$ span S, and let the vectors $\beta_1, \beta_2, \cdots, \beta_m$ be defined by the equation

$$P\begin{pmatrix}\alpha_1\\ \alpha_2\\ \cdot\\ \cdot\\ \cdot\\ \alpha_m\end{pmatrix} = \begin{pmatrix}\beta_1\\ \beta_2\\ \cdot\\ \cdot\\ \cdot\\ \beta_m\end{pmatrix},$$

where P is an m-rowed square matrix with elements in F. Show that if P is non-singular, then $\beta_1, \beta_2, \cdots, \beta_m$ span S.

Exercise (26.7). Prove that there exists a nonsingular matrix P

such that $P\begin{pmatrix}\alpha_1\\ \alpha_2\\ \cdot\\ \cdot\\ \cdot\\ \alpha_m\end{pmatrix} = \begin{pmatrix}\beta_1\\ \beta_2\\ \cdot\\ \cdot\\ \cdot\\ \beta_k\\ 0\\ \cdot\\ \cdot\\ \cdot\\ 0\end{pmatrix}$ and $\beta_1, \beta_2, \cdots, \beta_k$ are linearly independent if and only if the rank of $\begin{pmatrix} \alpha_1 \\ \alpha_2 \\ \cdot \\ \cdot \\ \cdot \\ \alpha_m \end{pmatrix}$ is equal to k.

Exercise (26.8). Let the set M of vectors $\alpha_1, \alpha_2, \cdots, \alpha_m$ span S. Prove that if the rank of $\begin{pmatrix} \alpha_1 \\ \alpha_2 \\ \cdot \\ \cdot \\ \cdot \\ \alpha_m \end{pmatrix}$ is equal to k, then there is a subset of k vectors of M which is a basis of S.

Exercise (26.9). If S and T are subspaces of $V_n(F)$, let $S + T$ be defined as the smallest subspace of $V_n(F)$ containing S and T, and let $S \cap T$ be defined as the largest subspace of $V_n(F)$ contained in both S and T. Prove the following relation between the dimensions of S, T, $S + T$, and $S \cap T$:

$$\dim (S + T) = \dim (S) + \dim (T) - \dim (S \cap T).$$

Section 27. Change of Basis

If $u_1, u_2, \cdots, u_n$ is any basis of $V_n(F)$, then by Theorem (26.2), every vector $\alpha \in V_n(F)$ has a unique expression $\alpha = a_1u_1 + a_2u_2 + \cdots + a_nu_n$ with coefficients $a_1, a_2, \cdots, a_n \in F$. We call the coefficients $a_1, a_2, \cdots, a_n$ the *coordinates* of α with respect to the basis $u_1, u_2, \cdots, u_n$. Specifically, the components c_i of the vector $\alpha = (c_1, c_2, \cdots, c_n)$ are the coordinates of α with respect to the basis $\epsilon_i = (\delta_{i1}, \delta_{i2}, \cdots, \delta_{in})$, $i = 1, 2, \cdots, n$.

The equations of rotation,

$$x = x' \cos \theta - y' \sin \theta$$
$$y = x' \sin \theta + y' \cos \theta,$$

are interpreted in plane analytic geometry as the relation between the coordinates of a point P with respect to two coordinate systems. Making this same interpretation for a vector $\alpha = (x,y) = x \cdot \epsilon_1 + y \cdot \epsilon_2 \in V_2(R^\#)$, these equations give the relation between the coordinates of α relative to the two bases, ϵ_1, ϵ_2 and u_1, u_2, of $V_2(R^\#)$, where $u_1 =$

$(\cos\theta, \sin\theta)$ and $u_2 = (-\sin\theta, \cos\theta)$ are the rotated positions of ϵ_1 and ϵ_2.

The relation between the coordinates of a vector relative to two bases of $V_n(F)$ is a consequence of the following theorem.

(27.1) Theorem. Let $u_1, u_2, \cdots, u_n$ be a basis of $V_n(F)$ and let $\bar{u}_1, \bar{u}_2, \cdots, \bar{u}_n$ be any set of n vectors in $V_n(F)$. Then $\bar{u}_1, \bar{u}_2, \cdots, \bar{u}_n$ is a basis of $V_n(F)$ if and only if there exists a nonsingular n by n matrix $P = (p_{ij})$ with elements in F such that

$$\begin{pmatrix} \bar{u}_1 \\ \bar{u}_2 \\ \cdot \\ \cdot \\ \cdot \\ \bar{u}_n \end{pmatrix} = P \begin{pmatrix} u_1 \\ u_2 \\ \cdot \\ \cdot \\ \cdot \\ u_n \end{pmatrix}.$$

PROOF. Let the n by n matrices*

$$\begin{pmatrix} u_1 \\ u_2 \\ \cdot \\ \cdot \\ \cdot \\ u_n \end{pmatrix} \quad \text{and} \quad \begin{pmatrix} \bar{u}_1 \\ \bar{u}_2 \\ \cdot \\ \cdot \\ \cdot \\ \bar{u}_n \end{pmatrix}$$

be denoted by U and $\bar{U}$ respectively. Since $u_1, u_2, \cdots, u_n$ is a linearly independent set, the matrix U is nonsingular by Theorem (25.3).

If P is a nonsingular n by n matrix such that $\bar{U} = PU$, then $\bar{U}$ is nonsingular since it is the product of two nonsingular matrices. Thus $\bar{u}_1, \bar{u}_2, \cdots, \bar{u}_n$ is a linearly independent set of n vectors in $V_n(F)$, and is therefore a basis.

Conversely, if $\bar{u}_1, \bar{u}_2, \cdots, \bar{u}_n$ is a basis of $V_n(F)$, then the matrix $\bar{U}$ is nonsingular and $(U\bar{U}^{-1})\bar{U} = U$. Thus $P = \bar{U}U^{-1}$ is a nonsingular matrix such that $\bar{U} = PU$.

(27.2) Corollary. If $\alpha \in V_n(F)$ has coordinates $a_1, a_2, \cdots, a_n$ with respect to the basis $u_1, u_2, \cdots, u_n$, then the coordinates $\bar{a}_1, \bar{a}_2, \cdots, \bar{a}_n$ of α with respect to the basis $\bar{u}_1, \bar{u}_2, \cdots, \bar{u}_n$ are given by

$$(\bar{a}_1, \bar{a}_2, \cdots, \bar{a}_n) = (a_1, a_2, \cdots, a_n)P^{-1}$$

where $P = \bar{U}U^{-1}$ is the matrix of Theorem (27.1).

---

* Whenever we write the matrix of a set of vectors, the vectors are written in terms of their components.

PROOF. Using the notation of Theorem (27.1) we have

$$\alpha = a_1u_1 + a_2u_2 + \cdots + a_nu_n = (a_1, a_2, \cdots, a_n)U,$$

and

$$\alpha = \bar{a}_1\bar{u}_1 + \bar{a}_2\bar{u}_2 + \cdots + \bar{a}_n\bar{u}_n = (\bar{a}_1, \bar{a}_2, \cdots, \bar{a}_n)\bar{U}.$$

By the theorem, $\bar{U} = PU$ or $U = P^{-1}\bar{U}$. Thus we have

$$(\bar{a}_1, \bar{a}_2, \cdots, \bar{a}_n)\bar{U} = (a_1, a_2, \cdots, a_n)P^{-1}\bar{U},$$

and on multiplying this matrix equation by the inverse of the nonsingular matrix $\bar{U}$, we obtain the desired relation between the coordinates.

(27.3) Corollary. The coordinates $\bar{a}_1, \bar{a}_2, \cdots, \bar{a}_n$ of a vector α with respect to the basis $\bar{u}_1, \bar{u}_2, \cdots, \bar{u}_n$ are given by

$$(\bar{a}_1, \bar{a}_2, \cdots, \bar{a}_n) = (c_1, c_2, \cdots, c_n)\bar{U}^{-1}$$

where $c_1, c_2, \cdots, c_n$ are the components of α and

$$\bar{U} = \begin{pmatrix} \bar{u}_1 \\ \bar{u}_2 \\ \cdot \\ \cdot \\ \cdot \\ \bar{u}_n \end{pmatrix}.$$

PROOF. This is a special case of Corollary (27.2) with the basis $u_1, u_2, \cdots, u_n$ taken to be the special basis $\epsilon_1, \epsilon_2, \cdots, \epsilon_n$. Then $U = I_n$, and $P = \bar{U}U^{-1} = \bar{U}$.

Exercise (27.1). Show that (1,2,1), (3,−1,4), (2,0,1) and (1,0,0), (1,1,0), (1,1,1) are bases of $V_3(R)$. Compute the matrix P of Theorem (27.1). Find the coordinates of $\alpha = (3,-1,5)$ with respect to each basis and write out the equations connecting the two sets of coordinates.

Exercise (27.2). Find in two ways the coordinates of the vectors (5,0,−1) and (2,0,0) with respect to the basis (1,2,3), (2,1,3), (2,2,2) of $V_3(R)$.

Exercise (27.3). Prove that the rows of the matrix P of Theorem (27.1) are the coordinates of the basis vectors $\bar{u}_1, \bar{u}_2, \cdots, \bar{u}_n$ with respect to the basis $u_1, u_2, \cdots, u_n$.

Exercise (27.4). Show that $(2,i,-1)$, $(0,-2+i,2)$, $(1/2,0,-1)$ and $(-1,2,-1)$, $(2,i,-i)$, $(3,3+i,-1)$ are bases of $V_3(C)$. Compute the matrix P of Theorem (27.1) by the method of the preceding exercise.

Section 28. Linear Mappings

Let us consider the problem of mapping a vector space $V_n(F)$ into a vector space $V_m(F)$ in such a way that the operations in $V_n(F)$ of addition and multiplication by a scalar are preserved. If the mapping is denoted by $\mathfrak{L}$, so that $\mathfrak{L}(\alpha)$ is a uniquely defined vector in $V_m(F)$ for every $\alpha \in V_n(F)$, then both vector operations are preserved by $\mathfrak{L}$ if and only if $\mathfrak{L}(a\alpha + b\beta) = a\mathfrak{L}(\alpha) + b\mathfrak{L}(\beta)$ for every $\alpha,\beta \in V_n(F)$ and every $a,b \in F$.

(28.1) Definition. A single-valued mapping $\mathfrak{L}$ of $V_n(F)$ into $V_m(F)$ such that $\mathfrak{L}(a\alpha + b\beta) = a\mathfrak{L}(\alpha) + b\mathfrak{L}(\beta)$ for every $\alpha,\beta \in V_n(F)$ and every $a,b \in F$ is called a *linear mapping* of $V_n(F)$ into $V_m(F)$.

One of the consequences of the linearity of $\mathfrak{L}$ is that subspaces of $V_n(F)$ are mapped onto subspaces of $V_m(F)$. To show this, let $\mathfrak{L}(S)$ be the totality of the image vectors in $V_m(F)$ of the vectors in the subspace S of $V_n(F)$. Then if $\gamma,\delta \in \mathfrak{L}(S)$, there exists a pair $\alpha,\beta \in S$ such that $\gamma = \mathfrak{L}(\alpha)$ and $\delta = \mathfrak{L}(\beta)$. Since $a\gamma + b\delta = a\mathfrak{L}(\alpha) + b\mathfrak{L}(\beta) = \mathfrak{L}(a\alpha + b\beta)$, and since $a\alpha + b\beta \in S$ for every $a,b \in F$, $\mathfrak{L}(a\alpha + b\beta) \in \mathfrak{L}(S)$. By Theorem (24.4), $\mathfrak{L}(S)$ is a subspace of $V_m(F)$.

Another consequence of the linearity of $\mathfrak{L}$ is that $\mathfrak{L}$ is completely determined by its effect on the vectors of any basis of $V_n(F)$. For if $u_1, u_2, \cdots, u_n$ is any basis of $V_n(F)$ and if α is any vector in $V_n(F)$, then

$$\begin{aligned}\mathfrak{L}(\alpha) &= \mathfrak{L}(x_1u_1 + x_2u_2 + \cdots + x_nu_n)\\ &= x_1\mathfrak{L}(u_1) + x_2\mathfrak{L}(u_2) + \cdots + x_n\mathfrak{L}(u_n)\end{aligned}$$

where $x_1, x_2, \cdots, x_n$ are the coordinates of α with respect to the given basis.

In order to obtain an explicit expression for a linear mapping $\mathfrak{L}$, we select a basis $u_1, u_2, \cdots, u_n$ of $V_n(F)$ and a basis $v_1, v_2, \cdots, v_m$ of $V_m(F)$. Let $a_{1i}, a_{2i}, \cdots, a_{mi}$ be the coordinates of $\mathfrak{L}(u_i)$ with respect to the basis $v_1, v_2, \cdots, v_m$, that is, $\mathfrak{L}(u_i) = a_{1i}v_1 + a_{2i}v_2 + \cdots + a_{mi}v_m$ for $i = 1, 2, \cdots, n$. Then if $\alpha = x_1u_1 + x_2u_2 + \cdots + x_nu_n$ is any vector in $V_n(F)$,

$$\begin{aligned}\mathfrak{L}(\alpha) &= x_1\mathfrak{L}(u_1) + x_2\mathfrak{L}(u_2) + \cdots + x_n\mathfrak{L}(u_n)\\ &= x_1(a_{11}v_1 + a_{21}v_2 + \cdots + a_{m1}v_m)\\ &\qquad + x_2(a_{12}v_1 + a_{22}v_2 + \cdots + a_{m2}v_m)\\ &\qquad\qquad + \cdots + x_n(a_{1n}v_1 + a_{2n}v_2 + \cdots + a_{mn}v_m)\\ &= (x_1a_{11} + x_2a_{12} + \cdots + x_na_{1n})v_1\\ &\qquad + (x_1a_{21} + x_2a_{22} + \cdots + x_na_{2n})v_2\\ &\qquad\qquad + \cdots + (x_1a_{m1} + x_2a_{m2} + \cdots + x_na_{mn})v_m.\end{aligned}$$

The coefficients of $v_1, v_2, \cdots, v_m$ in the last expression are the coordinates $y_1, y_2, \cdots, y_m$ of $\mathcal{L}(\alpha)$ with respect to the basis $v_1, v_2, \cdots, v_m$. Thus the mapping $\mathcal{L}$ is given by the equations

$$\sum_{j=1}^{n} a_{ij}x_j = y_i, \qquad i = 1, 2, \cdots, m \tag{28.2}$$

where $\mathcal{L}(u_i) = a_{1i}v_1 + a_{2i}v_2 + \cdots + a_{mi}v_m$ for $i = 1, 2, \cdots, n$, $\alpha = x_1u_1 + x_2u_2 + \cdots + x_nu_n \in V_n(F)$, and $\mathcal{L}(\alpha) = y_1v_1 + y_2v_2 + \cdots + y_mv_m \in V_m(F)$. The matrix form of these equations is

$$\begin{pmatrix} a_{11} & a_{12} & \cdots & a_{1n} \\ a_{21} & a_{22} & \cdots & a_{2n} \\ \cdot & \cdot & & \cdot \\ \cdot & \cdot & & \cdot \\ \cdot & \cdot & & \cdot \\ a_{m1} & a_{m2} & \cdots & a_{mn} \end{pmatrix} \begin{pmatrix} x_1 \\ x_2 \\ \cdot \\ \cdot \\ \cdot \\ x_n \end{pmatrix} = \begin{pmatrix} y_1 \\ y_2 \\ \cdot \\ \cdot \\ \cdot \\ y_m \end{pmatrix}, \tag{28.3}$$

and the matrix $A = (a_{ij})$ with elements in F is called the *matrix of the linear mapping* with respect to the given bases.

Conversely, with given bases $u_1, u_2, \cdots, u_n$ of $V_n(F)$ and $v_1, v_2, \cdots, v_m$ of $V_m(F)$, if $A = (a_{ij})$ is any m by n matrix with elements in F, the equations (28.2) uniquely determine a vector $\beta = y_1v_1 + y_2v_2 + \cdots + y_mv_m \in V_m(F)$ for every vector $\alpha = x_1u_1 + x_2u_2 + \cdots + x_nu_n \in V_n(F)$. It is left for the reader as an exercise to prove that the mapping $\mathcal{L}$ defined by $\mathcal{L}(\alpha) = \beta$ is linear mapping and that A is the matrix of $\mathcal{L}$ with respect to the given bases.

The above argument shows that with respect to given bases in the two spaces, each linear mapping $\mathcal{L}$ corresponds to a unique m by n matrix A, and each such matrix determines a linear mapping.

EXAMPLE 1. The vectors $u_1 = (3,1,1)$, $u_2 = (1,1,0)$, $u_3 = (0,0,1)$ form a basis of $V_3(F)$, and the vectors $v_1 = (1,1)$, $v_2 = (2,0)$ a basis of $V_2(F)$. The mapping $\mathcal{L}$ of $V_3(F)$ into $V_2(F)$ defined by $\mathcal{L}(u_1) = v_1 + v_2$, $\mathcal{L}(u_2) = v_1 - v_2$, $\mathcal{L}(u_3) = 2v_1$ has the matrix

$$A = \begin{pmatrix} 1 & 1 & 2 \\ 1 & -1 & 0 \end{pmatrix}.$$

One should note that

$$\begin{aligned} \mathcal{L}(\alpha) &= \mathcal{L}(x_1u_1 + x_2u_2 + x_3u_3) \\ &= x_1\mathcal{L}(u_1) + x_2\mathcal{L}(u_2) + x_3\mathcal{L}(u_3) \\ &= x_1(v_1 + v_2) + x_2(v_1 - v_2) + x_3 2v_1 \\ &= (x_1 + x_2 + 2x_3)v_1 + (x_1 - x_2)v_2, \end{aligned}$$

so that $\begin{pmatrix} x_1 + x_2 + 2x_3 \\ x_1 - x_2 \end{pmatrix} = \begin{pmatrix} 1 & 1 & 2 \\ 1 & -1 & 0 \end{pmatrix} \begin{pmatrix} x_1 \\ x_2 \\ x_3 \end{pmatrix} = \begin{pmatrix} y_1 \\ y_2 \end{pmatrix}.$

EXAMPLE 2. With the bases as in Example 1, the matrix $B = \begin{pmatrix} 2 & 1 & 4 \\ 1 & -2 & 1 \end{pmatrix}$ defines a linear mapping $\mathcal{L}$ of $V_3(F)$ into $V_2(F)$ where $\mathcal{L}(u_1) = 2v_1 + v_2$, $\mathcal{L}(u_2) = v_1 - 2v_2$, $\mathcal{L}(u_3) = 4v_1 + v_2$, and $\mathcal{L}(\alpha) = \mathcal{L}(x_1u_1 + x_2u_2 + x_3u_3) = (2x_1 + x_2 + 4x_3)v_1 + (x_1 - 2x_2 + x_3)v_2$. If $\beta = (-1,3,2) \in V_3(F)$, to find $\mathcal{L}(\beta)$ we first find the coordinates of β with respect to u_1, u_2, u_3. By Corollary (27.3), $\beta = x_1u_1 + x_2u_2 + x_3u_3$ where

$$(x_1, x_2, x_3) = (-1,3,2) \begin{pmatrix} 3 & 1 & 1 \\ 1 & 1 & 0 \\ 0 & 0 & 1 \end{pmatrix}^{-1}$$

$$= (-1,3,2) \begin{pmatrix} 1/2 & -1/2 & -1/2 \\ -1/2 & 3/2 & 1/2 \\ 0 & 0 & 1 \end{pmatrix} = (-2,5,4).$$

Therefore $\begin{pmatrix} y_1 \\ y_2 \end{pmatrix} = \begin{pmatrix} 2 & 1 & 4 \\ 1 & -2 & 1 \end{pmatrix} \begin{pmatrix} -2 \\ 5 \\ 4 \end{pmatrix} = \begin{pmatrix} 17 \\ -8 \end{pmatrix},$

and

$$\mathcal{L}(\beta) = 17v_1 - 8v_2 = 17(1,1) - 8(2,0) = (1,17) \in V_2(F).$$

Since the matrix of a linear mapping $\mathcal{L}$ depends upon the bases selected in each space, we next wish to find the change in the matrix of $\mathcal{L}$ caused by a change of basis in each space. Let $\bar{u}_1, \bar{u}_2, \cdots, \bar{u}_n$ be a second basis of $V_n(F)$ and $\bar{v}_1, \bar{v}_2, \cdots, \bar{v}_m$ be a second basis of $V_m(F)$, and let the coordinates of $\alpha \in V_n(F)$ and $\mathcal{L}(\alpha) \in V_m(F)$ with respect to these bases be $\bar{x}_1, \bar{x}_2, \cdots, \bar{x}_n$ and $\bar{y}_1, \bar{y}_2, \cdots, \bar{y}_m$.

Then by Corollary (27.2)

$$(x_1, x_2, \cdots, x_n) = (\bar{x}_1, \bar{x}_2, \cdots, \bar{x}_n)P_n$$

and

$$(y_1, y_2, \cdots, y_m) = (\bar{y}_1, \bar{y}_2, \cdots, \bar{y}_m)P_m,$$

where P_n and P_m are nonsingular n by n and m by m matrices respectively. If we substitute in the matrix equation (28.3)

$$A(x_1, x_2, \cdots, x_n)' = (y_1, y_2, \cdots, y_m)',$$

we obtain

$$AP_n'(\bar{x}_1, \bar{x}_2, \cdots, \bar{x}_n)' = P_m'(\bar{y}_1, \bar{y}_2, \cdots, \bar{y}_m)',$$

or

$$(P_m')^{-1}AP_n'(\bar{x}_1, \bar{x}_2, \cdots, \bar{x}_n)' = (\bar{y}_1, \bar{y}_2, \cdots, \bar{y}_m)'.$$

Therefore the matrix $(P_m')^{-1}AP_n'$ of $\mathfrak{L}$ with respect to the new bases is rationally equivalent to A. The above results are summarized in the following theorem.

(28.4) Theorem. If A is the matrix of a linear mapping $\mathfrak{L}$ with respect to given bases in $V_n(F)$ and $V_m(F)$, then the matrix of $\mathfrak{L}$ relative to any other bases is rationally equivalent to A.

If the linear mapping $\mathfrak{L}$ is given by the matrix equation (28.3), and if B is any m by n matrix which is rationally equivalent to the matrix A of $\mathfrak{L}$, then there exist nonsingular matrices P and Q in F such that $B = PAQ$. If we then define new bases in $V_n(F)$ and $V_m(F)$ by

$$\text{(28.5)}\qquad \begin{pmatrix} \bar{u}_1 \\ \bar{u}_2 \\ \cdot \\ \cdot \\ \cdot \\ \bar{u}_n \end{pmatrix} = Q' \begin{pmatrix} u_1 \\ u_2 \\ \cdot \\ \cdot \\ \cdot \\ u_n \end{pmatrix} \quad \text{and} \quad \begin{pmatrix} \bar{v}_1 \\ \bar{v}_2 \\ \cdot \\ \cdot \\ \cdot \\ \bar{v}_m \end{pmatrix} = (P^{-1})' \begin{pmatrix} v_1 \\ v_2 \\ \cdot \\ \cdot \\ \cdot \\ v_m \end{pmatrix},$$

B is the matrix of $\mathfrak{L}$ relative to these new bases. This suggests that $\mathfrak{L}$ may be given in a particularly simple form if the new bases are chosen suitably in $V_n(F)$ and $V_m(F)$. In fact, if P and Q in equations (28.5) are selected so that $PAQ = D_r$, where r is the rank of A, then in terms of the new bases $\mathfrak{L}$ is given by

$$D_r(\bar{x}_1, \bar{x}_2, \cdots, \bar{x}_n)' = (\bar{y}_1, \bar{y}_2, \cdots, \bar{y}_m)',$$

or in equation form by

$$\text{(28.6)}\qquad \begin{aligned} \bar{x}_i &= \bar{y}_i \text{ for } i = 1, 2, \cdots, r; \\ 0 &= \bar{y}_i \text{ for } i = r+1, r+2, \cdots, m. \end{aligned}$$

EXAMPLE 3. To find the equation of the mapping in Example 2 with respect to the bases $\epsilon_1, \epsilon_2, \epsilon_3$ of $V_3(F)$ and $\epsilon_1, \epsilon_2,$ of $V_2(F)$, we must first find the equations for the change of coordinates in each space. In $V_3(F)$, $\alpha = x_1u_1 + x_2u_2 + x_3u_3 = (x_1,x_2,x_3)\begin{pmatrix} 3 & 1 & 1 \\ 1 & 1 & 0 \\ 0 & 0 & 1 \end{pmatrix} = (c_1,c_2,c_3)$, or

$$\begin{pmatrix} x_1 \\ x_2 \\ x_3 \end{pmatrix} = \begin{pmatrix} 3 & 1 & 1 \\ 1 & 1 & 0 \\ 0 & 0 & 1 \end{pmatrix}'^{-1} \begin{pmatrix} c_1 \\ c_2 \\ c_3 \end{pmatrix}.$$

Similarly in $V_2(F)$, $\begin{pmatrix} y_1 \\ y_2 \end{pmatrix} = \begin{pmatrix} 1 & 1 \\ 2 & 0 \end{pmatrix}'^{-1} \begin{pmatrix} d_1 \\ d_2 \end{pmatrix}$ where $\alpha = y_1v_1 + y_2v_2 = (d_1,d_2)$. Thus

$$B\begin{pmatrix} x_1 \\ x_2 \\ x_3 \end{pmatrix} = B\begin{pmatrix} 3 & 1 & 1 \\ 1 & 1 & 0 \\ 0 & 0 & 1 \end{pmatrix}'^{-1} \begin{pmatrix} c_1 \\ c_2 \\ c_3 \end{pmatrix} = \begin{pmatrix} y_1 \\ y_2 \end{pmatrix} = \begin{pmatrix} 1 & 1 \\ 2 & 0 \end{pmatrix}'^{-1} \begin{pmatrix} d_1 \\ d_2 \end{pmatrix},$$

or $$\begin{pmatrix} 1 & 1 \\ 2 & 0 \end{pmatrix}' B \begin{pmatrix} 3 & 1 & 1 \\ 1 & 1 & 0 \\ 0 & 0 & 1 \end{pmatrix}'^{-1} \begin{pmatrix} c_1 \\ c_2 \\ c_3 \end{pmatrix} = \begin{pmatrix} 1/2 & -7/2 & 6 \\ -3/2 & 5/2 & 4 \end{pmatrix} \begin{pmatrix} c_1 \\ c_2 \\ c_3 \end{pmatrix} = \begin{pmatrix} d_1 \\ d_2 \end{pmatrix}.$$

Therefore $\mathcal{L}(c_1,c_2,c_3) = (1/2\ c_1 - 7/2\ c_2 + 6c_3, -3/2\ c_1 + 5/2\ c_2 + 4c_3) \in V_2(F)$. In particular, if $\beta = (-1,3,2)$, $\mathcal{L}(\beta) = (1,17)$, in agreement with the previous calculation.

EXAMPLE 4. To find bases of $V_3(F)$ and $V_2(F)$ with respect to which the mapping in Example 1 has matrix D_r, we must first reduce the matrix A to this form. Using the methods of Section 20, we find

$$\begin{pmatrix} 1 & 0 \\ 1/2 & -1/2 \end{pmatrix} A \begin{pmatrix} 1 & -1 & -1 \\ 0 & 1 & -1 \\ 0 & 0 & 1 \end{pmatrix} = D_2 = \begin{pmatrix} 1 & 0 & 0 \\ 0 & 1 & 0 \end{pmatrix}.$$

Since $A\begin{pmatrix} x_1 \\ x_2 \\ x_3 \end{pmatrix} = \begin{pmatrix} y_1 \\ y_2 \end{pmatrix}$, we have

$$\begin{pmatrix} 1 & 0 \\ 1/2 & -1/2 \end{pmatrix} A \begin{pmatrix} 1 & -1 & -1 \\ 0 & 1 & -1 \\ 0 & 0 & 1 \end{pmatrix}\begin{pmatrix} 1 & -1 & -1 \\ 0 & 1 & -1 \\ 0 & 0 & 1 \end{pmatrix}^{-1} \begin{pmatrix} x_1 \\ x_2 \\ x_3 \end{pmatrix} = \begin{pmatrix} 1 & 0 \\ 1/2 & -1/2 \end{pmatrix}\begin{pmatrix} y_1 \\ y_2 \end{pmatrix}.$$

We let $$\begin{pmatrix} \bar{x}_1 \\ \bar{x}_2 \\ \bar{x}_3 \end{pmatrix} = \begin{pmatrix} 1 & -1 & -1 \\ 0 & 1 & -1 \\ 0 & 0 & 1 \end{pmatrix}^{-1} \begin{pmatrix} x_1 \\ x_2 \\ x_3 \end{pmatrix},$$

or $$(x_1,x_2,x_3) = (\bar{x}_1,\bar{x}_2,\bar{x}_3)\begin{pmatrix} 1 & 0 & 0 \\ -1 & 1 & 0 \\ -1 & -1 & 1 \end{pmatrix},$$

and $$\begin{pmatrix} \bar{y}_1 \\ \bar{y}_2 \end{pmatrix} = \begin{pmatrix} 1 & 0 \\ 1/2 & -1/2 \end{pmatrix}\begin{pmatrix} y_1 \\ y_2 \end{pmatrix},$$

or $$(y_1,y_2) = (\bar{y}_1,\bar{y}_2)\begin{pmatrix} 1 & 0 \\ 1/2 & -1/2 \end{pmatrix}'^{-1} = (\bar{y}_1,\bar{y}_2)\begin{pmatrix} 1 & 1 \\ 0 & -2 \end{pmatrix}.$$

This means that the new bases $\bar{u}_1$, $\bar{u}_2$, $\bar{u}_3$ and $\bar{v}_1$, $\bar{v}_2$ are given by

$$\begin{pmatrix}\bar{u}_1\\ \bar{u}_2\\ \bar{u}_3\end{pmatrix} = \begin{pmatrix}1 & 0 & 0\\ -1 & 1 & 0\\ -1 & -1 & 1\end{pmatrix}\begin{pmatrix}u_1\\ u_2\\ u_3\end{pmatrix} = \begin{pmatrix}1 & 0 & 0\\ -1 & 1 & 0\\ -1 & -1 & 1\end{pmatrix}\begin{pmatrix}3 & 1 & 1\\ 1 & 1 & 0\\ 0 & 0 & 1\end{pmatrix}$$

$$= \begin{pmatrix}3 & 1 & 1\\ -2 & 0 & -1\\ -4 & -2 & 0\end{pmatrix}$$

and $\begin{pmatrix}\bar{v}_1\\ \bar{v}_2\end{pmatrix} = \begin{pmatrix}1 & 1\\ 0 & -2\end{pmatrix}\begin{pmatrix}v_1\\ v_2\end{pmatrix} = \begin{pmatrix}1 & 1\\ 0 & -2\end{pmatrix}\begin{pmatrix}1 & 1\\ 2 & 0\end{pmatrix} = \begin{pmatrix}3 & 1\\ -4 & 0\end{pmatrix}.$

The equations of the mapping with respect to these bases are $\bar{y}_1 = \bar{x}_1$ and $\bar{y}_2 = \bar{x}_2$.

By Theorem (28.4), the rank of the matrix of a linear mapping is independent of the choice of bases in $V_n(F)$ and $V_m(F)$. Therefore, each linear mapping $\mathfrak{L}$ has a unique *rank*, which is the rank of the matrix of $\mathfrak{L}$ with respect to any pair of bases.

(28.7) Theorem. If $\mathfrak{L}$ is a linear mapping of rank r of $V_n(F)$ into $V_m(F)$, then the subspace $\mathfrak{L}(V_n(F))$ of $V_m(F)$ has dimension r.

PROOF. $\mathfrak{L}(V_n(F))$ is the complete set of image vectors by the mapping $\mathfrak{L}$ in $V_m(F)$. It is a subspace of $V_m(F)$, since we have shown that subspaces are mapped into subspaces by a linear mapping. Selecting bases $\bar{u}_1, \bar{u}_2, \cdots, \bar{u}_n$ and $\bar{v}_1, \bar{v}_2, \cdots, \bar{v}_m$ in the two spaces, so that relative to these bases $\mathfrak{L}$ is given by equations (28.6), it is evident that the vectors $\bar{v}_1, \bar{v}_2, \cdots, \bar{v}_r$ span $\mathfrak{L}(V_n(F))$. Since this set of vectors is linearly independent, it is a basis of $\mathfrak{L}(V_n(F))$. By Theorem (26.4), $\mathfrak{L}(V_n(F))$ has dimension r.

Exercise (28.1). Let S' be a subspace of $V_m(F)$ and S be a subset of $V_n(F)$ consisting of all the vectors in $V_n(F)$ which are mapped into S' by a linear mapping $\mathfrak{L}$. S is called the *complete inverse image* of S'. Prove that S is a subspace of $V_n(F)$.

Exercise (28.2). Prove that the mapping defined by equations (28.2) is a linear mapping with matrix A.

Exercise (28.3). Verify that if new bases are defined by equations (28.5), PAQ is the matrix of $\mathfrak{L}$ with respect to these new bases.

Exercise (28.4). The linear mapping $\mathfrak{L}$ of $V_4(R)$ into $V_3(R)$ is given by $\begin{pmatrix}3 & 1 & 2 & 5\\ -1 & 4 & 0 & 1\\ 0 & 0 & 2 & 2\end{pmatrix}\begin{pmatrix}x_1\\ x_2\\ x_3\\ x_4\end{pmatrix} = \begin{pmatrix}y_1\\ y_2\\ y_3\end{pmatrix}$ where x_1, x_2, x_3, x_4 are the components of a vector in $V_4(R)$ and y_1, y_2, y_3 are the components of the image vector in $V_3(R)$. Find bases in $V_4(R)$ and $V_3(R)$ with respect to which $\mathcal{L}$ has matrix D_r.

Exercise (28.5). In Exercise (28.4) let S be the subspace of $V_4(R)$ spanned by the vectors $\alpha = (2,-3,1,4)$ and $\beta = (1,0,1,0)$. Find a basis for the subspace $\mathcal{L}(S)$ in $V_3(R)$.

Exercise (28.6). Prove that if a linear mapping $\mathcal{L}$ of $V_n(F)$ into $V_m(F)$ has rank m, then $n \geq m$ and $\mathcal{L}(V_n(F)) = V_m(F)$.

Exercise (28.7). Construct a linear mapping $\mathcal{L}$ of $V_3(R)$ into $V_4(R)$ which maps (1,0,0) onto (3,1,3,1), (0,1,0) onto (0,1,0,1), and (0,0,1) onto (3,2,3,2).

Exercise (28.8). Let S be any subspace of $V_n(F)$, let N be the subspace of $V_n(F)$ consisting of those vectors mapped onto the zero vector of $V_m(F)$ by a linear mapping $\mathcal{L}$, and let $S \cap N$ be the largest subspace of $V_n(F)$ contained in both S and N. Prove the following relation between the dimensions of S and $\mathcal{L}(S)$:

$$\dim (S) = \dim (S \cap N) + \dim (\mathcal{L}(S)).$$

In particular, if $\mathcal{L}$ is of rank r, then $\dim (N) = n - r$.

Section 29. Bilinear Mappings

In the preceding section we saw how the theory of rational equivalence of rectangular matrices is connected with a discussion of a linear mapping from $V_n(F)$ into $V_m(F)$. Rational equivalence enters in a similar way in the discussion of a mapping from $V_m(F)$ and $V_n(F)$ into the number field F. Let $\mathcal{B}$ be a single-valued mapping such that for every pair α, β of vectors $\alpha \in V_m(F)$ and $\beta \in V_n(F)$, there exists a unique element $\mathcal{B}(\alpha,\beta) \in F$.

(29.1) Definition. A single-valued mapping $\mathcal{B}$ of $V_m(F)$ and $V_n(F)$ into F is called *bilinear* if

$$\mathcal{B}(c_1\alpha_1 + c_2\alpha_2, d_1\beta_1 + d_2\beta_2) = c_1d_1 \cdot \mathcal{B}(\alpha_1,\beta_1) + c_1d_2 \cdot \mathcal{B}(\alpha_1,\beta_2) + c_2d_1 \cdot \mathcal{B}(\alpha_2,\beta_1) + c_2d_2 \cdot \mathcal{B}(\alpha_2,\beta_2)$$

for all $\alpha_1,\alpha_2 \in V_m(F)$; $\beta_1,\beta_2 \in V_n(F)$; and $c_1,c_2,d_1,d_2 \in F$.

One important example of a bilinear mapping is the inner product defined in a vector space. Taking $m = n$ so that the two spaces are the same space $V_n(F)$, we define $\mathcal{B}(\alpha,\beta)$ to be the matrix product $(x_1, x_2, \cdots, x_n)(y_1, y_2, \cdots, y_n)'$ where $\alpha = (x_1, x_2, \cdots, x_n)$ and

$\beta = (y_1, y_2, \cdots, y_n)$ are any two vectors in $V_n(F)$. Thus $\mathcal{B}(\alpha,\beta) = x_1y_1 + x_2y_2 + \cdots + x_ny_n \in F$, and the bilinearity of $\mathcal{B}$ follows from the distributive laws and the identities of scalar multiplication of matrices. This example is of particular importance in the discussion of Euclidean vector spaces in Chapter VIII.

Let $u_1, u_2, \cdots, u_m \in V_m(F)$ and $v_1, v_2, \cdots, v_n \in V_n(F)$ be given bases in the two spaces and let $\alpha = x_1u_1 + x_2u_2 + \cdots + x_mu_m \in V_m(F)$ and $\beta = y_1v_1 + y_2v_2 + \cdots + y_nv_n \in V_n(F)$. Then in terms of the coordinates of α and β relative to these bases we can write a bilinear mapping as follows:

$$\begin{aligned}\mathcal{B}(\alpha,\beta) &= \mathcal{B}(x_1u_1 + x_2u_2 + \cdots + x_mu_m, y_1v_1 + y_2v_2 + \cdots + y_nv_n)\\ &= \sum_{i=1}^{m}\sum_{j=1}^{n} x_iy_j \cdot \mathcal{B}(u_i,v_j)\\ &= (x_1, x_2, \cdots, x_m)(\mathcal{B}(u_i,v_j))(y_1, y_2, \cdots, y_n)' = XAY'\end{aligned}$$

where $A = (a_{ij})$ is an m by n matrix with $a_{ij} = \mathcal{B}(u_i,v_j) \in F$ for all pairs i,j. Thus relative to given bases, each bilinear mapping can be written in matrix form. The matrix $A = (a_{ij})$ is called the *matrix of* $\mathcal{B}$ with respect to the bases $u_1, u_2, \cdots, u_m$ of $V_m(F)$ and $v_1, v_2, \cdots, v_n$ of $V_n(F)$.

Conversely, the reader may show that with respect to given bases $u_1, u_2, \cdots, u_m \in V_m(F)$ and $v_1, v_2, \cdots, v_n \in V_n(F)$, each m by n matrix $A = (a_{ij})$ in F defines a bilinear mapping $\mathcal{B}$ given by

$$\mathcal{B}(\alpha,\beta) = (x_1, x_2, \cdots, x_m)A(y_1, y_2, \cdots, y_n)'$$

for all $\alpha = \sum_{i=1}^{m} x_iu_i \in V_m(F)$ and $\beta = \sum_{j=1}^{n} y_jv_j \in V_n(F)$.

If $\bar{u}_1, \bar{u}_2, \cdots, \bar{u}_m$ and $\bar{v}_1, \bar{v}_2, \cdots, \bar{v}_n$ are new bases in $V_m(F)$ and $V_n(F)$ respectively, and if

$$\alpha = \sum_{i=1}^{m} \bar{x}_i\bar{u}_i,\ \beta = \sum_{j=1}^{n} \bar{y}_j\bar{v}_j,$$

then by (27.2)

$$\begin{aligned}(x_1, x_2, \cdots, x_m) &= (\bar{x}_1, \bar{x}_2, \cdots, \bar{x}_m)P \text{ or } X = \bar{X}P\\ (y_1, y_2, \cdots, y_n) &= (\bar{y}_1, \bar{y}_2, \cdots, \bar{y}_n)Q \text{ or } Y = \bar{Y}Q,\end{aligned}$$

where P and Q are nonsingular matrices in F. This means that

$$\mathcal{B}(\alpha,\beta) = XAY' = \bar{X}PAQ'\bar{Y}' = \bar{X}B\bar{Y}',$$

and the matrix B of $\mathcal{B}$ with respect to the new bases is rationally equivalent to A.

If P and Q are selected so that $PAQ' = D_r$, then the bilinear mapping assumes the form

$$\mathcal{B}(\alpha,\beta) = \bar{X}D_r\bar{Y}' = \bar{x}_1\bar{y}_1 + \bar{x}_2\bar{y}_2 + \cdots + \bar{x}_r\bar{y}_r$$

with respect to the new bases defined by P and Q. The integer r, which is the rank of the matrix of $\mathcal{B}$, is independent of the choice of the bases and is called the *rank* of $\mathcal{B}$.

Exercise (29.1). Prove $\mathcal{B}(\alpha,O) = \mathcal{B}(O,\beta) = 0 \in F$.

Exercise (29.2). Prove that if there exists a pair α,β such that $\mathcal{B}(\alpha,\beta) \neq 0$ while $\mathcal{B}(\gamma,\beta) = 0$ for all $\beta \in V_n(F)$, then $\gamma = O$.

Exercise (29.3). Prove that for a fixed $\alpha \in V_m(F)$, the set of all $\beta \in V_n(F)$ such that $\mathcal{B}(\alpha,\beta) = 0$ is a subspace of $V_n(F)$.

Exercise (29.4). Prove that

$$\mathcal{B}(\alpha,\beta) = (x_1, x_2, \cdots, x_n)(y_1, y_2, \cdots, y_n)'$$

defines a bilinear mapping. Also show that $\mathcal{B}(\alpha,\beta) = \mathcal{B}(\beta,\alpha)$.

Exercise (29.5). Given bases $u_1 = (1,1,0)$, $u_2 = (1,0,1)$, and $u_3 = (0,1,1)$ of $V_3(F)$ and $v_1 = (1,1)$, $v_2 = (2,0)$ of $V_2(F)$,

(a) Discuss the bilinear mapping defined by the matrix $A = \begin{pmatrix} 2 & 1 \\ 1 & -1 \\ 0 & 2 \end{pmatrix}$. Find the map of the pair of vectors α,β where $\alpha = 2u_1 - u_2 + 3u_3$, $\beta = v_1 - v_2$. Find the map of the pair $\alpha = (3,1,2)$, $\beta = (5,-3)$.

(b) Let $\mathcal{B}$ have matrix $\begin{pmatrix} 3 & -1 \\ -1 & 0 \\ 4 & 1 \end{pmatrix}$. Define new bases in the two spaces with respect to which $\mathcal{B}$ has matrix $\begin{pmatrix} 1 & 0 \\ 0 & 1 \\ 0 & 0 \end{pmatrix}$.

(c) Write the mapping $\mathcal{B}(\alpha,\beta) = 3x_1y_1 - 7x_2y_2 + 4x_3y_1 - x_3y_2$ in matrix form where $\alpha = x_1u_1 + x_2u_2 + x_3u_3$, $\beta = y_1v_1 + y_2v_2$. Find new bases with respect to which $\mathcal{B}(\alpha,\beta)$ has matrix D_r.

Exercise (29.6). Given the basis $u_1 = (1,i), u_2 = (i,1)$ of $V_2(C)$, let the bilinear mapping $\mathcal{B}$ of $V_2(C)$ and $V_2(C)$ into C be defined by

$$\mathcal{B}(u_1,u_1) = 2,\ \mathcal{B}(u_1,u_2) = \mathcal{B}(u_2,u_1) = i,\ \mathcal{B}(u_2,u_2) = 0.$$

(a) Give the matrix form of $\mathcal{B}$ and find $\mathcal{B}(\alpha,\beta)$ for $\alpha = (1,0)$, $\beta = (0,1)$, and for $\alpha = \beta = (2 + i, 2 - i)$.
(b) Find the matrix of $\mathcal{B}$ with respect to the basis ϵ_1,ϵ_2 of $V_2(C)$.

Exercise (29.7).

(a) Show that a single-valued mapping $\mathcal{B}$ of pairs of vectors $\alpha,\beta \in V_n(F)$ into F which satisfies (i) $\mathcal{B}(\alpha,\beta) = \mathcal{B}(\beta,\alpha)$; (ii) $\mathcal{B}(\alpha + \gamma,\beta) = \mathcal{B}(\alpha,\beta) + \mathcal{B}(\gamma,\beta)$; and (iii) $\mathcal{B}(c\alpha,\beta) = c\mathcal{B}(\alpha,\beta)$ is a bilinear mapping of $V_n(F)$ and $V_n(F)$ into F. Such a mapping is called a *symmetric bilinear mapping of* $V_n(F)$ into F.
(b) Show that a symmetric bilinear mapping $\mathcal{B}$ of $V_n(F)$ into F has a symmetric matrix with respect to any basis of $V_n(F)$.

Section 30. Linear Transformations

If we take $m = n$ in the discussion of Section 28, a linear mapping $\mathcal{L}$ becomes a transformation of the set $V_n(F)$. Relative to a fixed basis $u_1, u_2, \cdots, u_n$ of $V_n(F)$, $\mathcal{L}$ is given by the matrix equation

$$(30.1)\quad A\begin{pmatrix} x_1 \\ x_2 \\ \cdot \\ \cdot \\ \cdot \\ x_n \end{pmatrix} = \begin{pmatrix} y_1 \\ y_2 \\ \cdot \\ \cdot \\ \cdot \\ y_n \end{pmatrix} \qquad \text{or} \qquad (x_1, x_2, \cdots, x_n)A' = (y_1, y_2, \cdots, y_n),$$

which maps the vector $\alpha = x_1u_1 + x_2u_2 + \cdots + x_nu_n \in V_n(F)$ onto the vector $\mathcal{L}(\alpha) = y_1u_1 + y_2u_2 + \cdots + y_nu_n \in V_n(F)$. We call $\mathcal{L}$ a *linear transformation* of $V_n(F)$. The square n by n matrix $A = (a_{ij})$ is the matrix of $\mathcal{L}$ with respect to the given basis, and the columns of A are respectively the coordinates of $\mathcal{L}(u_1), \mathcal{L}(u_2), \cdots, \mathcal{L}(u_n)$.

Let $\mathcal{L}$ and $\mathcal{M}$ be linear transformations of $V_n(F)$ with matrices A and B respectively, relative to the given basis $u_1, u_2, \cdots, u_n \in V_n(F)$. Then the product $\mathcal{ML}$, defined by $\mathcal{ML}(\alpha) = \mathcal{M}[\mathcal{L}(\alpha)]$ for all $\alpha \in V_n(F)$, is a linear transformation of $V_n(F)$ since

$$\begin{aligned}\mathcal{ML}(a\alpha + b\beta) &= \mathcal{M}[\mathcal{L}(a\alpha + b\beta)] = \mathcal{M}[a\mathcal{L}(\alpha) + b\mathcal{L}(\beta)] \\ &= a\mathcal{M}[\mathcal{L}(\alpha)] + b\mathcal{M}[\mathcal{L}(\beta)] = a\mathcal{ML}(\alpha) + b\mathcal{ML}(\beta).\end{aligned}$$

The matrix equation for $\mathcal{M}$ is

$$(y_1, y_2, \cdots, y_n)B' = (z_1, z_2, \cdots, z_n),$$

where $\mathcal{M}$ maps the vector $\mathcal{L}(\alpha) = y_1u_1 + y_2u_2 + \cdots + y_nu_n$ onto the vector $\mathcal{M}[\mathcal{L}(\alpha)] = z_1u_1 + z_2u_2 + \cdots + z_nu_n$. Substituting equation

(30.1) into the matrix equation for $\mathfrak{M}$, we obtain

$$(x_1, x_2, \cdots, x_n)A'B' = (z_1, z_2, \cdots, z_n),$$

or

$$(x_1, x_2, \cdots, x_n)(BA)' = (z_1, z_2, \cdots, z_n).$$

Therefore, the linear transformation $\mathfrak{ML}$ which sends $\alpha = x_1u_1 + x_2u_2 + \cdots + x_nu_n$ onto $\mathfrak{ML}(\alpha) = z_1u_1 + z_2u_2 + \cdots + z_nu_n$ has matrix BA which is the product of the matrices of the transformations $\mathfrak{M}$ and $\mathfrak{L}$. As mentioned before, this result is the principal motivation for the definition of matrix multiplication.

If $\bar{u}_1, \bar{u}_2, \cdots, \bar{u}_n$ is a second basis of $V_n(F)$, then $\alpha = \bar{x}_1\bar{u}_1 + \bar{x}_2\bar{u}_2 + \cdots + \bar{x}_n\bar{u}_n$ and $\mathfrak{L}(\alpha) = \bar{y}_1\bar{u}_1 + \bar{y}_2\bar{u}_2 + \cdots + \bar{y}_n\bar{u}_n$ where

$$(\bar{x}_1, \bar{x}_2, \cdots, \bar{x}_n) = (x_1, x_2, \cdots, x_n)P^{-1}$$

and

$$(\bar{y}_1, \bar{y}_2, \cdots, \bar{y}_n) = (y_1, y_2, \cdots, y_n)P^{-1}$$

for a nonsingular matrix P, by Corollary (27.2). In terms of the new basis, the linear transformation $\mathfrak{L}$ has matrix $B = (P')^{-1}AP'$, since by equation (30.1)

$$\begin{aligned}(\bar{y}_1, \bar{y}_2, \cdots, \bar{y}_n) &= (x_1, x_2, \cdots, x_n)A'P^{-1} \\ &= (\bar{x}_1, \bar{x}_2, \cdots, \bar{x}_n)PA'P^{-1},\end{aligned}$$

or

$$(P')^{-1}AP'\begin{pmatrix}\bar{x}_1\\ \bar{x}_2\\ \cdot\\ \cdot\\ \cdot\\ \bar{x}_n\end{pmatrix} = \begin{pmatrix}\bar{y}_1\\ \bar{y}_2\\ \cdot\\ \cdot\\ \cdot\\ \bar{y}_n\end{pmatrix}. \tag{30.2}$$

The effect of the linear transformation $\mathfrak{L}$ on the space $V_n(F)$ is more likely to be apparent if a basis of $V_n(F)$ is chosen so that the matrix A of equation (30.1) has a simple form. It is clear from equation (30.2), that if $\mathfrak{L}$ has been given with matrix A in terms of a fixed basis $u_1, u_2, \cdots, u_n$ of $V_n(F)$, then the simplification of the matrix of $\mathfrak{L}$ relative to a new basis depends on how A can be transformed by an equivalence transformation of the type

$$T_{Q,Q^{-1}}(A) = QAQ^{-1} \qquad \text{with } Q \text{ in } F.$$

Such an equivalence transformation, which is a transformation of the set $\mathfrak{A}_n(F)$ of all n-rowed square matrices with elements in F, is called a *collineatory transformation* of $\mathfrak{A}_n(F)$. The set of all collineatory transformations of $\mathfrak{A}_n(F)$ is a group of transformations, a subgroup* of the

* A subset H of a group G of transformations of a set M which is itself a group of transformations, is called a *subgroup* of G.

group of equivalence transformations $\mathcal{E}(\mathfrak{A}_n(F))$, and the equivalence relation induced in $\mathfrak{A}_n(F)$ by the collineatory group is called *similarity of square matrices over F*.

If the matrix A of the linear transformation $\mathcal{L}$ relative to a given basis of $V_n(F)$ is nonsingular, $\mathcal{L}$ is called a *nonsingular linear transformation.* Since the rank of the matrix of $\mathcal{L}$ is unchanged by a change of basis in $V_n(F)$, the matrix of $\mathcal{L}$ with respect to any basis in $V_n(F)$ is nonsingular. If $\mathcal{L}$ is nonsingular, then

$$\begin{pmatrix} x_1 \\ x_2 \\ \cdot \\ \cdot \\ \cdot \\ x_n \end{pmatrix} = A^{-1} \begin{pmatrix} y_1 \\ y_2 \\ \cdot \\ \cdot \\ \cdot \\ y_n \end{pmatrix},$$

so that each vector $y_1u_1 + y_2u_2 + \cdots + y_nu_n \in V_n(F)$ is the map of a unique vector $x_1u_1 + x_2u_2 + \cdots + x_nu_n \in V_n(F)$ by $\mathcal{L}$. Thus $\mathcal{L}$ is a one-to-one transformation of $V_n(F)$ onto itself.

The proof of the following theorem, which depends upon the formula for multiplying linear transformations discussed above, is left to the reader as an exercise.

(30.3) Theorem. The set L of all nonsingular linear transformations of $V_n(F)$ is a group of transformations, called the *full linear group* on $V_n(F)$.

Exercise (30.1). Prove Theorem (30.3).

Exercise (30.2). Find the matrix of the product $\mathfrak{M}\mathcal{L}$ of the linear mapping $\mathcal{L}$ of $V_n(F)$ into $V_m(F)$ followed by the linear mapping $\mathfrak{M}$ of $V_m(F)$ into $V_k(F)$.

Exercise (30.3). If $\mathcal{L}$ has matrix D_n with respect to the basis $\epsilon_1, \epsilon_2, \cdots, \epsilon_n$, prove that $\mathcal{L}$ has matrix D_n with respect to every basis.

Exercise (30.4). Let $u_1 = (2,4,1)$, $u_2 = (5,1,1)$, $u_3 = (3,-3,1)$ be a basis of $V_3(R)$ and let

$$\begin{pmatrix} 3 & 1 & 3 \\ 1 & -1 & 0 \\ 0 & 0 & 1 \end{pmatrix}$$

be the matrix of $\mathcal{L}$ with respect to u_1, u_2, u_3. Find the matrix of $\mathcal{L}$ with respect to $\epsilon_1, \epsilon_2, \epsilon_3$. Also find the matrix of $\mathcal{L}$ with respect to $\bar{u}_1 = (1,-1,1)$, $\bar{u}_2 = (1,1,-1)$, $\bar{u}_3 = (2,0,2)$.

Exercise (30.5). Let $\mathfrak{M}$ be the linear transformation of $V_3(R)$ which has matrix $\begin{pmatrix} 2 & 4 & 2 \\ 1 & -1 & -2 \\ 3 & -1 & -4 \end{pmatrix}$ with respect to the basis u_1, u_2, u_3 given in the preceding exercise. With $\mathfrak{L}$ as in Exercise (30.4), find the product transformations $\mathfrak{M}\mathfrak{L}$ and $\mathfrak{L}\mathfrak{M}$. Discuss the subspaces $\mathfrak{L}(V_3(R))$, $\mathfrak{M}(V_3(R))$, $\mathfrak{M}\mathfrak{L}(V_3(R))$, and $\mathfrak{L}\mathfrak{M}(V_3(R))$.

Exercise (30.6).

(a) Prove that $u_1 = (2,0,0)$, $u_2 = (0,3,1)$, $u_3 = (0,1,1)$ is a basis of $V_3(R)$.

(b) Find the coordinates of $\alpha = (4,1,3)$ with respect to this basis.

(c) Let $A = \begin{pmatrix} 2 & 2 & -4 \\ 1 & -3 & 0 \\ 0 & 1 & 1 \end{pmatrix}$ be the matrix of a linear transformation $\mathfrak{L}$ of $V_3(R)$ with respect to the basis u_1, u_2, u_3. Find the coordinates of $\mathfrak{L}(\alpha)$ with respect to this basis, and then find the components of $\mathfrak{L}(\alpha)$.

(d) Find the matrix of $\mathfrak{L}$ with respect to the basis $\bar{u}_1 = (2,2,0)$, $\bar{u}_2 = (0,1,-1)$, $\bar{u}_3 = (0,2,2)$.

(e) Check your calculations by finding the components of $\mathfrak{L}(\alpha)$ using the new equation for the transformation.

Exercise (30.7). Show that the equivalence relation induced on $V_n(F)$ by the full linear group is a trivial one.

Exercise (30.8). Prove that the collineatory transformations of $\mathfrak{A}_n$ form a group of transformations.

IV GROUPS

Section 31. Binary Operations

Most sets of objects dealt with in mathematics are sets which have an algebraic structure. This means that operations, or rules of combination, are defined on the sets, which enable us to combine the elements in various useful ways. The most widely known examples of sets with an algebraic structure are the number systems of mathematics, which we will study in detail in Chapter V. The fundamental properties of the familiar operations defined for numbers are the same as those for the rules of combination which we have studied for matrices, vectors, and transformations, and as we shall see, are the same as those for many other basic mathematical systems. The abstraction of these properties leads to the concept of an algebraic system, called a group, which has a particularly simple structure. The following study of groups, which unifies the treatment of the various systems mentioned above, is an introduction to a theory which holds a central position in modern mathematics.

It was remarked in Section 7 that the set $\mathfrak{A}_n$ of square matrices with complex number elements is closed with respect to the operations of matrix addition and multiplication. By this we mean that for every ordered pair A,B of matrices in $\mathfrak{A}_n$, there exist uniquely determined matrices $A + B$ and AB in $\mathfrak{A}_n$. Similarly if S and T are transformations in $\mathfrak{T}(M)$ for an arbitrary set M, there is a uniquely defined product transformation TS in $\mathfrak{T}(M)$. These are examples of binary operations.

(31.1) Definition. A *binary operation* o on a set M is a rule which assigns to each ordered pair a,b of elements in M a unique element $c = a \circ b$ in M.

For convenience, we will call $a \circ b$ the product of a and b.

Other examples of binary operations are the rational operations of addition, subtraction, and multiplication in any number field.

(31.2) Definition. A set $N \subseteq M$ is *closed* with respect to the binary operation o, defined on M, if $a \circ b \in N$ for every ordered pair $a,b \in N$.

If $N \subseteq M$ is closed with respect to o, then o is a binary operation defined on N; and by Definition (31.1) any set M is closed with respect to a binary operation defined on it.

As an example of a set being closed with respect to a binary operation defined on a larger set, let o be the addition of matrices in $\mathfrak{A}_n$ and let $\mathfrak{B}$ be the subset of $\mathfrak{A}_n$ consisting of those matrices with integral elements. Then for $A,B \in \mathfrak{B} \subseteq \mathfrak{A}_n$, $A \, o \, B$ is a uniquely determined matrix in $\mathfrak{A}_n$. But since the sum of two integers is again an integer, $A \, o \, B \in \mathfrak{B}$. Thus matrix addition is a binary operation defined on $\mathfrak{B}$ by Definition (31.1). Similarly the set $\mathfrak{O}(M)$ of all one-to-one transformations of a set M is closed with respect to the composition of transformations, an operation defined on the set $\mathfrak{T}(M)$ of all transformations of M.

Most binary operations with which the reader is familiar, such as the operations of addition and multiplication in a number field, satisfy the simple algebraic identities which we have called the associative and commutative laws. These identities stated for an arbitrary binary operation defined on a set M are:

(31.3) Definition. The operation o is *associative* if

$$a \, o \, (b \, o \, c) = (a \, o \, b) \, o \, c \text{ for every } a,b,c \in M.$$

(31.4) Definition. The operation o is *commutative* if

$$a \, o \, b = b \, o \, a \qquad \text{for every } a,b \in M.$$

Of the binary operations considered in the second paragraph of this section, all are associative, but only the addition of matrices is commutative. The operation of subtraction in a number field is neither associative nor commutative.

If $N \subseteq M$ is closed with respect to a binary operation defined on M, then the identities satisfied by this operation in M hold automatically in N. For, in performing any sequence of operations with elements of N, we make the calculations as they are defined in M. The closure of N assures us that the result of any such calculation is again an element of N. For example, the composition of transformations in $\mathfrak{O}(M)$ is associative by virtue of the associativity of transformation multiplication in $\mathfrak{T}(M)$.

Let $a_1, a_2, \cdots, a_n$ be any ordered set of n elements in the set M with a binary operation o. We may combine the elements of this ordered set in different ways by repeated application of this binary operation. We use parentheses and other signs of aggregation to indicate the sequence of operations, for example, $(a_1 \, o \, a_2) \, o \, [(a_3 \, o \, a_4) \, o \, a_5]$, $\{a_1 \, o \, [(a_2 \, o \, a_3) \, o \, a_4]\} \, o \, a_5$, and so forth. If o is an associative operation, we may prove the general associative law, which states that all such products are equal for a given ordered set of n elements.

We first define inductively a *general product* of n elements of M: $\prod_{i=1}^{2} a_i = a_1 \, o \, a_2$, $\prod_{i=1}^{n} a_i = \left(\prod_{i=1}^{n-1} a_i\right) o \, a_n$ for all $n > 2$. For example, $\prod_{i=1}^{4} a_i$

$$= \left(\prod_{i=1}^{3} a_i\right) o \, a_4 = \left[\left(\prod_{i=1}^{2} a_i\right) o \, a_3\right] o \, a_4 = [(a_1 \, o \, a_2) \, o \, a_3] \, o \, a_4.$$

(31.5) Theorem. Let the set M be closed with respect to an associative binary operation o. Then all products formed from the factors $a_1, a_2, \cdots, a_n$, $(n \geq 2)$, multiplied in that order and with the parentheses placed in any positions whatever, are equal to the general product

$$\prod_{i=1}^{n} a_i.$$

PROOF. The theorem is true for $n = 2$, since in this case the general product

$$\prod_{i=1}^{2} a_i = a_1 \, o \, a_2$$

is the only product defined. Assume that the theorem is true for all products of m factors where $2 \leq m < n$, and let $\prod$ be any product of n factors. Since $\prod$ is formed by the repeated application of o, there must be a last multiplication, so that $\prod = \prod_1 o \prod_2$ where $\prod_1$ and $\prod_2$ are products of k and $n - k$ factors respectively, and where $1 \leq k < n$. If $k = n - 1$, then $\prod = \left(\prod_1\right) o \, a_n$ where $\prod_1 = \prod_{i=1}^{n-1} a_i$ by the induction hypothesis. Then $\prod = \left(\prod_{i=1}^{n-1} a_i\right) o \, a_n = \prod_{i=1}^{n} a_i$ by the definition of the general product.

If $k < n - 1$, $\prod = \left(\prod_{i=1}^{k} a_i\right) o \left(\prod_{i=k+1}^{n} a_i\right)$, applying the induction hypothesis* to both $\prod_1$ and $\prod_2$. But using the definition of the general

---

* We make the convention that $\prod_{i=1}^{1} a_i = a_1$. This definition is necessary here if $k = 1$ and later if $k = n - 2$.

product,

$$\prod = \left(\prod_{i=1}^{k} a_i\right) o \left[\left(\prod_{i=k+1}^{n-1} a_i\right) o\, a_n\right],$$

and using the associative law (31.3),

$$\left(\prod_{i=1}^{k} a_i\right) o \left[\left(\prod_{i=k+1}^{n-1} a_i\right) o\, a_n\right] = \left[\left(\prod_{i=1}^{k} a_i\right) o \left(\prod_{i=k+1}^{n-1} a_i\right)\right] o\, a_n.$$

Applying first the induction hypothesis, and then the definition of the general product,

$$\prod = \left[\left(\prod_{i=1}^{k} a_i\right) o \left(\prod_{i=k+1}^{n-1} a_i\right)\right] o\, a_n = \left(\prod_{i=1}^{n-1} a_i\right) o\, a_n = \prod_{i=1}^{n} a_i.$$

This completes the proof of the theorem.

By this theorem, all the ordered products of $a_1, a_2, \cdots, a_n$ are therefore equal, and, as in Section 2, we may use the notation $a_1\, o\, a_2\, o \cdots o\, a_n$ for this uniquely determined product.

If M is closed with respect to an associative binary operation, we can introduce exponents by

$$a^1 = a,\ a^n = \prod_{i=1}^{n} a_i \text{ for all } n > 1, \text{ where } a_1 = a_2 = \cdots = a_n = a,$$

and we can prove the laws of exponents for positive integers m and n:

$$a^m\, o\, a^n = a^{m+n},\ (a^m)^n = a^{m \cdot n}.$$

We have observed that the zero matrix, O, and the identity matrix, I_n, satisfy the relations $A + O = O + A = A$ and $A \cdot I_n = I_n \cdot A = A$ for every $A \in \mathfrak{A}_n$. Similarly the identity transformation, I, in $\mathfrak{I}(M)$ satisfies $I \cdot T = T \cdot I = T$ for every $T \in \mathfrak{I}(M)$. We abstract the concept of an identity element for an arbitrary binary operation o.

(31.6) Definition. An element $e \in M$ is an *identity* for the binary operation o if $a\, o\, e = e\, o\, a = a$ for every $a \in M$.

(31.7) Definition. If M contains an identity element e for the binary operation o, then $b \in M$ is an *inverse* of $a \in M$ with respect to o if $a\, o\, b = b\, o\, a = e$.

The proofs of the following results are like those for matrices and transformations, and are left to the reader as an exercise.

(31.8) Theorem. The set M contains at most one identity for the binary operation o.

(31.9) Theorem. An element of M can have at most one inverse if the operation o is associative.

Therefore in the associative case we may speak of *the* inverse of a, if it exists. We denote this element by a^{-1}. It follows from the symmetry of Definition (31.7) that $(a^{-1})^{-1} = a$.

Exercise (31.1). Which of the following are binary operations on the given sets?

(a) $a \, o \, b = a/b$ where M is a number field;
(b) $A \, o \, B = ABA^{-1}$ where M is the set of all nonsingular square matrices of order n;
(c) $a \, o \, b = a - b$ where M is the set of all positive integers;
(d) $A \, o \, B = A^2B^2$ where $M = \mathfrak{A}_n$;
(e) $a \, o \, b = 1$ where M is the set of all integers.

Exercise (31.2). Which of the binary operations of Exercise (31.1) are associative and which are commutative? Which sets contain an identity element for the given operation?

Exercise (31.3). How many different binary operations can be defined on a finite set M with n elements? How many of these have an identity? How many are commutative?

Exercise (31.4). Prove (31.8) and (31.9).

Exercise (31.5). Prove that if the binary operation o on M is associative and also commutative, the phrase "taken in that order" may be replaced by "taken in any order" in Theorem (31.5).

Exercise (31.6). Prove that if o is an associative operation with an identity, and if a^{-1} and b^{-1} exist, then $(a \, o \, b)^{-1}$ exists and $(a \, o \, b)^{-1} = b^{-1} \, o \, a^{-1}$. Generalize to a product of n factors.

Exercise (31.7). Let M be closed with respect to the operation o. An element $l \in M$ is a *left-identity* for o if $l \, o \, a = a$ for every $a \in M$. Similarly r is a *right-identity* if $a \, o \, r = a$ for every $a \in M$. Show that if M contains a left-identity l and a right-identity r, then $l = r$ is the identity element e in M.

Exercise (31.8). Prove that if M contains an identity e, then any left-identity or right-identity is equal to e.

Exercise (31.9). Show by repeated application of the associative law (31.3) how to transform $[a_1 \, o \, (a_2 \, o \, a_3)] \, o \, (a_4 \, o \, a_5)$ into the general product.

Exercise (31.10). Show by constructing an example that the hypothesis that o is associative is necessary in Theorem (31.9).

Exercise (31.11). Show that if a has an inverse b with respect to an associative operation o, then any left- or right-inverse of a is equal to b.

Section 32. One-to-One Correspondences and Isomorphism

Let M be the set of all positive integers $1, 2, 3, \cdots$, and N the set of all positive even integers $2, 4, 6, \cdots$. Let the even integer $2m \in N$ correspond to each integer $m \in M$. We write $m \to 2m$ or $f(m) = 2m$ and call $2m$ the correspondent of m by the correspondence f. The correspondence f has the properties that every $m \in M$ has one, and only one, correspondent $2m \in N$, and every $n \in N$ is the correspondent of one, and only one, element $n/2 \in M$. Because of these properties, f is called a one-to-one correspondence, generally written (1–1). The (1–1) transformations defined in Chapter II are (1–1) correspondences of a set M onto itself, that is, with $N = M$.

Let M and N be arbitrary sets.

(32.1) Definition. A *(1–1) correspondence* f of M onto N is a correspondence with the following properties:

(i) For every $m \in M$, there exists a unique correspondent $f(m) \in N$.
(ii) For every $n \in N$, there exists a unique element $m \in M$ such that $n = f(m)$.

In Definition (32.1), f is defined from M to N; but it is easy to see that g, defined by $g(n) = m$ if $f(m) = n$, is a (1–1) correspondence of N onto M. The definition is therefore symmetric, and we are justified in saying that there is a (1–1) *correspondence between M and N*. We denote this correspondence by $m \leftrightarrow n$.

The sets M and N are said to have the *same number of elements* if there is a (1–1) correspondence between M and N. A non-empty set M is called a *finite set with n elements* if there is a (1–1) correspondence between M and the set of positive integers $\{1, 2, \cdots, n\}$. When we write $M = \{a_1, a_2, \cdots, a_n\}$, we are exhibiting such a correspondence. An *infinite set* may now be defined as one which is neither empty nor finite. Alternately, an infinite set may be defined as a set M such that there exists a (1–1) correspondence between M and some proper subset of M.

In the example at the beginning of this section, the sets M and N are each closed with respect to the binary operations of addition and multiplication. With $f(m) = 2m$ and $f(m') = 2m'$ we have $f(m + m') = f(m) + f(m')$, since $f(m + m') = 2(m + m') = 2m + 2m' = f(m) + f(m')$. This proves that the correspondent of the sum of two elements of M is the same element of N as the sum of the correspondents. We say that f "preserves" addition.

The implications of this fact are far-reaching. Any property of the set M which can be expressed as an identity involving the operation of addition alone is also a property of N, and conversely. For example, every $m \in M$ can be written as a sum $m = 1 + 1 + \cdots + 1$. We say that $1 \in M$ generates M. Now if n is any element of N, there exists an $m \in M$ such that $n = f(m)$. Since $m = 1 + 1 + \cdots + 1$, $n = f(m) = f(1 + 1 + \cdots + 1) = f(1) + f(1) + \cdots + f(1) = 2 + 2 + \cdots + 2$, and we see that $2 \in N$ generates N.

On the other hand, $f(m \cdot m') \neq f(m) \cdot f(m')$ since $f(m \cdot m') = 2mm'$ while $f(m) \cdot f(m') = 2m \cdot 2m' = 4mm'$. Thus f does not preserve multiplication. As a matter of fact the multiplicative properties of M are different from those of N. For example, the element 1 is an identity for multiplication in M, while N contains no identity for multiplication.

Let the set M be closed with respect to the binary operation o, and let the set N be closed with respect to the binary operation $*$.

(32.2) Definition. An $(M, o; N, *)$-*isomorphism* of M onto N is a (1–1) correspondence f of M onto N such that $f(m \; o \; m') = f(m) * f(m')$ for all $m, m' \in M$.

If o and $*$ are the only operations which have been defined on the sets, we simply say that M is isomorphic to N. If $o_1, o_2, \cdots, o_n$ and $*_1, *_2, \cdots, *_n$ are binary operations on M and N respectively, then an $(M, o_1, o_2, \cdots, o_n; N, *_1, *_2, \cdots, *_n)$-isomorphism is a (1–1) correspondence f of M onto N such that $f(m \; o_i \; m') = f(m) *_i f(m')$ for all $m, m' \in M$ and all $i = 1, 2, \cdots, n$. In the above example, f is an $(M, +; N, +)$-isomorphism, but is not an $(M, \cdot\,; N, \cdot)$-isomorphism, and therefore not an $(M, +, \cdot\,; N, +, \cdot)$-isomorphism.

If we take $N = M$ and the operation $*$ to be the operation o in Definition (32.2), we obtain the following important special case.

(32.3) Definition. If M is closed with respect to the binary operation o, an *o-automorphism* of M is a (1–1) correspondence f of M onto itself such that $f(m \; o \; m') = f(m) \; o \; f(m')$ for all $m, m' \in M$.

It was mentioned that the Definition (32.1) of a (1–1) correspondence of a set M onto a set N is symmetric. The verification that the same is true for Definition (32.2) is included in the proof of the following theorem.

(32.4) Theorem. Let $\mathcal{K}$ be a set with elements which are the sets M, N, P, $\cdots$, each closed with respect to a binary operation. Then isomorphism is an equivalence relation on $\mathcal{K}$.

PROOF. Every set M is isomorphic to itself since the identity transformation, $I(a) = a$, is an isomorphism of M. If f is an isomorphism of M onto N, then the correspondence g, defined by $g(n) = m$ if and only if $f(m) = n$, is an isomorphism of N onto M. This demonstrates the symmetry of Definition (32.2). Finally, if f is an isomorphism of M onto N and g an isomorphism of N onto P, then the correspondence h, defined by $h(m) = g(f(m))$, is an isomorphism of M onto P. Thus the relation of isomorphism defined on the elements of $\mathcal{K}$ satisfies the reflexive, symmetric, and transitive laws and is an equivalence relation.

Again consider sets M and N with binary operations o and $*$ respectively. The algebraic properties of M are those properties which can be expressed as identities involving the operation o. The same statement applies to the set N and its operation $*$. If M and N are isomorphic, they have exactly the same algebraic properties, so that we regard M and N as being essentially the same algebraically. Their difference lies only in the names we give the elements and the way we denote the law of combination.

In concluding this section, we again emphasize the invariance of algebraic properties under isomorphism by stating the following theorem, the proof of which is left to the reader.

(32.5) Theorem. If M and N are $(M, o; N, *)$-isomorphic, then

(i) o is associative if and only if $*$ is associative.
(ii) o is commutative if and only if $*$ is commutative.
(iii) M contains an identity for o if and only if N contains an identity for $*$. Furthermore, the identities correspond.

Exercise (32.1). Construct a (1–1) correspondence between the set of all integers and the set of all positive integers.

Exercise (32.2). Prove that the correspondences I, g, and h defined in the proof of Theorem (32.4) are isomorphisms.

Exercise (32.3). Prove Theorem (32.5).

Exercise (32.4). Show that there is no isomorphism between the set of all integers with the operation $+$ and the set of all positive integers with the operation $+$.

Exercise (32.5)

(a) Show that the set M of nonsingular 2 by 2 matrices A with real elements which satisfy $A^{-1} = A'$ is closed with respect to matrix multiplication.

(b) Show that if $A \in M$, $|A| = \pm 1$. Let N be the subset of all $A \in M$ such that $|A| = +1$. Show that N is closed with respect to matrix multiplication.

(c) Show that N is isomorphic to the group of rotations about the origin in the plane, where a rotation through an angle θ is given by

$$x' = x \cos \theta - y \sin \theta$$
$$y' = x \sin \theta + y \cos \theta.$$

Exercise (32.6). Show that $A \rightarrow A'$ is an $({}_m\mathfrak{A}_n, +; {}_n\mathfrak{A}_m, +)$-isomorphism.

Exercise (32.7). Show that $(a) \rightarrow a$ is a $(\mathfrak{A}_1, +, \cdot; F, +, \cdot)$-isomorphism where $\mathfrak{A}_1$ is the set of all 1 by 1 matrices with elements from the number field F.

Section 33. Groups

We now give a set of postulates which define a group. The groups of transformations studied in the preceding chapter are examples of groups and, as we shall see, are of particular importance in the general theory of groups.

(33.1) Definition. A set G is a *group* with respect to the binary operation o if

(i) G is closed with respect to o;
(ii) the operation o is associative;
(iii) G contains an identity element e for o;
(iv) for each $a \in G$, there is an element $b \in G$ such that b is an inverse of a with respect to o.

(33.2) Definition. A group is called *abelian*, or *commutative*, if the operation o is commutative.

For groups of transformations the binary operation o is always the composition of transformations. Since this operation is associative by (13.2), a set G of transformations of a set M is a group if (i), (iii), and (iv) are satisfied [see Definition (15.1)].

Other examples of groups which the reader has already encountered are:

(1) The set of all m by n matrices with elements in a number field F with respect to the operation of matrix addition.

(2) The set of all nonsingular n-rowed square matrices in a number field F with respect to the operation of matrix multiplication.

(3) The elements of any number field F with respect to the addition defined in the field. This group is called the additive group of F.

(4) The set of non-zero elements of any number field F with respect to the multiplication defined in the field.

(5) The set of all vectors in any subspace S of $V_n(F)$ with respect to addition of vectors.

If a group G has a finite number of elements, G is called a *finite group*. Other groups, such as those in examples (1) through (5), are called *infinite groups*, or *groups* of *infinite order*.

(33.3) Definition. A finite group G has *order* n if G contains n elements.

(6) As an example of a finite group, consider the set G consisting of the sixteen 2 by 2 diagonal matrices with diagonal elements 1, -1, i, and $-i$. This set is a group with respect to matrix multiplication.

(7) Consider the set J_n consisting of the integers 0, 1, 2, $\cdots$, $n - 1$. This set is a group of order n under the operation $a \oplus b = r$ where r is the remainder after dividing the ordinary sum $a + b$ by n. Since every sum $a + b$ can be written uniquely in the form $a + b = nq + r$ where $0 \leq r < n$, J_n is closed under the binary operation $\oplus$. J_n is called the *additive group of integers modulo n*. This example shows that there exists at least one group of order n for every positive integer n.

There are sets of postulates other than Definition (33.1) which serve to define a group. We have assumed more than is necessary [see Exercise (33.6)], but this set is one that is easily remembered. Of course, all such postulate sets are logically equivalent to the one we have given. Since a group is not empty by postulate (iii), every set of postulates for a group must assert the existence of at least one element.

Several consequences of the group postulates were given in Section 31. From (i) and (ii) we have the general associative law (31.5) and the laws of positive integral exponents. Using (31.8), postulates (i) and (iii) imply that a group contains exactly one identity element e. And by (31.9), the four group postulates imply that each group element has exactly one inverse.

One property of a group which follows immediately from our postulates pertains to the solution of equations.

(33.4). The equations $a \circ x = c$ and $y \circ a = c$ have unique solutions x and y in G for all $a, c \in G$.

PROOF. Let b be the inverse of $a \in G$. Then $x = b \circ c$ is a solution of $a \circ x = c$ since $a \circ (b \circ c) = (a \circ b) \circ c = e \circ c = c$ by (ii) and (iii). If d is any element of G such that $a \circ d = c$, then $d = e \circ d = (b \circ a) \circ d = b \circ (a \circ d) = b \circ c$, so that the solution is unique. The proof of the second part of the theorem is left to the reader.

As a corollary to (33.4) we obtain the cancellation laws; namely

(33.5). If $a \circ c = a \circ d$ or $c \circ a = d \circ a$, then $c = d$.

For if $a \circ c = a \circ d$, then c and d are both solutions of the equation $a \circ x = a \circ d$, and are equal by (33.4). The proof is similar if $c \circ a = d \circ a$.

Exercise (33.1). In Example (6) of the text prove that G is a group by checking the postulates of Definition (33.1). Similarly prove that J_n of Example (7) is a group.

Exercise (33.2). Which of the examples in the text are abelian groups?

Exercise (33.3). Generalize the laws of exponents in a group by defining a^0 and a^{-n} suitably.

Exercise (33.4). Complete the proofs of (33.4) and (33.5). Also prove (33.5) directly from the postulates.

Exercise (33.5). Show that the mapping $a \to a^{-1}$ is an automorphism of an abelian group.

Exercise (33.6). If in Definition (33.1) we replace (iii) and (iv) by

(iii′) G contains a left identity l for $\circ$, and
(iv′) for every $a \in G$, there exists a $b \in G$ which is a left inverse of a with respect to $\circ$,

prove that the resulting definition is equivalent to Definition (33.1).

Exercise (33.7). Prove that M is a group with respect to the binary operation $\circ$ if M is a non-empty set of elements such that

(a) M is closed with respect to $\circ$;
(b) the operation $\circ$ is associative;
(c) the equations $a \circ x = b$ and $y \circ a = b$ have solutions x and y in M for all $a, b \in M$.

Exercise (33.8). Prove that M is a group if M is a finite set closed with respect to an associative operation o, and in which the cancellation laws (33.5) hold.

Exercise (33.9). Give examples of groups with 1, 2, and 3 elements. Prove that all groups with n elements are isomorphic if $n = 1$, 2, or 3.

Section 34. Isomorphic Groups

It has previously been emphasized that isomorphic systems have the same algebraic properties. The statement of this fact for groups takes the form of the following theorem.

(34.1) Theorem. Let G be a group with respect to o, and let the set M be closed with respect to $*$. If there exists a $(G, o; M, *)$-isomorphism between G and M, then M is a group with respect to $*$.

PROOF. By hypothesis, M is closed with respect to $*$. It follows from Theorem (32.5) that $*$ is associative, and, further, that M contains an identity e' which is the correspondent of the identity $e \in G$. Finally, if α is any element of M, then α is the correspondent of some $a \in G$. But G contains an element a^{-1} such that $a \; o \; a^{-1} = a^{-1} \; o \; a = e$, and a^{-1} corresponds to some element $\beta \in M$. From the isomorphism, $\alpha * \beta = \beta * \alpha = e'$, so that $\beta = \alpha^{-1} \in M$.

This theorem can be used in proving that a given system is a group. It is an important consequence of the proof of the above theorem that if $a \leftrightarrow \alpha$ in an isomorphism between two groups, then $a^{-1} \leftrightarrow \alpha^{-1}$.

When nothing is assumed about the binary operation o or the nature of the elements of the set G except that G satisfies postulates (i) through (iv) in Definition (33.1), we refer to G as an *abstract group*. On the other hand, each example of a group which we have given has had for its elements definite quantities (for example, numbers, matrices, transformations) combined in a specifically defined way. If an abstract group G is isomorphic to a group G' of this latter type, we call G' a *realization* of G. The following theorem says that every abstract group can be realized by a group of transformations.

(34.2) Theorem. Every group G is isomorphic to a group of transformations.

PROOF. The set of elements on which we define the transformations is the set of elements in G. If a is any element in G, we define a transformation T_a by

$$T_a(b) = a \; o \; b \qquad \text{for every } b \in G.$$

Since $a \circ b$ is a uniquely determined element of G for every $b \in G$, $T_a \in \mathfrak{J}(G)$. Moreover, $T_a \in \mathcal{O}(G)$. For the equation $a \circ x = c$ has a unique solution $x = d \in G$ for every $c \in G$ by Theorem (33.4), and therefore there exists a unique $d \in G$ such that $T_a(d) = c$ for every $c \in G$.

Let $\mathcal{H}(G)$ be the set of transformations T_a for all $a \in G$. If T_a and T_b are in $\mathcal{H}(G)$, then $T_aT_b(c) = T_a(b \circ c) = a \circ (b \circ c)$ for every $c \in G$. Since $a \circ b \in G$, $T_{a \circ b} \in \mathcal{H}(G)$, and $T_{a\circ b}(c) = (a \circ b) \circ c$ for every $c \in G$. But $a \circ (b \circ c) = (a \circ b) \circ c$, so that $T_aT_b = T_{a\circ b}$, and $\mathcal{H}(G)$ is closed with respect to transformation multiplication. If e is the identity in G, then $T_e \in \mathcal{H}(G)$ is the identity transformation, since $T_e(a) = e \circ a = a$ for every $a \in G$. Finally, if $T_a \in \mathcal{H}(G)$, then $T_{a^{-1}} \in \mathcal{H}(G)$, and $T_{a^{-1}} = (T_a)^{-1}$ since $T_aT_{a^{-1}} = T_{a\circ a^{-1}} = T_e = T_{a^{-1}}T_a$. Therefore $\mathcal{H}(G)$ is a group of transformations.

We complete the proof by showing that the correspondence $a \leftrightarrow T_a$, by which each $a \in G$ has a unique correspondent $T_a \in \mathcal{H}(G)$, is an isomorphism. If $T_a = T_b$, then $T_a(c) = a \circ c = T_b(c) = b \circ c$ for $c \in G$, and $a = b$ by (33.5). Thus $a \leftrightarrow T_a$ is a (1–1) correspondence. It is an isomorphism since $a \circ b \leftrightarrow T_{a\circ b} = T_aT_b$.

This theorem means that the theory of abstract groups is the same as the theory of groups of transformations, although the properties of groups are studied most conveniently using the abstract definition of a group as we did in Section 33.

Exercise (34.1). Find a realization in geometry of the group consisting of the elements e,a,a^2,a^3,a^4,a^5 where $a^6 = e$, the identity of the group.

Exercise (34.2). Given that the integers under addition form a group, show that each of the following is a group:

(a) The powers of a rotation Φ through an angle of 1 radian.
(b) The set of all n by n scalar matrices under addition, where the scalar is an even integer.
(c) The set of all numbers of the form 2^i under multiplication for i an integer.

Exercise (34.3). Show that S and S' are isomorphic groups with respect to addition if S and S' are subspaces of dimension r of $V_n(F)$ and $V_m(F)$ respectively. In particular, S and $V_r(F)$ are isomorphic groups.

Exercise (34.4). Show that the real numbers under addition form a group isomorphic to the positive reals under multiplication.

Exercise (34.5). If we define transformations T_a by the rule $T_a(b) = b \circ a^{-1}$ for all $b \in G$, show that as in Theorem (34.2), we get a realization of G.

Exercise (34.6). Show that the identity transformation in $\mathcal{O}(G)$ is an automorphism of G. Exhibit all automorphisms of the group G consisting of the three elements e, a, and a^2 where $a^3 = e$.

Exercise (34.7). Given the two transformations of $M = \{a,b,c,d\}$,

$$E: \begin{matrix} a \rightarrow a \\ b \rightarrow c \\ c \rightarrow c \\ d \rightarrow c \end{matrix} \qquad A: \begin{matrix} a \rightarrow c \\ b \rightarrow a \\ c \rightarrow a \\ d \rightarrow a, \end{matrix}$$

verify that E and A form a group. Is this a group of transformations of the set M?

Section 35. Subgroups

(35.1) Definition. A subset H of a group G is a *subgroup* of G if H is a group with respect to the binary operation defined in G.

Let C_+ denote the additive group of all complex numbers. Then the additive group of every number field is a subgroup of C_+. Examples are $R_+^{\#}$, the additive group of real numbers, and R_+, the additive group of rational numbers. Another subgroup of C_+ is the additive group of integers. The set of rotations through 0°, 90°, 180°, and 270° is a subgroup of the group of all rotations about the origin in the plane.

The identity $e \in G$ is a one-element subgroup E of G, and G itself is a subgroup of G. A subgroup H of G is called a *proper subgroup* of G if $H \neq E$ and $H \neq G$.

(35.2) Theorem. If H is a subgroup of G, then the identity in H is the identity $e \in G$, and the inverse of an element $a \in H$ is its inverse $a^{-1} \in G$.

PROOF. Since a group is non-empty, H contains at least one element c. Further, H must contain the solution x of the equation $c \circ x = c$. But $x = e$ is the unique solution of this equation in G, and therefore e is in H since the law of combination in H is that of G. Similarly if $a \in H$, the unique solution $a^{-1} \in G$ of the equation $a \circ y = e$ is in H.

If a non-empty subset H is closed with respect to the operation in G, this operation is associative in H. Therefore if H contains the inverse of each of its elements, it will contain the identity e by closure, and will be a subgroup of G.

The following theorem gives a useful criterion for a subset $H \subseteq G$ to be a subgroup of G.

(35.3) Theorem. The subset H of a group G is a subgroup of G if and only if H is non-empty and $a \circ b^{-1} \in H$ for every pair $a,b \in H$.

PROOF. If H is a subgroup of G, then H is non-empty; and if a, b is any pair of elements in H, $b^{-1} \in H$ by Theorem (35.2) and $a \circ b^{-1} \in H$ by closure. Conversely, let H be a non-empty subset of G which contains the element $a \circ b^{-1}$ for every pair $a,b \in H$. Since H contains some element c, H contains $c \circ c^{-1} = e$, applying the hypothesis to the pair $c,c \in H$. If $b \in H$, $e \circ b^{-1} = b^{-1} \in H$, using the pair $e,b \in H$. Therefore if a, $b \in H$, $a \circ (b^{-1})^{-1} = a \circ b \in H$ using the pair $a,b^{-1} \in H$. Since the operation o is associative, H is a subgroup of G.

Let S be any subset of G and let $S' \subseteq G$ consist of the elements of S and their inverses. We denote by $\{S\}$ the set of all finite combinations of the elements of S', that is, $\{S\}$ is the set of all finite power products of the elements of S. It follows immediately that $S \subseteq S' \subseteq \{S\} \subseteq G$ and that $\{S'\} = \{S\}$, since $(S')' = S'$. For example, let $G = R_+$ and let S consist of the elements 2 and 5. Then 2, 5, -2, and -5 are the elements of S', and since $1 = 5 + (-2) + (-2)$ and $-1 = (-5) + 2 + 2$, $\{S\}$ is the set of all integers.

(35.4) Theorem. If S is a non-empty subset of a group G, then $\{S\}$ is a subgroup of G, and is the smallest subgroup of G containing S.

PROOF. The set $\{S\}$ is non-empty since $\{S\} \supseteq S$ which is non-empty. Let a,b be any pair of elements of $\{S\}$. Then

$$a = a_1 \circ a_2 \circ \cdots \circ a_n \text{ and } b = b_1 \circ b_2 \circ \cdots \circ b_m$$

where $a_i,b_j \in S'$ for $i = 1, 2, \cdots, n$ and $j = 1, 2, \cdots, m$ by the definition of $\{S\}$. It follows that

$$b^{-1} = (b_1 \circ b_2 \circ \cdots \circ b_m)^{-1} = b_m^{-1} \circ b_{m-1}^{-1} \circ \cdots \circ b_1^{-1}$$

with $b_j^{-1} \in S'$ for all j. Therefore

$$a \circ b^{-1} = a_1 \circ a_2 \circ \cdots \circ a_n \circ b_m^{-1} \circ b_{m-1}^{-1} \circ \cdots \circ b_1^{-1}$$

with all a_i, $b_j^{-1} \in S'$, so that $a \circ b^{-1} \in \{S\}$, again using the definition of $\{S\}$.

Now if H is any subgroup of G which contains S, then $H \supseteq S'$ and H contains all finite combinations of elements in S'. Thus $H \supseteq \{S\}$, and $\{S\}$ is the smallest subgroup of G which contains S.

(35.5) Definition. We call $\{S\}$ the *subgroup generated by the set* S.

In particular, if S contains the single element $a \in G$, we write $\{a\}$ for the subgroup of G generated by a. The elements of $\{a\}$ are the powers $a^0 = e, a, a^{-1}, a^2, a^{-2}, \cdots$.

(35.6) Definition. A group G is *cyclic* if $G = \{a\}$ for some $a \in G$.

If there are infinitely many distinct powers of a, $G = \{a\}$ is called an *infinite cyclic group*. Otherwise, $\{a\}$ is a *finite cyclic group*.

In the examples given at the beginning of this section, the additive group of integers is an infinite cyclic group generated by 1, while the group of rotations through 0°, 90°, 180°, and 270° is a finite cyclic group generated by the rotation through 90°.

(35.7) Theorem. Let a be any element of a group G. If for every positive integer i, $a^i \neq e$, then the different powers of a are all distinct elements of $\{a\}$, and $\{a\}$ is an infinite cyclic group. Otherwise there exists a unique positive integer n such that $a^n = e$ while for every positive $m < n$, $a^m \neq e$. In this case $\{a\}$ is a finite cyclic group of order n consisting of the elements $a, a^2, \cdots, a^{n-1}, a^n = e$.

PROOF. Assume first that for every positive integer i, $a^i \neq e$, and suppose that $a^j = a^k$ for any two integers j and k, where $j \neq k$ (say $j < k$). Then $a^{k-j} = a^k \circ (a^j)^{-1} = e$, contradicting the hypothesis since $k - j$ is a positive integer. Thus the different powers of a are distinct, and $\{a\}$ is an infinite cyclic group.

If on the other hand $a^i = e$ for some positive integer i, let n be the smallest positive integer such that $a^n = e$. The elements $a, a^2, \cdots, a^{n-1}, a^n = e$ are distinct elements of $\{a\}$, for if $a^j = a^k$ with $1 \leq j < k \leq n$, then $a^{k-j} = e$ with $1 \leq k - j < n$. Moreover, every element of $\{a\}$ is one of these. For if $\alpha \in \{a\}$, then $\alpha = a^t$ for some integer t. Dividing t by n, we obtain

$$a^t = a^{qn+r} = (a^n)^q \circ a^r = e^q \circ a^r = e \circ a^r = a^r$$

where $0 \leq r < n$. Thus α is one of the elements $a^0 = e, a, a^2, \cdots, a^{n-1}$.

(35.8) Definition. The *order* of an element $a \in G$ is the order of the subgroup $\{a\} \subseteq G$.

It follows from Theorem (35.7) that each element of G has a uniquely determined order. The element e has order 1, and it is the only element with order 1.

Exercise (35.1). Prove that $a = a^{-1}$ if and only if a has order 1 or 2.

Exercise (35.2). Prove that $(S')' = S'$ and therefore $\{S'\} = \{S\}$.

Exercise (35.3). If H is a subgroup of G, show that $H = H' = \{H\}$.

Exercise (35.4). If every element of S has finite order, prove that the elements of $\{S\}$ are finite combinations of the elements of S alone.

Exercise (35.5). List all subgroups of S_3, the group of all one-to-one transformations of the set $M = \{a,b,c\}$.

Exercise (35.6). What is the subgroup of $\mathcal{E}({}_m\mathfrak{A}_n)$, the group of equivalence transformations of ${}_m\mathfrak{A}_n$, generated by the set S of elementary transformations?

Exercise (35.7). Verify that a group of order 3 has no proper subgroups.

Exercise (35.8). If $\mathcal{A}(G)$ is the set of all automorphisms of the group G, prove that $\mathcal{A}(G)$ is a subgroup of $\mathcal{O}(G)$.

Exercise (35.9). State the results of this section for a group with its operation written as addition.

Exercise (35.10). Give an example of a subgroup of $V_n(F)$ which is not a subspace of $V_n(F)$.

Exercise (35.11). Show that every infinite cyclic group is isomorphic to the additive group of the integers, and that every finite cyclic group of order n is isomorphic to the additive group of integers mod n. This gives a realization for every cyclic group.

Exercise (35.12). If H and K are subgroups of an abelian group G, show that $\{H,K\}$ is the set of all products hk with $h \in H$, $k \in K$. Show that the order of $\{H,K\}$ is equal to the product of the orders of H and K if they have only the identity in common.

Exercise (35.13). Let the groups G and G' be isomorphic, and let H be a subgroup of G. Prove that H', the set of all images of the elements of H, is a subgroup of G'.

Exercise (35.14). The set $M_1 \cap M_2$ of all elements common to two sets M_1 and M_2 is called their *intersection*. Prove that the intersection of two subgroups of G is a subgroup of G.

Exercise (35.15). Prove that $\{a_1, a_2, \cdots, a_k\}$ is the intersection of all subgroups of G which contain these elements.

Section 36. Permutation Groups

If M is a finite set with n elements, then $\mathcal{O}(M)$, the group of all (1–1) transformations of M, is a finite group of order $n!$, and is called the *symmetric group S_n on n letters*. Each element of S_n is called a *permutation*, and a subgroup of S_n is called a *permutation group on n letters*. Theorem (34.2) states that if G is a finite group of order n, G is isomorphic to a permutation group on n letters. Much of the early work in the theory of finite groups was done using the language of permutations, which we consider in this section.

(36.1) Definition. A permutation T on the elements $a_1, a_2, \cdots, a_n$ is called a *cycle* if there exists a subset* $j_1, j_2, \cdots, j_k$ with $1 \leq k \leq n$ of the integers $1, 2, \cdots, n$, such that T sends $a_{j_1} \to a_{j_2}, a_{j_2} \to a_{j_3}, \cdots, a_{j_{k-1}} \to a_{j_k}, a_{j_k} \to a_{j_1}$, and $a_i \to a_i$ if i is not in the subset $j_1, j_2, \cdots, j_k$.

When $k = 1$ in this definition, the cycle is the identity permutation I. For in this case $a_{j_1} \to a_{j_1}$, so that every element is sent into itself. A cycle with $k = 2$ is called a *transposition*. If M contains seven elements, the permutation T defined by $a_1 \to a_4, a_2 \to a_2, a_3 \to a_1, a_4 \to a_7, a_5 \to a_5, a_6 \to a_6, a_7 \to a_3$ is a cycle.

A permutation which is a cycle can be written quite simply as $(j_1\ j_2 \cdots j_k)$, where this symbol indicates that $a_{j_r} \to a_{j_{r+1}}$ for $r = 1, 2, \cdots, k-1$, $a_{j_k} \to a_{j_1}$, and $a_i \to a_i$ if i does not appear in the symbol. For example, the cycle defined above can be written as (1473). The same cycle may be written in many ways, for example, $(1473) = (4731) = (7314) = (3147)$, since it is the circular order of the digits in the cycle which determines the permutation. It is customary to indicate the identity cycle by (1).

Since cycles are transformations of M, they are combined by transformation multiplication. If $S = (413)$ and $T = (3157)$, then $TS = (3157)(413) = (3457)$, performing first the transformation S and then T. Two or more cycles which have no digits in common are called *mutually disjoint*. If S and T are disjoint cycles, $ST = TS$ since each permutation affects only elements left fixed by the other.

The powers of a cycle are computed readily. If $T = (1\ 2 \cdots k)$, then T^h maps a_i onto a_j where j is the hth digit following i in the circular ordering of $1, 2, \cdots, k$. For example, $(1234567)^2 = (1357246)$ and $(1234567)^{11} = (1234567)^4 = (1526374)$. Since the kth digit following i in the circular ordering of $1, 2, \cdots, k$ is i itself, T^k maps each a_i onto itself and is therefore the identity permutation. But if $1 \leq h < k$, then $T^h(a_1) = a_{1+h} \neq a_1$, so that $T^h \neq (1)$. We have shown that k is the least positive integer such that $T^k = (1)$, and therefore that a cycle of k digits is a permutation of order k. It follows that $(1\ 2 \cdots k)^{-1} = (1\ 2 \cdots k)^{k-1} = (1\ k\ k-1 \cdots 2)$, and that a transposition is its own inverse.

Not every permutation of M is a cycle. For example $(1234)^2 = (13)(24) = (24)(13)$ is a product of two transpositions. But we will now prove that every permutation is a product of cycles.

* It is understood that $j_1, j_2, \cdots, j_k$ are distinct integers.

(36.2) Theorem. Every permutation is a product of mutually disjoint cycles.

PROOF. We will prove the theorem by induction on n, the number of elements in the set M. The theorem is true for $n = 1$ since the only permutation of a set $M = \{a_1\}$ is the identity cycle (1). Assume that the theorem is true for every set containing less than n elements, and let T be any permutation of $M = \{a_1, a_2, \cdots, a_n\}$. We may assume that we have the elements of M numbered so that $T(a_1) = a_2$, $T(a_2) = a_3, \cdots$. Since M is finite, there will be some smallest integer k such that $T(a_k) = a_i$ with $1 \leq i \leq k \leq n$. Then we must have that $i = 1$, for if $i > 1$, a_i is the map of the unique element a_{i-1} and therefore is not the map of a_k. Now if $k = n$, T is the cycle $(1\,2 \cdots n)$. Otherwise T is the product of the cycle $(1\,2 \cdots k)$ and a permutation S which leaves the elements $a_1, a_2, \cdots, a_k$ fixed. But S defines a permutation of the elements $a_{k+1}, \cdots, a_n$ which by the induction hypothesis is equal to a product of mutually disjoint cycles on the digits $k + 1, \cdots, n$. Thus $T = S(1\,2 \cdots k)$ is a product of mutually disjoint cycles on the digits $1, 2, \cdots, n$.

(36.3) Corollary. Every permutation can be written as a product of transpositions.

PROOF. We notice that any cycle

$$(1\,2 \cdots k) = (1\,k)(1\,k-1) \cdots (1\,2).$$

If we express the permutation T as a product of mutually disjoint cycles of $k_1, k_2, \cdots, k_h$ digits respectively, the order of T is k, the least common multiple of $k_1, k_2, \cdots, k_h$, that is, the smallest positive integer k such that each k_j is a factor of k.

Realizations of the abstract groups of orders 1 through 4 as permutation groups are $\{(1)\}$, $\{(12)\}$, $\{(123)\}$, $\{(1234)\}$, and $\{(12), (34)\}$. When the generators of a permutation group are given, the group is completely defined since it must be the subgroup of S_n generated by the given permutations.

Exercise (36.1). Compute (134)(217)(3567), (235)(14)(25), and (1342)(23)(124).

Exercise (36.2). Compute $(1\,2 \cdots k)^2$ and $(1\,2 \cdots k)^3$.

Exercise (36.3). Show that S_3 is generated by (12) and (123).

Exercise (36.4). Show that S_3 is isomorphic to

$$\{(12)(34)(56), (135)(264)\}.$$

This is an example of a regular permutation group, a group in which no element, except the identity, leaves a digit fixed. Obtain a regular permutation group isomorphic to $\{(12), (34)\}$.

Exercise (36.5). Prove that the permutation group obtained in the proof of Theorem (34.2) is a regular permutation group.

Exercise (36.6). Write out S_4 on $M = \{a,b,c,d\}$ in cyclic notation. Find subgroups of orders 1, 2, 3, 6, 12, and the two types of order 4.

Exercise (36.7). Which S_n are abelian?

Exercise (36.8). Show that S_n contains a subgroup isomorphic to S_m if $n \geq m$.

Exercise (36.9). Write out in cyclic notation the group of all transformations of the equilateral triangle ABC onto itself which can be performed in the plane of the triangle. Also find the group of such transformations in space. Similarly treat the square and the regular pentagon.

Exercise (36.10). Write out the group of all space transformations of a cube into itself.

Section 37. Even and Odd Permutations

We have seen that every permutation in S_n can be written as a product of transpositions. The example $(12) = (13)(23)(13)$ shows that this representation is not unique. But it is a consequence of Theorem (8.3) that in the various expressions for a given permutation as a product of transpositions, the number of transpositions is always even or always odd. For each arrangement $j_1, j_2, \cdots, j_n$ of the numbers $1, 2, \cdots, n$ defines a permutation T which sends $1 \to j_1$, $2 \to j_2$, $\cdots$, $n \to j_n$. Since a transposition corresponds to an interchange of two digits, if T could be written as a product of an even number of transpositions and also as a product of an odd number of transpositions, this would amount to sending the numbers $1, 2, \cdots, n$ into the arrangement $j_1, j_2, \cdots, j_n$ by both an even and an odd number of interchanges.

(37.1) Definition. A permutation is called *even* if it can be expressed as a product of an even number of transpositions. Otherwise it is called *odd*.

The identity permutation on a set of at least two elements is even since $(1) = (12)(12)$. We define the identity permutation on a set $M = \{a_1\}$ to be even.

(37.2) Theorem. The even permutations in any permutation group form a subgroup.

PROOF. Since (1) is even, every permutation group contains at least one even permutation. Since a transposition is its own inverse, the inverse of a product of transpositions is the product of these transpositions taken in reverse order. Thus if S and T are even permutations in G, T^{-1} is an even permutation, and therefore ST^{-1} is even. By Theorem (35.3) the even permutations in G form a subgroup of G.

(37.3) Theorem. Let G be a permutation group of order m, and let E be the subgroup of even permutations in G. Then either $E = G$ or E has the order $m/2$.

PROOF. Let $q \geq 1$ be the order of E. If $q < m$, G contains an odd permutation T. The set of permutations TX for every $X \in E$ contains q distinct odd permutations since $TX_1 = TX_2$ implies $X_1 = X_2$ by the cancellation law in G. Thus if p is the number of odd permutations in G, $q \leq p$. But similarly the set of permutations TY for every odd permutation Y in G contains at least p distinct even permutations so that $p \leq q$. Therefore $p = q = m/2$, since every permutation in G is either even or odd.

(37.4) Definition. The subgroup A_n of even permutations in S_n is called the *alternating group on n letters.*

If $n > 1$, S_n contains the odd permutation (12), so that the order of A_n is $n!/2$ by Theorem (37.3).

Exercise (37.1). List the even and odd permutations in S_1, S_2, and S_3.

Exercise (37.2). Show that a cycle of order k is even if k is odd, and odd if k is even.

Exercise (37.3). Let $\Delta = \prod_{i<k} (x_i - x_k)$ be a polynomial in n independent variables $x_1, x_2, \cdots, x_n$. Show that every permutation of $x_1, x_2, \cdots, x_n$ sends Δ into $\pm\Delta$, and that every even permutation sends Δ into itself.

Section 38. Multiplication Tables. Defining Relations

Let the elements of the finite set M be enumerated $a_1, a_2, \cdots, a_n$. If M is closed with respect to a binary operation o, we can construct an n-rowed square M-matrix $A = (a_{ij})$ where $a_{ij} = a_i \, o \, a_j \in M$ for all pairs i,j. Conversely, given an n-rowed square M-matrix $A = (a_{ij})$, we can define a binary operation o on M by $a_i \, o \, a_j = a_{ij}$. The matrix A is called the *multiplication table* for the operation o. For example, the multiplication table

$$A = \begin{pmatrix} a_1 & a_1 & a_1 \\ a_2 & a_2 & a_2 \\ a_3 & a_3 & a_3 \end{pmatrix}$$

corresponds to the operation $a_i \, o \, a_j = a_i$ defined on the set $M = \{a_1,a_2,a_3\}$.

The various properties of the operation o correspond to special forms* for the matrix A. For example, the operation o is commutative if and only if the matrix A is symmetric. The set M contains an identity e, which we may take as the element a_1, if and only if the first row and first column of A consist of the elements $a_1, a_2, \cdots, a_n$ in order. And in this case the element a_i is the inverse of the element a_j if and only if $a_{ij} = a_{ji} = a_1 = e$.

If the set M is a group with respect to o, each row and column of A will consist of the elements $a_1, a_2, \cdots, a_n$ in some order. For if $a_{ij} = a_{ik}$ with $j \neq k$, then $a_i \, o \, a_j = a_i \, o \, a_k$, which implies $a_j = a_k$ by the cancellation law. A similar contradiction is obtained if $a_{ij} = a_{kj}$ for $i \neq k$. Conversely, if each $a_i \in M$ appears exactly once in each row and each column of A, the cancellation law is valid for the corresponding operation o. If we can also prove the associative law for o, then M is a group with respect to o, using the postulate set given in Exercise (33.8).

Two finite groups are isomorphic only if they have the same order, for otherwise there does not exist a (1–1) correspondence between their elements. If G and G' are finite groups of order n, they are isomorphic if and only if it is possible to enumerate their elements so that their multiplication tables are identical.

It is the unsolved problem in the theory of finite groups to find all non-isomorphic groups of order n for every positive integer n. One can list all the non-isomorphic groups of order n by considering the possible multiplication tables, but the calculations are prohibitive except for very small n.

It would be cumbersome to describe finite groups of large order n by means of a multiplication table, and infinite groups would require a matrix with infinitely many rows and columns. Therefore, we will investigate the possibility of describing a group in another way.

---

* The associative law for o is not immediately evident in the matrix A. For a discussion of this in the case of a group, see H. Zassenhaus, *Theory of Groups*, (New York, 1949), p. 4.

Let S be a subset of a group G and let there be given a set of relations of the form*

$$a_{i_1}^{n_1}a_{i_2}^{n_2} \cdots a_{i_r}^{n_r} = e$$

which are satisfied by elements $a_{i_j} \in S$. The exponents n_i are any integers, positive, negative, or zero. If $G = \{S\}$, and if multiplication in G is completely determined by the given relations and relations implied by them, then the given relations are called *defining relations* of G.

For example, consider the group G which has multiplication table

$$\begin{pmatrix} a_1 & a_2 & a_3 & a_4 & a_5 & a_6 \\ a_2 & a_1 & a_4 & a_3 & a_6 & a_5 \\ a_3 & a_6 & a_5 & a_2 & a_1 & a_4 \\ a_4 & a_5 & a_6 & a_1 & a_2 & a_3 \\ a_5 & a_4 & a_1 & a_6 & a_3 & a_2 \\ a_6 & a_3 & a_2 & a_5 & a_4 & a_1 \end{pmatrix}.$$

The relations $a_2^2 = a_3^3 = (a_2a_3)^2 = e$ are defining relations for G. The reader may check that these relations are satisfied in G. Further $G = \{a_2,a_3\}$ since $a_1 = a_2^2 = e$, $a_2 = a_2$, $a_3 = a_3$, $a_4 = a_2a_3$, $a_5 = a_3^2$, and $a_6 = a_2a_3^2$. Finally these relations determine the complete multiplication table of G. For each $a_i \in G$ may be written as $a_i = a_2^{n_2}a_3^{n_3}$ with $n_2 = 0, 1$; $n_3 = 0, 1, 2$, and the relation $(a_2a_3)^2 = e$, which implies $a_3a_2 = a_2a_3^2$ and $a_3^2a_2 = a_2a_3$, enables us to collect the terms a_2 and a_3 in any product a_ia_j. For example,

$$\begin{aligned} a_4a_5 &= a_2a_3a_3^2 = a_2, \\ a_5a_4 &= a_3^2a_2a_3 = a_2a_3a_3 = a_2a_3^2 = a_6, \\ a_4a_6 &= a_2a_3a_2a_3^2 = a_2a_2a_3^2a_3^2 = a_3. \end{aligned}$$

In the above example we have determined a set of defining relations for a given group G. We wish to show now that G is uniquely determined by these relations.

Let $H = \{s,t\}$ be any group generated by the elements s,t satisfying only the relations $s^2 = t^3 = (st)^2 = e$ and relations implied by these. Then without knowing any further facts about multiplication in H, we can prove that H is isomorphic to G. Since for the known group $G = \{a_2,a_3\}$ with $a_2^2 = a_3^3 = (a_2a_3)^2 = e$, the elements a_2,a_3, and e are distinct, the given relations do not imply any of the relations $st^{-1} = e$, $s = e$, or $t = e$, and we have that s,t, and e are distinct elements of H. Every element of H is a power product of the elements s and t, and since from $s^2 = t^3 = e$ we have that $s^{-1} = s$ and $t^{-1} = t^2$, every element of H

* In the remainder of the chapter, we will simplify our notation by writing ab for $a \circ b$.

is a power product of s and t with non-negative exponents. Using $ts = st^2$, which is a consequence of $(st)^2 = e$, we can reduce every element of H to the form $s^\alpha t^\beta$ where α and β are non-negative integers. And using $s^2 = t^3 = e$, we can reduce each $s^\alpha t^\beta$ to the form $s^m t^n$ where $m = 0,1$ and $n = 0,1,2$. Thus every element of H is equal to one of the six elements e,s,t,st,t^2,st^2. Since e,s, and t are distinct elements of H, we can prove that these six elements are distinct. If $t^2 = e,s$, or t, we could prove $t = e$. The relations $st = e,s,t$, or t^2 imply $t = s$, $t = e$, $s = e$, or $s = t$ respectively, while $st^2 = e,s,t,st$, or t^2 imply respectively $s = t$, $t^2 = e$, $st = e$, $t = e$, or $s = e$. Therefore we have shown that H is a group of order six. The isomorphism between G and H is established by letting a_1,a_2,a_3,a_4,a_5, and a_6 correspond respectively to e,s,t,st,t^2, and st^2.

Thus G is uniquely determined up to isomorphism by the given defining relations. It is in this sense that a given set of defining relations determine a group.

As another example, let us determine the group $H = \{s,t\}$ subject only to the relation $sts^{-1}t^{-1} = e$, or $st = ts$. The set of all 1 by 2 matrices with integral elements is a group G with respect to addition such that $G = \{(1,0), (0,1)\}$ and $(1,0) + (0,1) = (0,1) + (1,0)$. In this example $s = (1,0)$, $t = (0,1)$, $e = (0,0)$, and since

$$(m,n) = m(1,0) + n(0,1) = p(1,0) + q(0,1) = (p,q)$$

if and only if $m = p$ and $n = q$, the given relation does not imply $s^m t^n = s^p t^q$ in H unless $m = p$ and $n = q$. Therefore, we have shown that $s^m t^n = s^p t^q$ in H if and only if $m = p$ and $n = q$. It follows from $st = ts$ that every element of H, which is a power product of the elements s and t, can be written in the form $s^m t^n$ where m and n are integers, positive, negative, or zero. Therefore, H is the infinite group consisting of the distinct elements $s^m t^n$. H is isomorphic to the group G by the correspondence f given by $f(s^m t^n) = (m,n)$.

It should be remarked that any given set of relations defines some group, for the identity group $H = \{e\}$ satisfies all relations. Also if one of the generators a does not appear in the defining relations, the relations do not imply $a^n = e$ for any positive integer n, and therefore a has infinite order.

If we have defining relations for the groups G and G', and if we can find a (1–1) correspondence between their generators which preserves all defining relations, the groups G and G' are isomorphic. For multiplication in each group is defined in terms of the generators. The isomorphism given in the first example above is completely determined by the correspondence $a_2 \leftrightarrow s$ and $a_3 \leftrightarrow t$.

Exercise (38.1). Prove that a finite group G is abelian if and only if its multiplication table is symmetric.

Exercise (38.2). Construct a multiplication table which satisfies postulates (i), (iii), and (iv) of a group, but not postulate (ii). Also construct one which satisfies (i), (ii), and (iii), but not (iv).

Exercise (38.3). If $G = \{a\}$ of order n is enumerated $a_1 = e$, $a_i = a^{i-1}$ for $i = 2, 3, \cdots, n - 1$, what is the form of the ith row of the multiplication table of G?

Exercise (38.4). List all groups of orders 1 through 4 by considering all possible multiplication tables which define a group. Give defining relations and a realization as a permutation group for each.

Exercise (38.5). Prove that $s^2 = t^3 = e$, $ts = st$ defines the cyclic group of order 6.

Exercise (38.6). Find the group determined by each set of defining relations:

(a) $s^3 = t^3 = e,\ ts = st;$
(b) $s^4 = t^4 = e,\ ts = st;$
(c) $s^4 = t^4 = e,\ ts = st,\ t^2 = s^2,$
(d) $s^2 = t^3 = r^n = e,\ (st)^2 = e,\ sr = rs,\ tr = rt;$
(e) $s^2 = t^2 = e.$

Give a realization of each as a group of transformations.

Section 39. Complexes and Cosets

We now turn to a systematic study of abstract groups leading to some theorems which describe a group G in terms of certain subgroups of G. Since this study requires the concept of a product of subsets of G, we will devote the first part of this section to the properties of this multiplication.

(39.1) Definition. A *complex* is any non-empty subset of a group G.

The equality of complexes is the equality of sets; that is, two complexes are equal if and only if they contain the same elements. Included among the complexes of G are the subgroups of G and the individual elements of G.

The product of complexes of G is defined in terms of the operation o of G.

(39.2) Definition. The *product* H_1H_2 of the complexes H_1 and H_2 of G is the set of all elements $h_1 \circ h_2 \in G$ where $h_1 \in H_1$ and $h_2 \in H_2$.

Since H_1 and H_2 are non-empty, H_1H_2 is a non-empty subset of G and therefore a complex. Thus the multiplication of complexes is a binary operation on the set of all complexes of G. For example, if G is the group S_4, and if H_1 contains the elements (12), (132), (1234) and H_2 the elements (24), (134), then H_1H_2 contains the five elements (124), (12)(34), (1324), (1342), and (1423) since (12)(24) = (124), (12)(134) = (1342), (132)(24) = (1324), (132)(134) = (12)(34), (1234)(24) = (12)(34), (1234)(134) = (1423).

In Chapter I we saw how the properties of the matrix operations were a consequence of the corresponding properties of addition and multiplication of the elements. Here, in the same way, the properties of the multiplication of complexes depend on the corresponding ones for the operation o of G. For one-element complexes, the complex product is the ordinary product in G. The identity $e \in G$ is an identity with respect to complex multiplication, since $eH = He = H$ for every complex H of G. Moreover, the multiplication of complexes is associative, for if $x \in (H_1H_2)H_3$, then $x = (h_1h_2)h_3$ where $h_i \in H_i$, $i = 1, 2, 3$. Since $(h_1h_2)h_3 = h_1(h_2h_3)$, $x \in H_1(H_2H_3)$. Thus $(H_1H_2)H_3 \subseteq H_1(H_2H_3)$, and similarly $H_1(H_2H_3) \subseteq (H_1H_2)H_3$.

Of particular importance are the complex products involving a subgroup H of G.

(39.3) Definition. If H is a subgroup of G and $a \in G$, then aH is called a *left-coset* of H in G, and Ha is called a *right-coset* of H in G.

Since $eH = He = H$, H itself is both a left- and right-coset of H.

In the following discussion we will consider only left-cosets of a subgroup. It will be clear that there is a parallel theory for right-cosets. Our first theorem characterizes the equality of cosets.

(39.4) Theorem. $aH = bH$ if and only if $a^{-1}b \in H$.

PROOF. Assume first that $aH = bH$. Then if h_1 is any element of H, there exists an $h_2 \in H$ such that $ah_1 = bh_2$. This implies that $a^{-1}b = h_1h_2^{-1} \in H$. Conversely, assume that $a^{-1}b = h \in H$, and therefore that $b^{-1}a = h^{-1} \in H$. If $x \in aH$, then $x = ah_1$ for $h_1 \in H$. This implies that $x = ah_1 = (bb^{-1})ah_1 = b(b^{-1}a)h_1 = bh^{-1}h_1 \in bH$, so that $aH \subseteq bH$. Similarly $bH \subseteq aH$ since $bh_2 = aa^{-1}bh_2 = ahh_2 \in aH$, and we have $aH = bH$.

Thus if a is any element in a left-coset, then this coset is the coset aH. For if $a \in bH$, then $a^{-1}b \in H$ and $bH = aH$ by the theorem. In particular, if $a \in H$, $H = eH = aH$.

(39.5) Theorem. If $aH \neq bH$, then aH and bH are disjoint.

PROOF. If aH and bH contain any element c in common, then $c = ah_1 = bh_2$ for h_1 and $h_2 \in H$. Thus $a^{-1}b = h_1h_2^{-1} \in H$, and $aH = bH$ by Theorem (39.4).

It follows from this result that H is the only coset of H which is a subgroup of G. For if any coset aH were a subgroup of G, then $aH = H$ since they would both contain the identity e of G.

The most important consequence of Theorem (39.5) is that a subgroup H defines a partition of G into mutually disjoint left-cosets of H. Since each $a = ae \in G$ is in the coset aH, G is separated into mutually disjoint subsets. By Theorem (39.4) each subset can be written as aH where a is any element of the subset.

In Section 15, we saw that each partition of a set defines an equivalence relation on the set, where the sets in the partition are the equivalence classes of the derived relation. The partition of a group G into left-cosets of a subgroup H leads to the equivalence relation, $a \sim b$ if and only if a and b are in the same left-coset. By (39.4), $a \sim b$ if and only if $a^{-1}b \in H$. This relation is called *left-congruence modulo H*. When G is an abelian group, so that each left-coset aH is a right-coset Ha, the relation is called *congruence modulo H* and is written $a \equiv b \mod H$.

The significance of the partition of G by the left-cosets of H is a consequence of the following theorem.

(39.6) Theorem. Any two left-cosets of H in G have the same number of elements.

PROOF. Let aH be any left-coset of H, and define the mapping from H to aH by $h \to ah$ for every $h \in H$. This mapping is clearly single-valued, and it is onto aH since every element of aH is of the form ah for $h \in H$. Moreover it is a (1–1)-mapping, since $ah_1 = ah_2$ if and only if $h_1 = h_2$ by the cancellation law in G. Thus H and aH have the same number of elements, since by the definition given in Section 32, two sets are said to have the same number of elements if there is a (1–1) correspondence between them. Therefore, any two left-cosets of H have the same number of elements, the number of elements in H. This leads at once to the following numerical identity.

(39.7) Theorem. If G is a finite group of order n, then $n = j \cdot m$ where m is the order of the subgroup H and j is the number of left-cosets of H in G. If G is an infinite group, then either m or j is infinite.

PROOF. Both results follow from the remark that G is partitioned into j subsets, each containing m elements.

For example, if G is the additive group of all integers and H is the subgroup of even integers, n and m are infinite and $j = 2$. The reader may verify that the left-cosets of H in G are H and $1 + H$. The left-cosets of $H = \{(1),(12)\}$ in $G = S_3$ are H, $(13)H$, and $(23)H$. In this example, $n = 6$, $m = 2$, and $j = 3$.

(39.8) Definition. The number j of left-cosets of H in G is called the *index* of H in G.

For finite groups, the following important results appear as immediate consequences of Theorem (39.7).

(39.9) Theorem. If H is a subgroup of G, the order of H divides the order of G.

(39.10) Theorem. The order of an element $a \in G$ divides the order of G.

PROOF. For the order of a is the same as the order of the cyclic subgroup $\{a\}$.

A prime number is an integer $p > 1$ which is divisible only by 1 and p. Using this we obtain:

(39.11) Theorem. A group G of order p, where p is a prime number, is cyclic.

PROOF. Since $p > 1$, G contains an element $a \neq e$. If a has order n, then $n > 1$ and n divides p. Therefore $n = p$ and $G = \{a\}$.

The preceding theorems show that the order of a finite group is of great importance in determining the structure of the group. For example, let G be a group of order 4. Then G contains the identity e of order 1 and the remaining elements of G are either of order 2 or 4. If G contains any element a of order 4, then $G = \{a\}$ must be the cyclic group of order 4. Otherwise, G must contain the distinct elements a and b of order 2, and their product ab must be the fourth element of G since $ab \neq e$, $ab \neq a$ and $ab \neq b$. Since ab is of order 2, $ab = (ab)^{-1} = b^{-1}a^{-1} = ba$. This group must be the group $G = \{a,b\}$ with defining relations $a^2 = b^2 = e$, $ab = ba$.

Exercise (39.1). Show by example that S_1S_2 is not necessarily a subgroup of G for subgroups S_1 and S_2 of G.

Exercise (39.2). Prove that $SS = S$ if S is a subgroup of G.

Exercise (39.3). Prove that multiplication of complexes of G is commutative if and only if G is abelian.

Exercise (39.4). Outline the theory of right-cosets of H in G. Prove that the index defined using right-cosets is equal to that using left-cosets.

Exercise (39.5). Prove directly that the relation $a \sim b$ if and only if $a^{-1}b \in H$ is an equivalence relation, and that the left-cosets of H are the equivalence classes of this relation.

Exercise (39.6). Construct the left- and right-cosets of S_3 in S_4, of $\{(12),(34)\}$ in S_4, and of $\{(12)(34),(13)(24)\}$ in S_4.

Exercise (39.7). Prove that there exist two, and only two, groups of order 6.

Exercise (39.8). Prove that there exist five, and only five, groups of order 8.

Exercise (39.9). Show that the elementary row transformations of type I generate a subgroup of $\mathcal{E}({}_m\mathfrak{A}_n)$ isomorphic to S_m. What is the index of this subgroup?

Exercise (39.10). Show that if $caH = cbH$, then $aH = bH$. State this result in words in terms of left-congruence modulo H.

Section 40. Normal Subgroups

If H is any subgroup of G, there is a theory of right-cosets of H in G which is parallel to that developed in the preceding section for left-cosets, and the number of right-cosets of H is the same as the number of left-cosets [see Exercise (39.4)]. Those subgroups of G for which every right-coset is a left-coset are of particular interest.

(40.1) Definition. A subgroup H of G is *normal* if every right-coset of H in G is a left-coset of H in G.

If H is any subgroup of G, and if the right-coset Ha is a left-coset, then it is the left-coset aH. For if $Ha = cH$, then $a \in cH$ since $a = ea \in Ha$, and $cH = aH$ by Theorem (39.5). Therefore H is a normal subgroup of G if and only if $Ha = aH$ for all $a \in G$.

The identity subgroup E, and G itself, are normal subgroups of G. Further, every subgroup of an abelian group is normal. The subgroup $\{(123)\}$ is a normal subgroup of S_3. The right-cosets of $\{(123)\}$ in S_3 are $\{(123)\}$ and $\{(123)\}(12)$ where the latter coset contains the elements $(123)(12) = (13)$, $(132)(12) = (23)$, and $(1)(12) = (12)$. The left-cosets are $\{(123)\}$ and $(12)\{(123)\}$, and $(12)\{(123)\}$ also contains the three elements $(12),(13)$, and (23). The subgroup $\{(12)\}$ is not a normal subgroup since the right-coset $\{(12)\}(23)$ contains (123) and (23) while the left-coset $(23)\{(12)\}$ contains (132) and (23).

(40.2) Theorem. If H is a normal subgroup of G, then $HK = KH$ for every complex K of G.

PROOF. Every element of HK has the form hk for $h \in H$ and $k \in K$. Since H is normal, the coset $Hk = kH$, so that $hk = kh'$ for some $h' \in H$. Hence $hk \in KH$ and $HK \subseteq KH$. By the same argument $KH \subseteq HK$, and therefore $HK = KH$.

The reader is cautioned to remember that $H_1H_2 = H_2H_1$ for complexes H_1 and H_2 of G does not require that every element of H_1 commute with every element of H_2. The statement $H_1H_2 = H_2H_1$ means that given any $h_1 \in H_1$ and $h_2 \in H_2$, there exists some pair of elements $h_1' \in H_1$ and $h_2' \in H_2$ such that $h_1h_2 = h_2'h_1'$, and some pair of elements $h_1'' \in H_1$ and $h_2'' \in H_2$ such that $h_1''h_2'' = h_2h_1$.

(40.3) Theorem. If H is a normal subgroup of G and K is any subgroup of G, then $HK = KH$ is a subgroup of G.

PROOF. That $HK = KH$ follows from Theorem (40.2). Let x and y be any pair of elements of HK. Then $x = h_1k_1$ and $y = h_2k_2$ for $h_1,h_2 \in H$ and $k_1,k_2 \in K$. Therefore, $xy^{-1} = (h_1k_1)(k_2^{-1}h_2^{-1}) = h_1(k_1k_2^{-1})h_2^{-1} = h_1(k_3h_2^{-1})$ where $k_3 = k_1k_2^{-1} \in K$. But $k_3h_2^{-1} = h_3k_3$ for some $h_3 \in H$ since $Hk_3 = k_3H$, and therefore $xy^{-1} = h_1(h_3k_3) = (h_1h_3)k_3 \in HK$. Since HK is a product of complexes, HK is non-empty and therefore a subgroup of G by (35.3).

The following theorem is of fundamental importance in determining the structure of a group.

(40.4) Theorem. If H is a normal subgroup of G, the left-cosets of H form a group with respect to the operation of complex multiplication.

PROOF. Since $(aH)(bH) = a(Hb)H = a(bH)H = (ab)(HH) = (ab)H$, using the associativity of complex multiplication, the set of left-cosets is closed with respect to this multiplication and the product of two cosets may be represented by the product of the representatives. The coset $H = eH$ is the identity, since $(eH)(aH) = (ea)H = aH$ and $(aH)(eH) = (ae)H = aH$. Finally the coset $a^{-1}H$ is the inverse of the coset aH since $(a^{-1}H)(aH) = (a^{-1}a)H = eH = (aa^{-1})H = (aH)(a^{-1}H)$.

(40.5) Definition. The group of left-cosets of a normal subgroup H of G is called the *quotient group* of G by H and is denoted by G/H.

This group G/H is the same as the group of right-cosets of H since $Ha = aH$ for all $a \in G$. The order of G/H is j, the index of H in G. If the operation of G is written as addition, the left-cosets of H in G are written $a + H$, and the group of cosets of a normal subgroup H is called the *difference group* of G by H and is denoted by $G - H$.

EXAMPLE 1. The subgroup $V_4 = \{I,(ab)(cd), (ac)(bd), (ad)(bc)\}$ is a normal subgroup of S_4 [see Exercise (39.6)]. The cosets of V_4 can be written as V_4, $(ab)V_4$, $(ac)V_4$, $(bc)V_4$, $(abc)V_4$, and $(acb)V_4$, so that S_4/V_4 is isomorphic to S_3 under the obvious correspondence $xV_4 \leftrightarrow x$ for all $x \in S_3$.

EXAMPLE 2. In the group J of integers under addition, the set $\{n\}$ of all multiples of the positive integer n is a subgroup, and $\{n\}$ is normal since J is abelian. The difference group $J - \{n\}$ consists of the cosets $\{n\}, 1 + \{n\}, 2 + \{n\}, \cdots, (n - 1) + \{n\}$, and $J - \{n\}$ is isomorphic to J_n under the correspondence $x \leftrightarrow x + \{n\}$. J_n is the additive group of integers modulo n as defined in Section 33.

The concept of a normal subgroup can be arrived at in a different way by defining an equivalence relation called conjugacy between the complexes of a group G.

(40.6) Definition. The element $a \in G$ is *conjugate to* $b \in G$ if there exists $c \in G$ such that $a = cbc^{-1}$.

It is easy to verify that conjugacy is an equivalence relation defined on the elements of G. This equivalence is induced by the group of transformations of G consisting of those transformations A_x for $x \in G$ defined by

$$A_x(a) = xax^{-1} \qquad \text{for all } a \in G.$$

These transformations are (1–1), and they are automorphisms of G since $A_x(ab) = x(ab)x^{-1} = (xax^{-1})(xbx^{-1}) = A_x(a) \cdot A_x(b)$. These automorphisms are called *inner automorphisms* of G. We leave it to the reader to prove the statements of this paragraph, and also to prove that the inner automorphisms of G form a normal subgroup of the group of automorphisms of G.

If $A_x(a) = a$ for all $x \in G$, that is, if a is sent into itself by every inner automorphism of G, a is called *self-conjugate*. The identity $e \in G$ is self-conjugate since $A_x(e) = xex^{-1} = e$ for all $x \in G$. The element $a \in G$ is self-conjugate if and only if $xax^{-1} = a$ or $xa = ax$ for all $x \in G$, that is, if and only if a commutes with every element of G.

Conjugacy of elements is a special case of conjugacy of complexes, where the complex H_1 of G is conjugate to the complex H_2 of G if there exists an element $c \in G$ such that $H_1 = cH_2c^{-1}$. The complex H is self-conjugate if $xHx^{-1} = H$ for all $x \in G$, that is, if the subset H is mapped onto itself by every inner automorphism A_x of G. These ideas are of particular interest when applied to subgroups of G. All conjugates xHx^{-1} of a subgroup H are subgroups of G since H is isomorphic to xHx^{-1} under the correspondence $h \rightarrow xhx^{-1}$.

(40.7) Theorem. H is a normal subgroup of G if and only if H is self-conjugate.

PROOF. The condition that H be self-conjugate is that $xHx^{-1} = H$ for all $x \in G$, and this equality is equivalent to $xH = Hx$ for all $x \in G$, which is the condition that H be normal.

A normal (or self-conjugate) subgroup of a group G is sometimes called an *invariant* subgroup since it is mapped onto itself by the group of inner automorphisms of G.

The following application of Theorem (40.4) will be used in Section 42.

(40.8) Theorem. If G is a finite abelian group such that the order of every element of G is a product of powers of the prime numbers $p_1, p_2, \cdots, p_t$, then the order of G is $p_1^{\alpha_1}p_2^{\alpha_2} \cdots p_t^{\alpha_t}$ for some set of exponents $\alpha_i \geq 0$.

PROOF. The theorem is true for $G = E$ of order $p_1^0p_2^0 \cdots p_t^0 = 1$. Assume that the theorem is true for all groups of order less than $n > 1$, and let G have order n. Since $G \neq E$, G contains an element a of order $r = p_1^{\beta_1}p_2^{\beta_2} \cdots p_t^{\beta_t} > 1$. Then $\{a\}$ has order r and index $m = n/r < n$. Every element of $G/\{a\}$ has the form $b\{a\}$ for $b \in G$. Since $b^s = e$ where $s = p_1^{\gamma_1}p_2^{\gamma_2} \cdots p_t^{\gamma_t}$, $[b\{a\}]^s = b^s\{a\} = e\{a\} = \{a\}$, so that the order of $b\{a\}$ divides s. This means that $G/\{a\}$ of order $m = n/r < n$ has the property that the order of every element is a product of powers of the primes $p_1, p_2, \cdots, p_t$. By the induction hypothesis, $m = p_1^{\delta_1}p_2^{\delta_2} \cdots p_t^{\delta_t}$ for some set of exponents $\delta_i \geq 0$, and therefore $n = rm = p_1^{\beta_1+\delta_1}p_2^{\beta_2+\delta_2} \cdots p_t^{\beta_t+\delta_t}$. This completes the induction and proves the theorem.

(40.9) Corollary. If $G \neq E$ is a finite abelian group such that the order of every element divides p^α for p a prime, then the order of G is p^β for some $\beta \geq 1$.

Exercise (40.1). Show by example that if H is not a normal subgroup of G, the product of two left-cosets of H in G is not necessarily a coset.

Exercise (40.2). Show that any subgroup of index 2 in G is normal.

Exercise (40.3). Show that $V_n(F) - S$ is isomorphic to F_+, the additive group of F, if S is a subspace of $V_n(F)$ of dimension $n - 1$.

Exercise (40.4). Discuss the quotient group G/H if G and H are cyclic groups of orders $n = rs$ and r respectively.

Exercise (40.5). Show that $C_+ - R_+^{\#}$ is isomorphic to $R_+^{\#}$ where C_+ and $R_+^{\#}$ are the additive groups of the complex and real number fields respectively.

Exercise (40.6). Prove that H is a normal subgroup of G and find the quotient group G/H where

(a) $G = \{(1\,2\,3\,4\,5),\ (6\,7)\};\ H = \{(6\,7)\}$,
(b) $G = \{(1\,2\,3\,4),\ (5\,6\,7)\};\ H = \{(1\,3)(2\,4)\}$,
(c) $G = \{s,t\}$ where $s^4 = t^4 = e,\ ts = st;\ H = \{s^2,t^2\}$.

Exercise (40.7). Find the classes of conjugate elements in S_3 and in the cyclic group of order 6. Find the classes of conjugate subgroups in each.

Exercise (40.8). Prove that if a is a self-conjugate element in G, then $\{a\}$ is a normal subgroup of G.

Exercise (40.9). Verify the following statements in the text:

(i) Conjugacy of elements is an equivalence relation in G;
(ii) The transformations A_x form a group of (1–1) transformations of G which induces the relation of conjugacy;
(iii) This group of transformations is a normal subgroup of the group of automorphisms of G.

Exercise (40.10). Prove that if a is conjugate to b in G, a and b have the same order.

Exercise (40.11). Prove that if the subgroup H is conjugate to the complex K, then K is a subgroup isomorphic to H. In particular, conjugate subgroups are isomorphic.

Exercise (40.12). Prove that the set of all self-conjugate elements of G is a normal subgroup of G. This subgroup of G is called the *center* of G.

Exercise (40.13). If $a,\ b \in G$, then $aba^{-1}b^{-1}$ is called their *commutator*, and the group C generated by all commutators of G is called the *commutator subgroup*. Prove that C is a normal subgroup of G and that G/C is abelian.

Section 41. Homomorphism

Let H be a normal subgroup of a group G, and consider the mapping f of G onto the quotient group G/H, defined by $f(g) = gH$ for all $g \in G$. Since all of the elements of a given left-coset of H in G are mapped onto the same element of G/H, this mapping is not (1–1) unless $H = E$, the identity subgroup. However, this mapping is like an isomorphism in that it preserves products. For if g_1 and g_2 are in G, $f(g_1g_2) = f(g_1) \cdot f(g_2)$ since $f(g_1g_2) = (g_1g_2)H = (g_1H)(g_2H) = f(g_1) \cdot f(g_2)$, using the multiplication rule which we proved for cosets of a normal subgroup. The mapping f is an example of a homomorphism of a group G onto a group G'. We will show in this section that this example is typical of all group homomorphisms.

Let the set M be closed with respect to the binary operation o, and let N be closed with respect to the operation $*$.

(41.1) Definition. An $(M, o; N, *)$-*homomorphism* of M onto N is a single-valued mapping f of M onto N such that $f(a \, o \, b) = f(a) * f(b)$ for all $a,b \in M$.

We write $M \sim N$ and say that M is *homomorphic* to N. The reader should recall that "single-valued" means that every $a \in M$ has a uniquely defined image $f(a) \in N$, and onto means that every element of N is the map of at least one element of M. If the homomorphism is (1–1), that is, if $a \neq b$ implies $f(a) \neq f(b)$, then it is an isomorphism, and we write $M \cong N$.

The following theorem gives some of the properties of the operation o in M which are preserved by homomorphism.

(41.2) Theorem. Let f be an $(M, o; N, *)$-homomorphism of M onto N.

(i) If o is associative, then $*$ is associative.
(ii) If o is commutative, then $*$ is commutative.
(iii) If M contains an identity e for o, its map $f(e) \in N$ is an identity for $*$.

PROOF. Since f is a mapping of M onto N, given any three elements of N, they may be written as $f(a)$, $f(b)$, and $f(c)$ for some triple a,b,c of elements of M. By the homomorphism $f((a \, o \, b) \, o \, c) = f(a \, o \, b) * f(c) = [f(a) * f(b)] * f(c)$ and $f(a \, o \, (b \, o \, c)) = f(a) * f(b \, o \, c) = f(a) * [f(b) * f(c)]$. If $(a \, o \, b) \, o \, c = a \, o \, (b \, o \, c)$ for all $a,b,c \in M$, then $f((a \, o \, b) \, o \, c) = f(a \, o \, (b \, o \, c))$, or $[f(a) * f(b)] * f(c) = f(a) * [f(b) * f(c)]$ for any three elements of N, proving (i). The proof of (ii) is similar and is left to the reader as an exercise. Finally assume that M contains an identity e for o. Then $e \, o \, a = a \, o \, e = a$ implies that $f(e \, o \, a) = f(a \, o \, e) = f(a)$ and that $f(e) * f(a) = f(a) * f(e) = f(a)$ for all $a \in M$. But since every element of N is of the form $f(a)$ for some $a \in M$, $f(e) \in N$ is an identity for $*$.

(41.3) Theorem. If G is a group with respect to o and if f is a $(G, o; M, *)$-homomorphism of G onto M, then M is a group with respect to $*$,

PROOF. It follows from (i) and (iii) of Theorem (41.2) that we have only to verify that each element of M has an inverse in M. Given any element of M, it may be written as $f(a)$ for some $a \in G$. Now there exists $a^{-1} \in G$ such that $a \circ a^{-1} = a^{-1} \circ a = e$ since G is a group. By the homomorphism $f(a) * f(a^{-1}) = f(a \circ a^{-1}) = f(e) = f(a^{-1} \circ a) = f(a^{-1}) * f(a)$, where $f(e)$ is the identity of M. Therefore $f(a^{-1})$ is the inverse in M of $f(a)$.

Homomorphism is not a symmetric relation. If G and G' are groups such that $G \sim G'$, every equality such as $a^n = e$ or $ab = ba$ which involves the elements of G remains true for their images in G'. But if the homomorphism is not an isomorphism, the elements of G' may satisfy additional relations not found in G. For example, S_n/A_n is abelian since it is a cyclic group of order 2, while S_n is non-abelian if $n > 2$.

In the introductory paragraph of this section, we proved that if H is a normal subgroup of a group G, then G is homomorphic to the quotient group G/H. Conversely, the following theorem shows that the only homomorphic images of a group G are the quotient groups of G with respect to its normal subgroups.

(41.4) Theorem. If the group G is homomorphic to the group G', then the set K of all elements of G mapped onto the identity $e' \in G'$ is a normal subgroup of G, and G' is isomorphic to G/K.

PROOF. Let f be the homomorphism of G onto G'. Since $f(e) = e'$ for the identity $e \in G$, K is not empty. If $c,d \in K$, then $f(c) = f(d) = e' \in G'$. As in the proof of Theorem (41.3), $f(d^{-1}) = f(d)^{-1} = e'^{-1} = e'$, and therefore $f(c \circ d^{-1}) = f(c) * f(d^{-1}) = e' * e' = e'$. Thus $c \circ d^{-1} \in K$ and K is a subgroup of G.

To show that K is a normal subgroup of G, we first prove that for $a,b \in G$, $f(a) = f(b)$ if and only if $aK = bK$. If $aK = bK$, then $b \in aK$, so that $b = a \circ k_1$ for $k_1 \in K$. This implies that $f(b) = f(a \circ k_1) = f(a) * f(k_1) = f(a) * e' = f(a)$. Conversely if $f(a) = f(b)$, then $f(a^{-1} \circ b) = f(a^{-1}) * f(b) = f(a)^{-1} * f(a) = e'$. Therefore, $a^{-1} \circ b \in K$, so that $aK = bK$ by Theorem (39.4).

By the same argument, $f(a) = f(b)$ if and only if $Ka = Kb$. Now if $b \in Ka$, then $Kb = Ka$, $f(b) = f(a)$, $bK = aK$, and $b \in aK$, so that $Ka \subseteq aK$. The inequality $aK \subseteq Ka$ is proved similarly, so that $aK = Ka$ for all $a \in G$, and K is a normal subgroup of G.

The isomorphism of G' onto G/K is the mapping Φ defined by $\Phi(f(a)) = aK$. Since every element of G' is of the form $f(a)$ for some $a \in G$, this defines a map for every element of G', and since every element in G/K can be written as aK for an element $a \in G$, it is a mapping onto G/K. Also Φ is a (1–1) mapping since $f(a) = f(b)$ if and only if $aK = bK$. Finally Φ is an isomorphism since $\Phi(f(a) * f(b)) = \Phi(f(a \circ b)) = (a \circ b)K = (aK)(bK) = \Phi(f(a)) \cdot \Phi(f(b))$. This completes the proof of the theorem.

A group G which does not contain a proper normal subgroup is called *simple*. Its homomorphic images are therefore only itself, since $G \cong G/E$, and the identity group $E \cong G/G$. An example of a simple group is a cyclic group of prime order. It can be proved that the alternating group A_n is simple if $n \neq 4$. This is a very important result in the theory of equations. The only abelian simple groups are the cyclic groups of prime order since every subgroup of an abelian group is normal.

Exercise (41.1). Find all homomorphic images of S_3.

Exercise (41.2). If f is a homomorphism of a group G onto G', prove that the order of $f(a)$ divides the order of a for all $a \in G$ of finite order. If G is a finite group, prove that the order of G' divides the order of G.

Exercise (41.3). Use Theorem (41.4) to prove that the set of even permutations in a permutation group G is a normal subgroup of G of index 1 or 2.

Exercise (41.4). Prove that if f is a homomorphism of a group G onto G' and if $e \in G$ is the only element mapped onto $e' \in G'$, then f is an isomorphism.

Exercise (41.5). An *endomorphism* of a group G is a homomorphism of G onto a subgroup H of G. If G is an abelian group, prove that the endomorphisms of G form a group with respect to the multiplication $\sigma\tau(a) = \sigma(a) \cdot \tau(a)$ for all $a \in G$. Why do they not form a group with respect to the customary multiplication of transformations?

Exercise (41.6). If G is homomorphic to an abelian group G', prove that the commutator subgroup of G is contained in the subgroup of G mapped onto the identity of G'.

Exercise (41.7). Let $G = \{S\}$ be a group which is given by a set of defining relations satisfied by the elements in S, and let N be a normal subgroup of G. Prove that G/N is generated by a set of elements S' which satisfy a set of relations which include the defining relations for G.

Section 42. Direct Products

In the preceding section we showed that the normal subgroups of a group G determine all of the homomorphic images of G. In this section we will show that in some cases there exist normal subgroups of G which completely determine the structure of G.

(42.1) Definition. The group G is the *direct product* of its normal subgroups H and K if $G = HK$ and H and K have only the identity $e \in G$ in common. We write $G = H \otimes K$.

As an example, let $G = \{a,b\}$ be the group of order 4 with defining relations $a^2 = b^2 = e$, $ab = ba$. Since G is abelian, every subgroup is normal. Let $H = \{a\}$ and $K = \{b\}$. The elements of G are $e = ee$, $a = ae$, $b = eb$, and ab, which are all in HK. Also H and K have only e in common, since H consists of e and a while K consists of e and b. Thus $G = H \otimes K$ is the direct product of two cyclic subgroups of order 2.

The following theorem collects the essential facts about direct products of subgroups.

(42.2) Theorem. If $G = H \otimes K$, then H and K have the following properties:

(i) every element $g \in G$ has a unique representation $g = hk$ for $h \in H$ and $k \in K$;
(ii) every element of H commutes with every element of K;
(iii) $G/H \cong K$ and $G/K \cong H$.

PROOF. Since $G = HK$, every element $g \in G$ has the form $g = hk$ for $h \in H$ and $k \in K$. If $g = h_1k_1$ for $h_1 \in H$ and $k_1 \in K$, then $hk = h_1k_1$, or $h_1^{-1}h = k_1k^{-1}$. But the element $x = h_1^{-1}h = k_1k^{-1}$ is in both H and K, so that $x = e$ by Definition (42.1). This implies that $h_1 = h$ and $k_1 = k$, proving (i).

Let h and k be any elements of H and K respectively, and consider the product kh. Since H is normal, $kH = Hk$ so that $kh = h_1k$ for $h_1 \in H$. Since K is normal, $Kh = hK$ so that $kh = hk_1$ for $k_1 \in K$. Thus $h_1k = hk_1$, and by (i) this implies $h_1 = h$ and $k_1 = k$. Therefore $hk = kh$, proving (ii).

The mapping f, defined by $f(g) = k$ if $g = hk$, is a homomorphism of G onto K. For the map of g is unique since the representation of $g \in G$ as $g = hk \in HK$ is unique. And if $g_1 = h_1k_1$ and $g_2 = h_2k_2$ are any two elements of G, then $g_1g_2 = (h_1k_1)(h_2k_2) = (h_1h_2)(k_1k_2)$ using (ii), so that $f(g_1g_2) = k_1k_2 = f(g_1) \cdot f(g_2)$. Since $f(g) = e$ if and only if $k = e$ in the representation $g = hk \in HK$, $f(g) = e$ if and only if $g \in H$. Therefore $G/H \cong K$ by (41.4). In the same way $f(g) = f(hk) = h$ is a homomorphism of G onto H and $G/K \cong H$.

It is a consequence of the following theorem that the structure of G

is uniquely determined by H and K whenever such normal subgroups exist.

(42.3) Theorem. If $G = H \otimes K$ and $G' = H' \otimes K'$ where $H \cong H'$ and $K \cong K'$, then $G \cong G'$.

PROOF. Let Φ and Ψ be the isomorphisms of H onto H' and K onto K' respectively. Then the correspondence f, defined by

$$f(g) = \Phi(h) \cdot \Psi(k) \qquad \text{where } g = hk,$$

is an isomorphism of G onto G'.

Returning to the example discussed earlier, we now see that any group which is the direct product of two cyclic subgroups of order 2 is essentially the group G defined there. By (*i*) of Theorem (42.2) if H and K are finite groups of orders m and n respectively, then $G = H \otimes K$ is a finite group of order mn.

Some groups have no direct factorization $G = H \otimes K$ other than the trivial one $G = G \otimes E = E \otimes G$. A simple group, which has no proper normal subgroups, is an example of such a group. Further, a proper normal subgroup of a group G is not necessarily a direct factor. For example, if $G = \{c\}$ is the cyclic group of order 4, then $H = \{c^2\}$ is not a direct factor. For if $G = H \otimes K$, then K must have order 2. Thus G would be the direct product of two cyclic groups of order 2 and would be isomorphic to the group $\{a,b\}$ with defining relations $a^2 = b^2 = e$, $ab = ba$.

In applications, an important result concerning direct products is that it is always possible to construct a group G which is the direct product of two given groups H and K.

(42.4) Theorem. The set G of all distinct pairs (h,k) for $h \in H$ and $k \in K$ is a group with respect to the multiplication defined by $(h,k)(h_1,k_1) = (hh_1,kk_1)$. Further, $G = H' \otimes K'$ where $H' \cong H$ and $K' \cong K$.

PROOF. Since the products hh_1 and kk_1 are uniquely defined in H and K, the multiplication of pairs is a binary operation on G. The associative law in G is an immediate consequence of the associative laws in H and K. The identity is the element (e_1,e_2) where e_1 and e_2 are the identities of H and K respectively, and $(h,k)^{-1} = (h^{-1},k^{-1})$.

The set of elements (h,e_2) is a subgroup H' of G since $(h_1,e_2) \cdot (h_2,e_2)^{-1} = (h_1,e_2)(h_2^{-1},e_2) = (h_1h_2^{-1},e_2) \in H'$. Further, H' is a normal subgroup of G. For if (h,k) is any element of G, $(h,k) \cdot (h_1,e_2) = (hh_1,ke_2) = (h_2h,e_2k) = (h_2,e_2)(h,k)$, so that $gH' = H'g$ for all $g \in G$. Similarly, the elements (e_1,k) form a normal subgroup K' of G.

Since $(h,k) = (h,e_2)(e_1,k) \in H'K'$, $G = H'K'$. Further, if (h,k) is in

H', then $k = e_2$, and if $(h,k) \in K'$, then $h = e_1$, so that if (h,k) is in both H' and K', then $(h,k) = (e_1,e_2)$, the identity in G. Therefore, $G = H' \otimes K'$ by (42.1). The correspondences $(h,e_2) \leftrightarrow h$ and $(e_1,k) \leftrightarrow k$ are the isomorphisms $H' \cong H$ and $K' \cong K$ respectively.

The following theorem is an example of a case in which a group may be expressed as a direct product of certain subgroups.

(42.5) Theorem. Let G be an abelian group of order $n = rs$ where r and s are relatively prime, let H consist of all $x \in G$ such that $x^r = e$, and let K consist of all $x \in G$ such that $x^s = e$. Then H and K are subgroups of G of orders r and s respectively, and $G = H \otimes K$.

PROOF. Since $e^r = e$, H is not empty. If a and b are in H, then $ab^{-1} \in H$ since $(ab^{-1})^r = a^r(b^r)^{-1} = ee^{-1} = e$ in an abelian group. Thus H is a subgroup of G, and similarly K is a subgroup of G. Both H and K are normal subgroups since G is abelian.

Since r and s are relatively prime, there exist integers u and v such that $1 = su + rv$. If $g \in G$, $g = g^1 = g^{su+rv} = g^{su}g^{rv}$. Since $(g^{su})^r = g^{rsu} = g^{nu} = (g^n)^u = e^u = e$, $g^{su} = h \in H$. Similarly $g^{rv} = k \in K$ and $g = hk \in HK$. Therefore $G = HK$.

If $x \in G$ is in both H and K, then $x^r = x^s = e$. This implies that $x = x^1 = x^{su+rv} = (x^s)^u(x^r)^v = e^ue^v = e$. Therefore H and K have only the identity element $e \in G$ in common, and $G = H \otimes K$ by (42.1).

Finally, since r and s are relatively prime, $r = p_1^{\alpha_1}p_2^{\alpha_2} \cdots p_u^{\alpha_u}$ and $s = q_1^{\beta_1}q_2^{\beta_2} \cdots q_v^{\beta_v}$ where the p_i and q_j are primes and $p_i \neq q_j$ for $i = 1, 2, \cdots, u$ and $j = 1, 2, \cdots, v$. By Theorem (40.8) H has order $p_1^{\gamma_1}p_2^{\gamma_2} \cdots p_u^{\gamma_u}$ and K has order $q_1^{\delta_1}q_2^{\delta_2} \cdots q_v^{\delta_v}$. Now $n = rs = p_1^{\alpha_1}p_2^{\alpha_2} \cdots p_u^{\alpha_u}q_1^{\beta_1}q_2^{\beta_2} \cdots q_v^{\beta_v} = p_1^{\gamma_1}p_2^{\gamma_2} \cdots p_u^{\gamma_u}q_1^{\delta_1}q_2^{\delta_2} \cdots q_v^{\delta_v}$ since by (i) of (42.2), the order n of G is the product of the orders of H and K. Since the factorization of n into prime power factors is unique, we obtain $\alpha_i = \gamma_i$ for $i = 1, 2, \cdots, u$ and $\beta_j = \delta_j$ for $j = 1, 2, \cdots, v$. Therefore H has order $p_1^{\gamma_1}p_2^{\gamma_2} \cdots p_u^{\gamma_u} = p_1^{\alpha_1}p_2^{\alpha_2} \cdots p_u^{\alpha_u} = r$, and K has order s.

We can extend the concept of a direct product to include any finite number of factors by defining inductively $G = H_1 \otimes H_2 \otimes \cdots \otimes H_n$ if $G = H' \otimes H_n$ where $H' = H_1 \otimes H_2 \otimes \cdots \otimes H_{n-1}$, each H_i being a normal subgroup of G. Theorem (42.4) can be extended to construct the direct product of any finite set of given groups. The following corollary is an immediate consequence of Theorem (42.5) and the above inductive definition of the direct product.

(42.6) Corollary. If G is a finite abelian group of order $n = p_1^{\alpha_1}p_2^{\alpha_2} \cdots p_t^{\alpha_t}$ where $p_1, p_2, \cdots, p_t$ are distinct primes, then $G = H_1 \otimes H_2 \otimes \cdots \otimes H_t$ where each H_i has order $p_i^{\alpha_i}$.

(42.7) Corollary. If the order of a finite abelian group G is divisible by p, then G contains an element of order p.

The proofs of these corollaries are left for the reader as exercises.

Results similar to Corollary (42.6) can be proved for certain infinite abelian groups, but comparatively little is known for non-abelian groups. The factorization given in (42.6) is not necessarily complete, since each H_i may be further factored into a direct product of cyclic groups if it is not itself cyclic.

Exercise (42.1). Prove that $H \otimes K \cong K \otimes H$ for the direct product of two abstract groups H and K.

Exercise (42.2). Show that there are only two groups of order 8 which can be written as a direct product of two or more nontrivial factors.

Exercise (42.3). Prove that the direct product $H \otimes K$ of two finite cyclic groups of orders m and n is cyclic if and only if m and n are relatively prime.

Exercise (42.4). Show that S_3 is not a direct product by showing that any direct product of order 6 must be a cyclic group.

Exercise (42.5). What is the smallest non-abelian group which can be written as a direct product of nontrivial subgroups?

Exercise (42.6). Prove that a cyclic group of order p^α has only the trivial direct factorization.

Exercise (42.7). Show that the additive group of m by n matrices over a number field F is a direct sum of mn summands each of which is isomorphic to the additive group of F.

Exercises (42.8). State and prove the generalization of Theorem (42.2) for $G = H_1 \otimes H_2 \otimes \cdots \otimes H_n$.

Exercise (42.9). State and prove the generalization of Theorem (42.4) for the construction of the direct product of given groups $H_1, H_2, \cdots, H_n$.

Exercise (42.10). Prove Corollary (42.6).

Exercise (42.11). Prove Corollary (42.7).

V PROPERTIES OF NUMBER SYSTEMS

Section 43. Rings

In this chapter we will study algebraic systems which are closed with respect to two binary operations. The models of these abstract systems are the well-known number systems of mathematics such as the integers and the rational numbers. Our discussion will be limited to systems with properties which are immediate abstractions of the properties of ordinary numbers. Such a study has the twofold purpose of obtaining general results which are valid in a wide variety of applications as well as examining the logical relationships between the familiar properties of numbers.

(43.1) Definition. A set R is a *ring* with respect to two binary operations, called addition and multiplication, if

A R is an abelian group with respect to addition.
M M_1. R is closed with respect to multiplication.
M_2. Multiplication is associative.
D Multiplication is distributive with respect to addition, that is, $a(b + c) = ab + ac$ and $(a + b)c = ac + bc$ for all $a,b,c \in R$.

Since R is an abelian group with respect to addition, the results of Chapter IV hold for R as far as addition is concerned. The identity for addition is called the *zero* of the ring and is denoted by 0. The additive inverse of an element $a \in R$ is denoted by $-a$. Since the equation $a + x = b$ has a unique solution $x = b - a$ in an additive abelian group, subtraction is possible and is unique in R.

It follows from Theorem (31.5) that the general associative law holds for both operations. Further, we may prove inductively from postulate D of Definition (43.1) that general distributive laws, such as

$$a\left(\sum_{j=1}^{m} b_j\right) = \sum_{j=1}^{m} ab_j \text{ and } \left(\sum_{i=1}^{n} a_i\right)\left(\sum_{j=1}^{m} b_j\right) = \sum_{i=1}^{n}\sum_{j=1}^{m} a_ib_j = \sum_{j=1}^{m}\sum_{i=1}^{n} a_ib_j,$$

hold in R. The latter of these two laws depends upon the fact that addition is both associative and commutative.

The concept of a ring can be specialized in many ways by introducing additional hypotheses which restrict the multiplication in the ring. The following two immediate specializations are of particular importance in the theory of rings. A ring R is called a *commutative ring* if the multiplication in R is commutative. And a ring R is called a *ring with identity* if R contains an identity element e for multiplication.

EXAMPLE 1. The elements of any number field form a commutative ring with identity with respect to the complex number operations of addition and multiplication.

EXAMPLE 2. The set J of all integers is a commutative ring with identity with respect to the usual operations.

EXAMPLE 3. The set E of all even integers is a commutative ring with respect to the addition and multiplication in J. Since the sum and product of two even integers is again even, E is closed with respect to the two operations. Since $E \subseteq J$, the identities of addition and multiplication required by A, M, and D of Definition (43.1) are satisfied in E. Finally $0 \in E$, and if $a \in E$, $-a \in E$, so that postulate A of (43.1) is satisfied. This ring does not have an identity, for if it contained an identity e, then $ea = a$ for all $a \in E$. But $1 \in J$ is the only solution in J of the equation $xa = a$, and $1 \notin E$.

EXAMPLE 4. The additive group J_n of integers modulo n, which was defined in Section 33, is a ring with respect to the operation $\oplus$ defined there and the operation $\otimes$ defined by $a \otimes b = s$, where s is the remainder after dividing the ordinary product ab by n. This ring is called the ring of integers modulo n, and is also denoted by J_n.

EXAMPLE 5. The set of all n-rowed square matrices with elements in a number field F is a ring with identity with respect to matrix addition and multiplication. That such a matrix ring is never commutative if $n > 1$ is seen from the following products:

$$\left(\begin{array}{cc|c} 1 & 1 & \\ 0 & 1 & O \\ \hline \multicolumn{2}{c|}{O} & I_{n-2} \end{array}\right)\left(\begin{array}{cc|c} 1 & 0 & \\ 1 & 1 & O \\ \hline \multicolumn{2}{c|}{O} & I_{n-2} \end{array}\right) = \left(\begin{array}{cc|c} 2 & 1 & \\ 1 & 1 & O \\ \hline \multicolumn{2}{c|}{O} & I_{n-2} \end{array}\right)$$

$$\left(\begin{array}{cc|c} 1 & 0 & \\ 1 & 1 & O \\ \hline \multicolumn{2}{c|}{O} & I_{n-2} \end{array}\right)\left(\begin{array}{cc|c} 1 & 1 & \\ 0 & 1 & O \\ \hline \multicolumn{2}{c|}{O} & I_{n-2} \end{array}\right) = \left(\begin{array}{cc|c} 1 & 1 & \\ 1 & 2 & O \\ \hline \multicolumn{2}{c|}{O} & I_{n-2} \end{array}\right).$$

In Chapter I, we defined an m by n S-matrix with elements in an arbitrary set S and then immediately restricted S to be the set of all complex numbers in order to define the matrix operations and prove the identities satisfied by these operations. If we take S to be a ring R, then the ring postulates are just the properties of addition and multiplication of the elements which we used in Chapter I to prove the properties of matrix addition, subtraction, and multiplication. Consequently, Example 5 may be generalized, and the set of all n-rowed square matrices with elements in a ring R is again a ring.

EXAMPLE 6. The ring of all n-rowed square matrices for $n > 1$ with elements in the ring E of even integers is an example of a ring which is not commutative and does not contain an identity.

EXAMPLE 7. The set of all real-valued functions continuous in a variable x over an interval $[a,b]$ is a ring with respect to the operations $h = f + g$ and $k = f \cdot g$ defined by $h(x) = f(x) + g(x)$ and $k(x) = f(x)g(x)$ for all x in $[a,b]$. Many properties of this important class of functions are conveniently described in ring terminology.

The first simple properties of a ring R beyond those which are essentially group properties are consequences of the distributive laws.

(43.2) $$a \cdot 0 = 0 \cdot a = 0 \quad \text{for all} \quad a \in R.$$

PROOF. Using the fact that 0 is an identity for addition and using the distributive laws, postulate D of Definition (43.1), we have

$$\begin{aligned} a \cdot 0 = 0 + a \cdot 0 &= [-(aa) + aa] + a \cdot 0 = -(aa) + (aa + a \cdot 0) \\ &= -(aa) + a(a + 0) = -(aa) + aa = 0, \end{aligned}$$

and

$$\begin{aligned} 0 \cdot a = 0 \cdot a + 0 &= 0 \cdot a + [aa + \{-(aa)\}] = (0 \cdot a + aa) + [-(aa)] \\ &= (0 + a)a + [-(aa)] = aa + [-(aa)] = 0. \end{aligned}$$

(43.3) $$-(ab) = (-a)b = a(-b) \quad \text{and} \quad (-a)(-b) = ab.$$

PROOF. By postulate D of (43.1), $0 = 0 \cdot b = (-a + a)b = (-a)b + ab$. This proves that $(-a)b = -(ab)$, the unique inverse of ab with respect to addition. Similarly, $0 = a \cdot 0 = a(-b + b) = a(-b) + ab$ proves that $a(-b) = -(ab)$. Finally, using these two results, $(-a)(-b) = -[a(-b)] = -[-(ab)] = ab$ since $-(-c) = c$ if c is an element of an additive group.

Exercise (43.1). Prove the general distributive laws given in the text. Also prove that $a(b - c) = ab - ac$.

Exercise (43.2). Prove that the ring described in Example 6 is not commutative and does not contain an identity.

Exercise (43.3). Show that every additive abelian group G can be made into a ring by defining the multiplication $ab = 0$ for all $a,b \in G$.

Exercise (43.4). Prove that the ring of matrices with elements in a ring R has an identity if and only if R has an identity, and that this ring is not commutative if $n > 1$ and R contains two elements a and b such that $ab \neq 0$.

Exercise (43.5). Prove that a non-empty set of complex numbers is a ring (with respect to the addition and multiplication of complex numbers) if it contains the difference and product of any two numbers in the set.

Exercise (43.6). Which of the following sets of complex numbers are rings?

(a) all numbers of the form $a + b\sqrt{2}$ where a and b are integers;
(b) all numbers of the form $a + bi$ with a and b rational;
(c) the four fourth roots of unity, $1, -1, i, -i$;
(d) the numbers $a + b\sqrt[3]{5} + c\sqrt[3]{25}$ where a,b,c are integers;
(e) the numbers $a/2$ where a is an integer;
(f) the numbers $a + b\sqrt[3]{2}$ where a and b are integers.

Exercise (43.7). Construct all rings which have as their additive group the cyclic group of order 3.

Exercise (43.8). Consider the integers with their ordinary addition $+$ and a "multiplication" $\otimes$ defined by $a \otimes b = 2(ab)$ where ab is the ordinary product. Prove that this system is a ring.

Exercise (43.9). Prove that the integers under ordinary addition and under "multiplication" $a \otimes b = a$ satisfy all ring postulates except one.

Exercise (43.10). Discuss the set of all matrices $\begin{pmatrix} a & 0 \\ 0 & 2a \end{pmatrix}$ for a in a ring R.

Exercise (43.11). Discuss the set of all matrices $\begin{pmatrix} a & 0 \\ 0 & a^2 \end{pmatrix}$ for a in a ring R.

Section 44. Complexes. Subrings. Ideals

Just as for groups, a non-empty subset H of a ring R is called a complex, and corresponding to the two operations in R, we define two operations for complexes. If H and K are complexes of R, $H + K$ is the complex consisting of all sums $h + k$ and HK consists of all products hk for $h \in H$ and $k \in K$. It follows from the corresponding properties of the operations in R that complex multiplication is associative. In place of the distributive laws, we have the relations

$$H(K_1 + K_2) \subseteq HK_1 + HK_2 \qquad \text{and} \qquad (H_1 + H_2)K \subseteq H_1K + H_2K.$$

These relations imply that

$$(H_1 + H_2 + \cdots + H_n)(K_1 + K_2 + \cdots + K_m) \subseteq \Sigma H_iK_j.$$

A *subring* of R is a complex S of R which is itself a ring with respect to the operations of R. Subrings are characterized by the following theorem which is an immediate consequence of Theorem (35.3).

(44.1) Theorem. The subset S of a ring R is a subring of R if and only if S is non-empty and $a - b$ and ab are in S for all $a,b \in S$.

The subrings of a ring R which play a role analogous to that of the normal subgroups of a group are called ideals.

(44.2) Definition. An *ideal* I of a ring R is a subring of R such that $rI \subseteq I$ and $Ir \subseteq I$ for every $r \in R$.

(44.3) Theorem. The subset S of a ring R is an ideal of R if and only if S is non-empty and $a - b$, ac, and ca are in S for all $a,b \in S$, $c \in R$.

The proof of this theorem, which is an immediate consequence of (44.1) and (44.2), is left for the reader.

The subring consisting of the zero element alone, as well as R itself, are ideals of R. In the ring E of even integers, the set of all multiples of any one element is an ideal of E, and E is itself an ideal of the ring J of all integers.

(44.4) Definition. If I is an ideal of the ring R, the complex $I + r$ for $r \in R$ is called a *residue class* of R modulo the ideal I.

Since R is an abelian group with respect to addition, each subring, and, in particular, each ideal, is a normal subgroup of the additive group of R. Therefore, a residue class $I + r = r + I$ is just a coset of I in R. From Theorem (40.4), the residue classes of R modulo I form an additive group, and the sum of two residue classes may be represented by the sum of the representatives of the two classes since the formula for addition is

$$(I + r) + (I + s) = I + (r + s).$$

The set of residue classes of R modulo I is not closed under complex multiplication. For example, in the ring J of integers, the square of the residue class $E = E + 0$ is only part of the residue class E, since EE consists of all integers which are a multiple of 4. However, the complex product of two residue classes of R modulo I is contained in a residue class, since

$$(I + r)(I + s) \subseteq II + rI + Is + rs \subseteq I + I + I + rs = I + rs.$$

Moreover this residue class is uniquely determined by the residue classes $I + r$ and $I + s$, since the complex product $(I + r)(I + s)$ is uniquely defined and since distinct residue classes, that is, cosets of I, have no elements in common. In particular, we have shown that this class may be represented by the product of the elements used to represent the two given classes. We use these facts to define a multiplication on the additive group of residue classes of R modulo I.

(44.5) Theorem. The set of residue classes of a ring R modulo an ideal I is a ring with respect to the operations of addition and multiplication defined by

$$(I + r) + (I + s) = I + (r + s)$$
$$(I + r) \times (I + s) = I + rs.$$

PROOF. The additive properties of this system follow from (40.4), since the addition is the addition of cosets which is commutative for an abelian group. By the remarks above, this multiplication is a binary operation on the set, and the identities M_2 and D may be verified by direct calculation. For example, since $(r + s)t = rt + st$ for all $r,s,t \in R$, we have

$$\begin{aligned}[(I + r) + (I + s)] \times (I + t) &= (I + (r + s)) \times (I + t) \\ &= I + (r + s)t = I + (rt + st) = (I + rt) + (I + st) \\ &= [(I + r) \times (I + t)] + [(I + s) \times (I + t)].\end{aligned}$$

This ring is called the *residue class ring of R modulo I* and is denoted by $R - I$. As in the case of quotient groups, the residue class rings of R may be associated with homomorphisms of R.

(44.6) Definition. A *ring-homomorphism* of a ring R, with operations $+$ and $\cdot$, onto a ring R', with operations $\oplus$ and $\odot$, is a single-valued mapping f of R onto R' such that for all $r, s \in R$

$$f(r + s) = f(r) \oplus f(s) \text{ and } f(r \cdot s) = f(r) \odot f(s).$$

If the mapping f is (1–1), it is a *ring-isomorphism*, and we write $R \cong R'$.

(44.7) Theorem. If I is an ideal of the ring R, then R is homomorphic to $R - I$; and conversely if R is homomorphic to the ring S, then the set I of all elements of R mapped onto the zero of S is an ideal of R, and S is isomorphic to $R - I$.

PROOF. The homomorphism of R onto $R - I$ is the mapping f defined by $f(r) = I + r$ for all $r \in R$. Conversely let f be a homomorphism of R onto S, and let I be the set of all $a \in R$ such that $f(a) = 0' \in S$. If $a,b \in I$, then $f(a - b) = f(a) - f(b) = 0' - 0' = 0'$. And if c is any element of R, then $f(a \cdot c) = f(a) \odot f(c) = 0' \odot f(c) = 0'$ and $f(c \cdot a) = f(c) \odot f(a) = f(c) \odot 0' = 0'$. Therefore I is an ideal by Theorem (44.3). The isomorphism of S onto $R - I$ is the mapping φ defined by

$$\varphi(f(a)) = I + a \qquad \text{for all} \qquad a \in R.$$

If n is any positive integer, the set (n) of all multiples of n is an ideal of the ring J of all integers, and the residue class ring $J - (n)$ is isomorphic to the ring J_n defined in Example 4 of Section 43. Each residue class of J modulo (n) has a unique representative r such that $0 \leq r < n$. These representatives were the symbols used for the elements of J_n as defined in Example 4. Because of this isomorphism, we also denote the residue class ring $J - (n)$ by J_n.

Exercise (44.1). Prove that the addition of complexes is commutative, and prove the relations $H(K_1 + K_2) \subseteq HK_1 + HK_2$, $(H_1 + H_2)K \subseteq H_1K + H_2K$. Give an example to show that complex multiplication is not distributive with respect to addition.

Exercise (44.2). Find all the subrings of the ring of integers. [*Hint:* Use the well-ordering principle (0.1) and Theorem (0.4), of the Introduction.] Show that they are ideals.

Exercise (44.3). Prove that if R contains an identity e, and if $e \in I$, an ideal of R, then $I = R$.

Exercise (44.4). Which of the following sets are ideals of the ring R of all 2 by 2 matrices with integral elements?

(a) all matrices $\begin{pmatrix} a & a \\ b & b \end{pmatrix}$;

(b) all matrices $\begin{pmatrix} 2a & 2b \\ 2c & 2d \end{pmatrix}$;

(c) all matrices $\begin{pmatrix} a & 0 \\ 0 & 2a \end{pmatrix}$.

Which sets are subrings of R?

Exercise (44.5). A subring S of R is called a *left-ideal* if $aS \subseteq S$ for all $a \in R$ and a *right-ideal* if $Sa \subseteq S$ for all $a \in R$. In the ring R of the preceding exercise, find an example of a left-ideal which is not a right-ideal, and vice versa.

Exercise (44.6). Prove that the identity correspondence I is the only ring-automorphism of the integers.

Exercise (44.7). Show that the correspondence $a + bi \leftrightarrow \begin{pmatrix} a & b \\ -b & a \end{pmatrix}$ is a ring-isomorphism of C into $\mathfrak{A}_2(R^\#)$.

Section 45. Zero-Divisors. Integral Domains

The definition of a ring, (43.1), was made sufficiently general to include such examples as matrix rings and rings of continuous functions, as well as the ordinary number systems. The number systems are distinguished from the more general examples chiefly by the validity of the cancellation law of multiplication.

We know from our discussion of matrix multiplication in Chapter I that the product of two non-zero matrices may be zero. In fact, the ring of n-rowed square matrices with elements in a ring R, except for the case when $n = 1$ or R is the zero ring, always contains elements $A \neq 0$ and $B \neq 0$ such that $AB = 0$. Such elements, which do not occur in our ordinary number systems, are found in many useful examples of rings.

(45.1) Definition. An element $a \neq 0$ of a ring R is called a *zero-divisor* if there exists a $b \neq 0$ in R such that either $ab = 0$ or $ba = 0$.

By this definition, 0 is not a zero-divisor, and if R contains an identity $e \neq 0$, then e is not a zero-divisor, nor is any element of R which has a multiplicative inverse.

The *cancellation law* for an element $a \in R$ is as follows:

(45.2) If $a \neq 0$ and either $ab = ac$ or $ba = ca$ for $b,c \in R$, then $b = c$.

The validity of the cancellation law for $a \neq 0 \in R$ is equivalent to the statement that a is not a zero-divisor.

(45.3) Theorem. An element $a \neq 0$ in a ring R is not a zero-divisor if and only if the cancellation law holds for a.

PROOF. If $a \neq 0$ is not a zero-divisor, then $ab = ac$ gives $ab - ac = a(b - c) = 0$, which implies that $b - c = 0$ and $b = c$. The proof is the same for $ba = ca$. Conversely, if the cancellation law holds for a, and if $ab = 0$ for $b \in R$, then since $a \cdot 0 = 0$, we have $ab = a \cdot 0$

which implies that $b = 0$. Similarly $ba = 0$ implies $b = 0$, so that a is not a zero-divisor.

(45.4) Corollary. R is a ring without zero-divisors if and only if the cancellation law holds for all $a \neq 0$ in R.

A ring which possesses all the additional multiplicative properties which we have discussed is called an integral domain.

(45.5) Definition. An *integral domain* is a commutative ring with an identity $e \neq 0$ which is without zero-divisors.

An integral domain is an abstract algebraic system which has the properties of addition and multiplication assumed for the integers. Any result which is valid for all integral domains is a property of the integers which does not depend on their natural ordering.

Besides the integers, any number field is an example of an integral domain. An example of a finite integral domain is the ring J_p of the integers modulo p where p is a prime number.

Exercise (45.1). Show that the ring of n-rowed square matrices with elements in a ring R contains zero-divisors if $n > 1$ and $R \neq 0$.

Exercise (45.2). Give an example of a zero-divisor in the ring of continuous functions described in Example 7 of Section 43.

Exercise (45.3). Prove that the ring J_m of the integers modulo m contains zero-divisors if m is not a prime number. Find all zero divisors for $m = 14$, 16, and 18.

Exercise (45.4). Prove that if R is an integral domain, then any subring of R which contains the identity e is an integral domain.

Exercise (45.5). Which of the rings of Exercise (43.6) are integral domains?

Section 46. Divisibility and Units in an Integral Domain

In an additive abelian group, and therefore in any ring R, the equations $a + x = b$ and $x + a = b$ for $a,b \in R$ have a unique solution in R which we write as $x = b - a$. We express this fact by saying that subtraction is always possible and is unique in R. It is therefore not a significant statement to say that $b - a$ exists in R for a particular pair $a,b \in R$ since $b - a$ exists for every pair $a,b \in R$.

The corresponding equations for multiplication are $ax = b$ and $xa = b$ for $a \neq 0$. These equations may have no solution in R. For example, the equation $2x = 15$ has no solution in the ring of integers.

However, if R is an integral domain, it follows from the commutativity of multiplication that any solution in R of one of the equations is a solution of the other; and it is a consequence of the cancellation law, which holds in R by Corollary (45.4), that a solution of these equations, if it exists, is unique. We may write such a unique solution as b/a and say that division, though not always possible, is unique in an integral domain. Thus it is a significant statement to say that a particular quotient b/a exists in R, and in defining an integral domain we have assumed just enough to make division a meaningful and workable concept.

(46.1) Definition. Let a and b be elements of an integral domain D. Then *a divides* b, or a is a *factor* of b, if there exists an element $c \in D$ such that $ac = b$.

The relation $ae = ea = a$ shows that a divides a and e divides a for all $a \in D$. Using the notation of the introductory paragraph, $a/e = a$, and if $a \neq 0$, $a/a = e$. By the relation $a0 = 0a = 0$, every $a \in D$ divides zero, and zero divides only itself.

(46.2) Theorem. In an integral domain D, if a divides b and b divides c, then a divides c.

PROOF. By hypothesis, there exist d and f in D such that $ad = b$ and $bf = c$. Therefore $a(df) = (ad)f = bf = c$, so that a divides c.

(46.3) Definition. The elements a and b are called *associates* if each divides the other.

The relation $\sim$, defined by $a \sim b$ if and only if a and b are associates, is an equivalence relation on D with equivalence classes which are the sets of associated elements. If a divides b, then by Theorem (46.2) every associate of a divides every associate of b. Therefore, for any choice of representatives of these equivalence classes, an element a divides an element b in D if and only if the representative of the class containing a divides the representative of the class containing b. Thus, division in D is completely determined by the division of the representatives. For example, division in the domain of integers is determined by that of the non-negative integers since each equivalence class consists of a and $-a$ and therefore has a unique non-negative representative.

(46.4) Definition. An associate of e is called a *unit* of D.

The identity e is itself a unit, and since $(-e)(-e) = ee = e$, $-e$ is also a unit. By (46.2), the units of D divide every element of D.

(46.5) Theorem. An element $u \in D$ is a unit if and only if $u^{-1} \in D$.

PROOF. If u is a unit, u divides e, so that there exists a v in D such that $uv = vu = e$. Therefore $v = u^{-1}$. Conversely, if $u^{-1} \in D$, the relation $uu^{-1} = e$ says that u divides e. Since e divides every element of D, u and e are associates.

The reader will find other characterizations of the units of an integral domain in the exercises. In the examples of integral domains given in Section 45, the units of the integers are $+1$ and -1, while every non-zero element of a number field is a unit.

(46.6) Definition. An element $a \in D$ which is not zero and not a unit is called a *prime* or *irreducible element* of D if its only divisors are its associates and the units.

Since the discussion of division may be restricted to a canonical set of representatives of the equivalence classes of associated elements, it is often convenient to define a prime as an irreducible element of this set of representatives. Thus for the integers, primes are defined to be positive.

Elements other than zero, the units, and primes are called *composite*. Every composite element $a \in D$ has at least one factorization $a = bc$ where neither b nor c is a unit of D.

In order to prove that every composite element of an integral domain has a factorization as a product of primes which is unique (except, of course, for the order of the factors and for possible unit factors), it is necessary to make extra assumptions about the domain. For the integers, the natural ordering and the well-ordering principle are sufficient, as was indicated in the Introduction. The term *Unique Factorization Domain* is used for integral domains in which the complete factorization of composite elements is possible and unique. In domains, such as number fields, in which every non-zero element is a unit, the concepts of prime and composite have no significance.

Exercise (46.1). Prove that the relation of association is an equivalence relation.

Exercise (46.2). Prove that a is a unit of D if and only if a divides every element of D.

Exercise (46.3). Prove that a is a unit of D if and only if a divides $e \in D$.

Exercise (46.4). Prove that a and b are associates if and only if each is a unit multiple of the other.

Exercise (46.5). The set of numbers $a + bi$, where a and b are integers, is an integral domain. What are the units of this domain? Show that the set of all $a + bi$ with $a > 0$ and $b \geq 0$ is a set of representatives of the equivalence relation of association in this domain.

Exercise (46.6). Using (0.6) of the Introduction, show that every non-zero element of the ring of integers modulo a prime p is a unit.

Exercise (46.7). Prove that the units of D form a multiplicative group.

Section 47. Characteristic of an Integral Domain

Since the elements of a ring form an additive group, by Theorem (35.7) each element of a ring generates under addition a cyclic group which is either finite of order $m \geq 1$ or an infinite cyclic group, and the order of this cyclic group is the additive order of the generating element. There is an important classification of integral domains which is based on the additive order of the identity e of the domain.

(47.1) Definition. The *characteristic* of an integral domain D is the additive order of the identity element e.

The characteristic of any integral domain which contains the integers (for example, the integers, number fields) is infinite since a sum $1 + 1 + \cdots + 1$ is never zero. The identity element of the ring $J - (p)$, for p a prime, is the residue class $(p) + 1$, and $(p) + 1$ generates the additive group of this ring. Since this additive group has order p, the characteristic of this integral domain is p. By the following theorem, these examples exhaust the possibilities for the characteristic of an integral domain.

(47.2) Theorem. If the characteristic of an integral domain is finite, it is a prime.

PROOF. Assume that the characteristic $m \geq 1$ is composite. Then $m = rs$ where $1 < r < m$ and $1 < s < m$. Therefore

$$(re)(se) = (\overbrace{e + e + \cdots + e}^{r \text{ terms}})(\overbrace{e + e + \cdots + e}^{s \text{ terms}})$$

$$= \overbrace{e^2 + e^2 + \cdots + e^2}^{rs \text{ terms}}$$

$$= (rs)e^2 = (rs)e = me = 0.$$

But in an integral domain, $(re)(se) = 0$ implies that $re = 0$ or $se = 0$, and this contradicts the hypothesis that e has additive order m since $r < m$ and $s < m$. Therefore m is a prime.

(47.3) Theorem. In an integral domain, all non-zero elements have the same additive order, which is the characteristic of the domain.

PROOF. If $a \neq 0$, then $ka = k(ea) = (ke)a = 0$ if and only if $ke = 0$. Therefore the order of a is the same as the order of e.

(47.4) Theorem. The set of elements generated under addition by the identity e of an integral domain D is a subdomain of D. This subdomain is isomorphic to the ring J of integers or to the ring J_p of integers modulo a prime p, according as the characteristic of D is infinite or the prime p.

PROOF. We have remarked above that the set of elements generated by e is an additive group, and the closure of this set under multiplication follows from $(re)(se) = (rs)e$. By Exercise (45.4), this set is a subdomain of D, and its characteristic is that of D. This subdomain is a ring-homomorphic image of the integers under the mapping $k \to ke$ for all integers k. Therefore, if this subdomain has infinite characteristic, $ke = 0$ if and only if $k = 0$, and the correspondence is (1–1), that is, an isomorphism. If, on the other hand, D has characteristic p, $ke = 0$ for all k which are multiples of p, and the subdomain is isomorphic to the ring of integers modulo p by (44.7).

Exercise (47.1). Definition (47.1) may be given for any ring R with identity e. State and prove a theorem corresponding to (47.4) for rings with identity.

Exercise (47.2). For a general ring R, the characteristic m is defined to be the smallest positive integer such that $ma = 0$ for all $a \in R$. If no such integer exists, R is said to have infinite characteristic. Show that this definition is equivalent to (47.1) for rings with identity.

Exercise (47.3). Prove that in an integral domain of characteristic p, $(a + b)^p = a^p + b^p$.

Exercise (47.4). Prove that in any ring R, the subset of elements of finite additive order is an ideal of R.

Section 48. Order

Among the fundamental properties which we assumed for the integers in the Introduction was their natural ordering. We have seen that the integers form an integral domain, but this description of the integers concerns only those properties related to the operations of addition and multiplication and does not involve the concept of order. Therefore, our next step in discussing number systems is to consider the consequences of defining an order relation in an integral domain.

(48.1) Definition. An integral domain D is *ordered* by the relation $a < b$ (read "a is less than b") defined on D if the following conditions are satisfied:

(i) if $a,b \in D$, one, and only one, of the statements $a < b$, $a = b$, and $b < a$ is true;
(ii) if $a,b,c \in D$ and $a < b$, $b < c$, then $a < c$;
(iii) if $a,b \in D$ and $a < b$, then $a + c < b + c$ for all $c \in D$;
(iv) if $a,b,c \in D$ and $a < b$, $0 < c$, then $ac < bc$.

It is customary to use the notation $b > a$ (read "b is greater than a") to mean the same thing as $a < b$, and to use the notation $a \leq b$, or $b \geq a$, to mean that either $a < b$ or $a = b$. By condition (i), the relation is neither reflexive nor symmetric, although by (ii) it is assumed to be transitive. The order relation is linked to the operations in D by assumptions (iii) and (iv). These four postulates are all familiar properties of the natural order of the integers.

An element c in an ordered domain D is called *positive* if $c > 0$ and *negative* if $c < 0$. By (iii) of (48.1), $a < b$ if and only if $b - a$ is positive. The following theorem characterizes those integral domains which can be ordered.

(48.2) Theorem. Let P be any subset of an integral domain D. There exists an order relation $<$ in D for which the elements of P are positive if and only if P has the following properties:

(α) P is closed with respect to addition;
(β) P is closed with respect to multiplication;
(γ) If $c \in D$, one, and only one, of the statements $c = 0$, $c \in P$, $-c \in P$ is true.

PROOF. Let D be an integral domain ordered by the relation $<$, and let P be the set of positive elements. If $a,b \in P$, then $a > 0$ which implies that $a + b > 0 + b = b$ by (iii), and $b > 0$ which implies that $a + b > 0$ by (ii). Also $ab > 0 \cdot b = 0$ by (iv), proving (α) and (β). Since one, and only one, of the statements $c = 0$, $c < 0$, and $0 < c$ is true for $c \in D$, to prove (γ) it is only necessary to show that $c < 0$ if and only if $-c > 0$; this follows immediately from (iii).

Conversely, let P be any subset of an integral domain D which satisfies (α), (β), and (γ), and define for $a,b \in D$, $a < b$ if and only if $b - a \in P$. Then (i) follows immediately from (γ). If $a < b$ and $b < c$, then $b - a \in P$ and $c - b \in P$. By (α), $(b - a) + (c - b) =$

$c - a \in P$ and $a < c$, proving (ii). Since $b - a = (b + c) - (a + c)$ for all $c \in D$, condition (iii) is satisfied, and since $b - a \in P$ and $c \in P$ imply $(b - a)c = bc - ac \in P$, condition (iv) is satisfied. Finally P is the set of positive elements of this order relation, since $a > 0$ if and only if $a - 0 = a \in P$.

(48.3) Corollary. If D is an ordered domain and $0 \neq a \in D$, then $a^2 > 0$.

PROOF. If $a > 0$, then $a^2 = aa > 0$ by (β), and if $a < 0$, then $-a > 0$ and $a^2 = (-a)(-a) > 0$, using (β) and (43.3).

(48.4) Corollary. If D is an ordered domain, $e > 0$.

PROOF. This follows from (48.3) since $e \neq 0$ and $e = e^2$.

(48.5) Corollary. The characteristic of an ordered domain is infinite.

PROOF. If the characteristic of D were m, then $me = \overbrace{e + \cdots + e}^{m \text{ terms}} = 0$, while $e > 0$. This contradicts (α).

These corollaries show that the complex numbers cannot be ordered. For if the complex numbers were ordered by $<$, then $-1 < 0$ since $1 > 0$, while by (48.3), $-1 > 0$ since $-1 = i^2$. Also by (48.5), the integral domain J_p cannot be ordered. The usual order of the real numbers is an extension of the natural order of the integers and satisfies the conditions of (48.1). Therefore, all subdomains of the real numbers are ordered domains.

(48.6) Definition. Two ordered domains, D and D', are *order-isomorphic* if there exists a ring-isomorphism of D onto D' under which $a > b$ in D if and only if $a' > b'$ in D'.

(48.7) Theorem. Every ordered domain contains a subdomain which is order-isomorphic to the integers.

PROOF. We have shown that E, the subdomain of D generated by e, is ring-isomorphic to the integers with $e \leftrightarrow 1$. We will show that this is an order-isomorphism. The positive elements of E are finite sums of e with itself, and the positive integers are finite sums of the integer 1. Thus if $a > b$ in E, then $a - b > 0$ and $a - b = \overbrace{e + \cdots + e}^{k \text{ terms}}$. If $a \leftrightarrow a' \in J$ and $b \leftrightarrow b' \in J$, then $a - b \leftrightarrow a' - b' = \overbrace{1 + \cdots + 1}^{k \text{ terms}}$. Therefore $a' > b'$ in J. Since we may reverse this argument, the correspondence is an order-isomorphism.

Exercise (48.1). Prove that in an ordered domain

(a) $a < b$ and $c < d$ imply $a + c < b + d$,
(b) $a < b$ implies $ac > bc$ if $c < 0$,
(c) $a < b$ implies $-a > -b$,
(d) $a > e$ implies $a^2 > a$, and $0 < a < e$ implies $0 < a^2 < a$.

Exercise (48.2). In an ordered domain D we may define $|a|$ by $|a| = a$ if $a \geq 0$ and $|a| = -a$ if $a < 0$. Show that this is a single-valued function from D to the set of non-negative elements of D. Also show that $|a + b| \leq |a| + |b|$ and $|ab| = |a| \cdot |b|$ by examining the various possible cases.

Exercise (48.3). If $a > b > 0$ and if a^{-1} and b^{-1} exist in an ordered domain, prove that $a^{-1} < b^{-1}$.

Exercise (48.4). The set M of all complex numbers of the form $a + bi$, where a and b are integers, is an integral domain. Show that M is not an ordered domain with respect to the relation $\propto$ defined by:

$$a + bi \propto c + di \qquad \text{if either } a < c, \text{ or } a = c \text{ and } b < d.$$

Section 49. The Integers

In the present chapter, the concept of a ring has been systematically specialized by making additional assumptions on the elements of the ring. We have seen that all of these assumptions are familiar properties of the integers. The property which distinguishes the integers from other ordered domains is the well-ordering principle (0.1) which was seen in the Introduction to be the basis for several important theorems concerning the integers. Following our established pattern, we rephrase this well-ordering principle so that it is applicable to any ordered integral domain.

(49.1) Definition. An ordered integral domain is *integrally ordered* if every non-empty subset of the set P of positive elements contains a least element.

An element $a \in S \subseteq P$ is a least element of S if $a \leq b$ for all $b \in S$. In particular, P itself contains a least element, the least positive element in D, and this element is the identity $e \in D$. For let S be the set of all elements $m \in D$ such that $0 < m < e$, and assume that S is not empty. Then S contains a least element q by Definition (49.1). By (ii) and (iv) of Definition (48.1), $0 < q < e$ implies $0 < q^2 < q < e$. This implies that $q^2 \in S$ and $q^2 < q$, contradicting the assertion that q is the least element of S. Therefore, S is empty, and e is the least positive element of D.

(49.2) Theorem. Every integrally ordered domain is order-isomorphic to the integers.

PROOF. By Theorem (48.7) every integrally ordered domain D contains a subdomain E, generated by the identity $e \in D$, which is order-isomorphic to the integers. Thus the proof will be complete if we can show that $D = E$.

Let S be the set of positive elements of D which are not in E, and assume that S is not empty. Then by (49.1), S contains a least element, say a. Since $e \in E$, $a \neq e$, and therefore $a > e$ since e is the least positive element in D. Now $a - e > 0$ and $a - e \in S$. For if $a - e \in E$, then $(a - e) + e = a \in E$ which contradicts the choice of a. However, $a - (a - e) = e > 0$ implies $a - e < a$, and this contradicts the fact that a is the least member of S. Therefore, our original assumption that S is not empty is false, which means that every positive element of D is in E.

Now if b is any element of D, then $b = 0$, or $b > 0$, or $-b > 0$. In either of the first two cases $b \in E$, and if $-b > 0$, then $-b \in E$, and $-(-b) = b \in E$ since E is an integral domain. This completes the proof that $D = E$.

The meaning of Theorem (49.2) is that Definition (49.1) constitutes a complete algebraic characterization of the integers. For the integers, as we intuitively know them, form an integrally ordered domain, and it is a consequence of Theorem (49.2) that the properties of the operations of addition and multiplication and of the order relation in any integrally ordered domain are identical with those of the integers. Thus all algebraic properties of the integers are provable if we define them to be an integrally ordered domain. The theorems in the Introduction are examples of algebraic properties of the integers, but the number of digits in a particular notation for an integer is not an algebraic property since this number need not be preserved by order-isomorphism.

It was indicated in the Introduction that the integers could be constructed from a minimal set of postulates for the positive integers such as the Peano Postulates.* This definition of the integers based on the Peano Postulates is equivalent to the definition of the integers as an integrally ordered domain. For it may be shown that the integers as constructed from the Peano Postulates form an integrally ordered

*See B. L. van der Waerden, *Modern Algebra* (New York, 1949), I, 3.

domain, just as the positive elements in any integrally ordered domain satisfy the Peano Postulates. For example, we proved that the identity e is the least positive element in an integrally ordered domain, and this is just the statement that 1 is the least positive integer, which is one of the Peano Postulates.

Exercise (49.1). Give a non-empty set of rational numbers which has no least element.

Exercise (49.2). Show that the positive elements in an integrally ordered domain satisfy the Peano Postulates.

Exercise (49.3). For the integers written in the usual decimal notation, the following theorem is true: An integer is divisible by 9 if and only if the sum of its digits is divisible by 9. Is this an algebraic property of the integers?

Section 50. The Congruence of Integers

Calculations in the residue class ring $R-I$ of a ring R modulo I, where I is an ideal, are most conveniently expressed in terms of the equivalence relation on R defined by the partition of R into disjoint residue classes $a + I$. This relation, called *congruence modulo* I, is given by $a \equiv b(I)$ if and only if a and b are in the same residue class. Thus $a \equiv b(I)$ in R if and only if $a + I = b + I$ in $R-I$, and the calculations with congruences in R correspond to operations in the ring $R-I$.

(50.1) Theorem. If $a \equiv b(I)$ and $a' \equiv b'(I)$, then $a \pm a' \equiv b \pm b'(I)$ and $aa' \equiv bb'(I)$.

PROOF. By hypothesis, $a + I = b + I$ and $a' + I = b' + I$ in $R-I$. Therefore $(a \pm a') + I = [a + I] \pm [a' + I] = [b + I] \pm [b' + I] = (b \pm b') + I$, which means that $a \pm a' \equiv b \pm b'(I)$. Similarly $aa' + I = [a + I][a' + I] = [b + I][b' + I] = bb' + I$ and $aa' \equiv bb'(I)$.

(50.2) Corollary. If $a \equiv b(I)$, then $a \pm c \equiv b \pm c(I)$ and $ac \equiv bc(I)$ for every $c \in R$.

PROOF. Since $c \equiv c(I)$, the hypothesis of Theorem (50.1) is satisfied.

When we take the ring R to be the domain J of integers, the special properties of J enable us to characterize the congruence relation in terms of division. Many interesting divisibility properties of the integers are most easily stated and derived using the language of integral congruences. It is a consequence of the division algorithm (0.4), that the ideals in J are the sets (m) of all multiples of a positive integer m.

(50.3) Theorem. If a, b, and $m > 0$ are integers, then $a \equiv b(m)$ if and only if $a - b$ is divisible by m.

PROOF. Since $a \equiv b(m)$ means that $a + (m) = b + (m)$ in J_m, $a \equiv b(m)$ if and only if $a - b \in (m)$, or $a - b = km$ where k is an integer.

Because of this characterization of integral congruence, we say that a is congruent to b modulo m, where m is an integer, whenever $a \equiv b(m)$. In the remainder of this section, we will be working only with integral congruences. The cancellation law for such congruences is the following.

(50.4) Theorem. If $ca \equiv cb(m)$, then $a \equiv b(m/d)$ where d is the g.c.d. of c and m.

PROOF. We may write $c = c'd$ and $m = m'd$, where c' and m' are relatively prime. By hypothesis, $m = m'd$ divides $ca - cb = c(a - b) = c'd(a - b)$. Therefore, m' divides $c'(a - b)$, and since c' and m' are relatively prime, m' divides $a - b$ by (0.10). Thus $a \equiv b(m')$ where $m' = m/d$.

We next consider the problem of finding the solutions of the integral congruence $ax \equiv b(m)$. If the integer ξ is a solution, and if $\eta \equiv \xi(m)$, then $a\eta \equiv a\xi \equiv b(m)$ by Corollary (50.2), so that η is also a solution. It follows that every integer in the residue class $\xi + (m)$ is a solution, and that all these solutions may be represented by any member of the class. Therefore, the congruence is completely solved by giving a representative set of solutions $x_1, x_2, \cdots, x_s$ such that $x_i \not\equiv x_j(m)$, and such that if ξ is any solution, then $\xi \equiv x_k(m)$ for some $k = 1, 2, \cdots, s$. We say that $ax \equiv b(m)$ has exactly s incongruent solutions modulo m. In particular, if $s = 1$, we say that the congruence has a unique solution modulo m. The integers in a representative set of solutions of $ax \equiv b(m)$ are representatives of the residue classes which are the distinct solutions of the equation $[a + (m)]X = b + (m)$ in the ring J_m.

(50.5) Theorem. If a and m are relatively prime, the congruence $ax \equiv b(m)$ has a unique solution modulo m.

PROOF. By (0.6), there exist integers s and t such that $1 = sa + tm$. Then $b = bsa + btm$ and $a(bs) - b = (-bt)m$, which means that $abs \equiv b(m)$ by (50.3). Thus bs is a solution of $ax \equiv b(m)$. If ξ is any solution of the given congruence, it follows from (50.1) that

$a\xi - abs \equiv b - b \equiv 0(m)$ which may be written $a\xi \equiv abs(m)$. Using (50.4) with a and m relatively prime, we have $\xi \equiv bs(m)$. Therefore, there is only one integer in a representative set of solutions of the given congruence.

(50.6) Corollary. If a is not divisible by the prime p, the congruence $ax \equiv b(p)$ has a unique solution modulo p.

(50.7) Theorem. If d is the g.c.d of a and m, the congruence $ax \equiv b(m)$ has a solution if and only if d divides b. If d divides b, the congruence has exactly d incongruent solutions modulo m.

PROOF. We have $a = a'd$ and $m = m'd$ where a' and m' are relatively prime. If ξ is a solution of the congruence, then $a\xi - b = km$ by (50.3). Now $b = a\xi - km = a'd\xi - km'd = d(a'\xi - km')$, so that d divides b. Conversely, if d divides b, that is, $b = b'd$, consider the congruence $a'x \equiv b'(m')$. Since a' and m' are relatively prime, this congruence has a unique solution modulo m' by (50.5). If x_1 is such a solution, then x_1 represents a class of solutions of $a'x \equiv b'(m')$ which includes the integers

$$x_1,\ x_2 = x_1 + m',\ x_3 = x_1 + 2m',\ \cdots,\ x_d = x_1 + (d-1)m'.$$

Since $a'x_i \equiv b'(m')$, $a'x_i - b' = km'$, and, multiplying this equation by d, we obtain $ax_i - b = km$, or $ax_i \equiv b(m)$. Thus each x_i, $i = 1, 2, \cdots, d$, is a solution of the given congruence. We will show that this is a representative set of solutions.

If $x_i \equiv x_j(m)$ for $i \neq j$, say $i > j$, then

$$x_1 + (i-1)m' \equiv x_1 + (j-1)m'\ (m).$$

This means that $(i-j)m' \equiv 0(m)$ and $(i-j)m'$ is divisible by m. But $0 < i - j < d$, so that $0 < (i-j)m' < dm' = m$, which is a contradiction. Therefore, no two of the d solutions $x_1, x_2, \cdots, x_d$ are congruent modulo m. Finally, if ξ is any solution of $ax \equiv b(m)$, then $a'\xi \equiv b'(m')$, and $\xi \equiv x_1(m')$ by (50.5). Thus $\xi = x_1 + lm'$ for some integer l. By the division algorithm, $l = qd + r$ with $0 \leq r \leq d - 1$, and $\xi = x_1 + lm' = x_1 + qdm' + rm'$. Thus $\xi \equiv x_1 + rm' \equiv x_{r+1}(m)$.

EXAMPLE. To solve $36x \equiv 6\ (21)$, we first note that $36 \equiv 15\ (21)$ so that $36x \equiv 15x\ (21)$ for all x, and we may replace the given congruence by $15x \equiv 6\ (21)$. Since 3 is the g.c.d. of 15 and 21, and since 3 divides 6, there will be three solutions. As in the proof of (50.7) we first solve the congruence $5x \equiv 2\ (7)$ which has the unique solution represented by $x = 6$. Therefore, a representative set of solutions of $15x \equiv 6\ (21)$ is given by 6, $6 + 7 = 13$, and $6 + 2 \cdot 7 = 20$.

Exercise (50.1). Prove directly that congruence of integers is an equivalence relation, using (50.3) as the definition of congruence.

Exercise (50.2). Solve completely:

(a) $24x \equiv 17\ (31)$ (b) $15x \equiv 20\ (30)$
(c) $15x \equiv 20\ (35)$ (d) $243x \equiv 126\ (62)$.

Exercise (50.3). Prove that every non-zero element of J_p is a unit if p is a prime, using the methods of this section.

Exercise (50.4). Find the inverse of the class $4 + (m)$ if $m = 5$, if $m = 7$, and if $m = 13$.

Exercise (50.5). Prove that the residue classes $a + (m)$ with a prime to m form a multiplicative group.

Exercise (50.6). If p is a prime, show that $a^p \equiv a(p)$ for all integers a, and $a^{p-1} \equiv 1(p)$ if a is not divisible by p.

Exercise (50.7). Prove by induction on n that the congruences $x \equiv b_i(m_i)$, $i = 1, 2, \cdots, n$, have a unique solution $0 \leq x_i < m_1m_2 \cdots m_n$ if the m_i are relatively prime in pairs.

Section 51. Fields

A number field F, as defined in Section 22, is a commutative ring with identity element 1. Moreover, since $a/b \in F$ for all $a,b \neq 0 \in F$, every non-zero element $b \in F$ has an inverse $b^{-1} = 1/b \in F$ with respect to multiplication. The algebraic properties of addition and multiplication in a number field depend upon the foregoing description, and not upon the fact that the elements are complex numbers. We are led, therefore, to define a system with arbitrary elements which has these same algebraic properties.

(51.1) Definition. A *field* F is a commutative ring with an identity $e \neq 0$ such that every $a \neq 0$ in F has an inverse in F with respect to multiplication.

If a, b, c are elements of a field F and $a \neq 0$, then $ab = ac$ implies $b = c$, since we can multiply the given equation $ab = ac$ by $a^{-1} \in F$. Therefore, the cancellation law holds in F, and since $a^{-1} \in F$ for every $a \neq 0 \in F$, F is an integral domain in which each non-zero element is a unit. Thus, by Exercise (46.7), the non-zero elements of a field form an abelian group with respect to multiplication, so that the equations $bx = a$ and $yb = a$ for $b \neq 0$ have a unique solution $x = y = ab^{-1} = a/b \in F$. Therefore, division by a non-zero element is always possible in a field and is unique. This means that the concept of divisibility discussed in Section 46 loses its significance in a field, although other concepts studied for integral domains, such as the characteristic and order relations, do remain important in the discussion of fields.

It was pointed out in Section 22 that the results which had been obtained for matrices with complex number elements are valid for matrices with elements in any number field, since only the properties of the complex numbers as a number field had been used in obtaining these results. These properties are the algebraic properties referred to in the present section, and therefore the results of Chapters I and II can be extended to matrices with elements in an arbitrary field. In the same way, the results of Chapter III concerning sequence vector spaces $V_n(F)$ are valid for an arbitrary field F.

The ring J_p of integers modulo p, where p is a prime, is an integral domain of characteristic p and the calculations in this ring correspond to calculations with integral congruences. Since the congruence $ax \equiv 1(p)$ always has a solution if a is not divisible by p, each non-zero element of J_p has a multiplicative inverse, and J_p is a field.

A finite field must have prime characteristic p since the additive order of the identity element e cannot be infinite. Therefore, if F is a finite field, $pa = 0$ for all $a \in F$, and every element of F has an additive order which divides p. This implies that F has p^α elements for some integer $\alpha \geq 1$, for by Corollary (40.9) the order of the additive group of F is p^α.

If F is a finite field with p elements, then the subfield of F isomorphic to J_p by (47.4) must be F itself, so that there is one, and (up to isomorphism) only one, field with p elements. It can be shown that for every prime p and integer $\alpha \geq 1$, there exists one, and only one, field with p^α elements.

Exercise (51.1). Show that an integral domain in which every non-zero element is a unit is a field.

Exercise (51.2). Show that a set F with at least two elements is a field if the elements of F form an additive abelian group, if F is closed with respect to multiplication and the non-zero elements of F form a multiplicative abelian group, and if multiplication is distributive with respect to addition.

Exercise (51.3). Prove that a subset S of a field is a field if it contains at least two elements, if $a - b \in S$ for all $a,b \in S$, and if $a/b \in S$ for all $a,b \in S$, $b \neq 0$.

Exercise (51.4). Prove that every finite integral domain is a field.

Exercise (51.5). Show that the set of scalar matrices contained in the set of all n-rowed square matrices with elements in a field F form a subfield isomorphic to F.

Exercise (51.6). Let a be a non-zero element of a finite field F with p^α elements. Show that a has additive order p, and that a has multiplicative order n where n divides $p^\alpha - 1$.

Exercise (51.7). Construct fields with 2, 4, 5, and 8 elements by considering the possible addition and multiplication tables.

Section 52. The Field of Quotients of an Integral Domain

The remainder of this chapter will be devoted to the construction of the principal number systems of mathematics from the integers, which have been characterized in Section 49 as an integrally ordered domain. These number systems are the rational, real, and complex fields. Until now, we have assumed the existence of these well-known number systems along with their more familiar properties, many of which were included in their description as number fields. It is our purpose now to describe these number systems completely in terms of the integers and to prove their existence by construction.

The reader is familiar with the description of the rational numbers R as the set of quotients a/b of integers $a,b \neq 0$. We recall that the quotient a/b of elements $a,b \neq 0$ in an integral domain is defined as the solution of the equation $bx = a$. Thus, the construction of R involves inventing a field which contains the integers and which satisfies the above description. We will approach the problem more generally by showing that every integral domain D is contained in a field of quotients a/b of elements $a,b \neq 0$ in D.

In order to see how to define the operations in a field containing a given integral domain D, we first assume that such a field F does exist. Then for every pair of elements $a,b \neq 0$ in D, the quotient $a/b = ab^{-1}$ exists in F. Calculating with such quotients in the field F we obtain

$$\begin{aligned} a/b + c/d = ab^{-1} + cd^{-1} = adb^{-1}d^{-1} + bcb^{-1}d^{-1} &= (ad + bc)(b^{-1}d^{-1}) \\ &= (ad + bc)(bd)^{-1} = (ad + bc)/bd \end{aligned}$$

and

$$a/b \cdot c/d = (ab^{-1})(cd^{-1}) = (ac)(bd)^{-1} = ac/bd.$$

Since the numerators and denominators of these quotients are calculated in D, these formulas, which we recognize as the familiar rules for operating with fractions, indicate how to define the operations in the field which we will construct. This construction is carried out in the proof of the following theorem.

(52.1) Theorem. For every integral domain D there exists a field Q with the following properties:

(i) Q contains a subdomain D' which is isomorphic to D;
(ii) Q is the set of all quotients a'/b' of elements a' and $b' \neq 0$ in D';
(iii) if F is any field which contains a subdomain $\bar{D}$ isomorphic to D, then the set of quotients $\bar{a}/\bar{b}$ in F of elements $\bar{a},\bar{b} \neq 0$ in $\bar{D}$ is a subfield of F which is isomorphic to Q.

PROOF. Let M be the set of all ordered pairs (a,b) of elements a and $b \neq 0$ in D. The pair (a,b) will play a role analogous to that of the rational number a/b for integers a and b. We define an equivalence relation $\sim$ on M by $(a,b) \sim (c,d)$ if and only if $ad = bc$ in D. Both the commutativity of D and the fact that D has no zero-divisors are needed in the proof that this is an equivalence relation, the details of which are left to the reader. We will show that the equivalence classes $U_{(a,b)}$ of this relation form a field under suitably defined operations, and this will be the field Q with the desired properties.

Addition in Q is defined by

$$U_{(a,b)} + U_{(c,d)} = U_{(ad+bc,bd)}.$$

Since $b \neq 0$ and $d \neq 0$ in D imply $bd \neq 0$, the pair $(ad + bc,bd)$ is an element of M, and $U_{(ad+bc,bd)}$ is an equivalence class which is uniquely determined by the representatives (a,b) and (c,d) of the classes $U_{(a,b)}$ and $U_{(c,d)}$. But since addition must be a binary relation on the set Q of equivalence classes, we must show that this sum class is uniquely determined by the *classes* $U_{(a,b)}$ and $U_{(c,d)}$. We will do this by showing that the sum class is independent of the choice of representatives of the summands. Suppose therefore that $(a',b') \in U_{(a,b)}$ and $(c',d') \in U_{(c,d)}$, so that $U_{(a',b')} = U_{(a,b)}$ and $U_{(c',d')} = U_{(c,d)}$. By the above definition $U_{(a',b')} + U_{(c',d')} = U_{(a'd'+b'c',b'd')}$. Since $(a',b') \sim (a,b)$, $a'b = b'a$, and since $(c',d') \sim (c,d)$, $c'd = d'c$. Therefore, $(a'd' + b'c')bd = a'bd'd + c'db'b = b'ad'd + d'cb'b = (ad + bc)b'd'$, so that $(a'd' + b'c',b'd') \sim (ad + bc,bd)$ and $U_{(a'd'+b'c',b'd')} = U_{(ad+bc,bd)}$.

The next step is to show that Q is an abelian group with respect to the operation of addition. The reader may verify the associative and commutative laws, that the class $U_{(0,e)} = U_{(0,b)}$ for all $b \neq 0$ in D is the zero class, and that $U_{(-a,b)}$ is the negative of $U_{(a,b)}$.

Multiplication in Q is defined by

$$U_{(a,b)} \times U_{(c,d)} = U_{(ac,bd)}.$$

Just as for addition, it must be verified that multiplication is a binary operation on the classes, which are the elements of Q. This follows from the fact that if $(a',b') \sim (a,b)$ and $(c',d') \sim (c,d)$ then $(a'c',b'd') \sim (ac,bd)$. Again it may be shown that multiplication is associative and commutative, and that it is distributive with respect to addition. The class $U_{(e,e)} = U_{(a,a)}$ for all $a \neq 0$ in D is the identity element, and if $U_{(a,b)}$ is not the zero class, then $a \neq 0$, so that $U_{(b,a)}$ is in Q and is the inverse of the class $U_{(a,b)}$. This completes the proof that Q is a field.

Let D' be the subset of Q consisting of all classes $U_{(a,e)}$ where e is the identity element of D. The reader may verify that the correspondence f defined by $f(a) = U_{(a,e)}$ is an isomorphism of D onto D'. Therefore, D' is an integral domain, a subdomain of Q. Since Q is a field containing D', the quotient of two elements of D' is in Q. Moreover, every element of Q is a quotient of elements of D', since every element $U_{(a,b)} \in Q$ is the solution $U_{(a,e)}/U_{(b,e)}$ of an equation $U_{(b,e)} \times X = U_{(a,e)}$ in D'.

Finally, let F be any field which contains a subdomain $\bar{D}$ isomorphic to D. Let this isomorphism be defined by $g(a) = \bar{a} \in \bar{D}$ for all $a \in D$. Then the correspondence h, defined by $h(U_{(a,b)}) = g(a)/g(b) = \bar{a}/\bar{b} \in F$ for all $U_{(a,b)} \in Q$, is an isomorphism of Q onto the set of all quotients $\bar{a}/\bar{b}$ in F of elements $\bar{a},\bar{b} \neq 0$ in $\bar{D}$.

We call a theorem of the type of (52.1) an *embedding theorem.* Such theorems prove the existence of an algebraic system with preassigned properties which contains a subsystem isomorphic to a given system. In this case the given system was the integral domain D. Algebraically, this is all that is required of the construction, but it is possible to prove a general replacement theorem which asserts the existence of an algebraic system which is isomorphic to the one constructed and which actually contains the given system [see Exercise (52.9)]. Using this result, Theorem (52.1) may be restated in the following simpler form.

(52.2) Theorem. Every integral domain D is contained in a quotient field Q which is the smallest field containing D and which is uniquely determined up to isomorphism.

If we take D to be the domain J of integers, then Theorem (52.1) gives the construction of the rational numbers from the integers, and we may therefore define the rational numbers to be the quotient field of the domain of integers.

Since the quotient field Q is the smallest field containing D, we have at once the following corollary.

(52.3) Corollary. If D is a field, D is identical with its quotient field Q.

As an example, the quotient field of J_p is again J_p since J_p is a field.

(52.4) Theorem. A field of infinite characteristic contains a subfield isomorphic to the field R of rational numbers, and a field of characteristic p contains a subfield isomorphic to J_p, the ring of integers modulo p.

PROOF. Every field F contains an integral domain D generated by the identity $e \in F$ and hence contains the quotient field of D. If F has infinite characteristic, D is isomorphic to the integers by (47.4) and its quotient field is isomorphic to the field of rational numbers. If F has characteristic p, D is isomorphic to J_p by (47.4), and J_p is itself a field.

A *prime field* is a field which contains no proper subfields. Theorem (52.4) shows that every field contains a unique prime field, and that the only prime fields are R and the J_p.

Exercise (52.1). Prove that $(a,b) \sim (c,d)$ if and only if $ad = bc$ is an equivalence relation on M.

Exercise (52.2). Complete the details of the proof that Q is a field.

Exercise (52.3). Verify that the correspondences f and h are isomorphisms.

Exercise (52.4). Show that the construction of Q can be carried out for the even integers. Hence, the assumption that $e \in D$ is unnecessary.

Exercise (52.5). Prove that under an isomorphism of two fields, their prime fields correspond.

Exercise (52.6). Let D be an ordered domain. Show that each equivalence class $U_{(a,b)}$ in the proof of Theorem (52.1) has a representative (a,b) with $b > 0$. Using such representatives, prove that the relation $U_{(a,b)} > U_{(c,d)}$ if and only if $ad > bc$ in D is an order relation on Q. This is the way the order of the rational numbers is defined from the natural ordering of the integers.

Exercise (52.7). Show that the order relation defined in the previous exercise is the only order relation that can be defined on Q which coincides on the subdomain D with the given order relation in D. This proves that the usual order relation of the rational numbers is uniquely defined by the natural ordering of the integers.

Exercise (52.8). Prove that every ordered field contains a subfield which is order-isomorphic to the rational numbers.

Exercise (52.9). Let R and S be rings which have no elements in common, and let R contain a subring R' which is isomorphic to S. Let S' consist of all elements of S together with all elements of R which are not in R'. Define operations in S' so that S' is a ring isomorphic to R which contains S as a subring. This is the general replacement theorem mentioned in the text.

Section 53. The Real Numbers

In the preceding section, we defined the rational number field R to be the quotient field of the domain of integers J. Thus R is a uniquely defined field which is uniquely ordered by a natural extension of the order in J [see Exercises (52.6) and (52.7)]. We will see in the next section that it is possible to give a simple algebraic construction of the field of complex numbers C, assuming that the real field $R^{\#}$ is known. In this section, we will give a characterization of $R^{\#}$ and briefly outline the construction* of $R^{\#}$ from R.

By a characterization of $R^{\#}$ is meant a set of properties which provide a basis for the accepted theorems concerning the real numbers, and which distinguish $R^{\#}$ from other number systems. The characterization given here is based on the following three definitions.

(53.1) Definition. An ordered field F is called *Archimedean* if for every $a \in F$, there exists a positive integer n such that $ne > a$, where e is the identity of multiplication in F.

(53.2) Definition. The sequence $\{a_m\} = \{a_1, a_2, \cdots, a_m, \cdots\}$ of elements a_m in an ordered field F is called *fundamental*, if for every positive element $b \in F$, there exists a positive integer t such that $|a_i - a_j| < b$ for all $i > t$, $j > t$.

(53.3) Definition. The element $a \in F$ is a *limit of the sequence* $\{a_m\}$ in an ordered field F if for every positive $b \in F$ there exists a positive integer t such that $|a_i - a| < b$ for all $i > t$.

The real number system is characterized by saying that it is an Archimedean ordered field in which every fundamental sequence of elements in the field has a limit in the field. This description uniquely determines $R^{\#}$ since it may be shown that any two algebraic systems which satisfy this description are order-isomorphic. It should be noted that this characterization of $R^{\#}$ involves the concept of the limit of a sequence which is usually classified as a nonalgebraic concept.

The rational numbers form an Archimedean ordered field, but

* See B. L. van der Waerden, *Modern Algebra* (New York, 1949), I, Sec. 67.

there are fundamental sequences of rational numbers which do not have a rational limit. For example, if the sequence $\{1, 1.4, 1.41, 1.414, \cdots\}$, generated by the usual process for approximating a number whose square is 2, had a limit α in R, then $\alpha^2 = 2$. But it is not hard to show that there is no rational number whose square is 2 [see Exercise (53.1)].

The construction of $R^\#$ from R may be based on the notion of a fundamental sequence in the following way. Let S be the set of all fundamental sequences of elements in R. Addition and multiplication are defined in S by $\{a_m\} + \{b_m\} = \{a_m + b_m\}$ and $\{a_m\} \cdot \{b_m\} = \{a_m b_m\}$, and it may be shown that S is a ring with respect to these operations. The set N of all fundamental sequences which have zero as a limit (null sequences) is an ideal in S, and the residue class ring $S-N$ is a field. Those residue classes which contain a constant sequence $\{a\} = \{a, a, \cdots, a, \cdots\}$ form an ordered subfield of $S-N$ which is order-isomorphic to R by the correspondence $N + \{a\} \leftrightarrow a$. Order in $S-N$ can then be defined as an extension of the order in this subfield in such a way that $S-N$ satisfies the description of $R^\#$ given above.

The real numbers are usually written as infinite decimals $n.a_1a_2 \cdots$, where n is an integer and the a_i are digits between 0 and 9. This decimal stands for the fundamental sequence of rational numbers $\{n, n + a_1/10, n + a_1/10 + a_2/100, \cdots\}$, and every residue class in $S-N$ may be represented by a sequence of this type. In this notation, the rational numbers are the repeating decimals (for example, $2/7 = 0.285714\,285714 \cdots$).

A fundamental theorem concerning real numbers states that every non-empty set of real numbers bounded from above has a least upper bound, that is, a bound which is less than or equal to every other bound. Any ordered field for which this theorem holds satisfies the characterization of $R^\#$ which we have given, and in fact $R^\#$ is often characterized in terms of this statement on least upper bounds.

Analytic geometry is based on the fact that the points of a line may be designated by real number coordinates. The field $R^\#$ is the only number system which can be put into (1–1) correspondence with the points of a line in such a way that the difference between two numbers can be used to measure the directed distance between any two points. This (1–1) correspondence is the basis for the Cartesian coordinate systems in two- and three-dimensional space, and for this reason, $R^\#$ is the number system underlying most applications of mathematics to the physical world.

Exercise (53.1). Prove that $\sqrt{2}$ is not a rational number.

Exercise (53.2). Find the first three digits in the infinite decimal form of the following real numbers:

(a) $\sqrt{5}$, (b) $3/8$, (c) $2 - \sqrt{3}$, (d) $\sqrt[3]{3}$.

Exercise (53.3). Prove that the real number a is a rational number if and only if it is a repeating decimal.

Exercise (53.4). Write the following repeating decimals as ordinary fractions:

(a) $.37500 \cdots$, (b) $.066 \cdots$, (c) $.2727 \cdots$, (d) $.51325132 \cdots$.

Exercise (53.5). Which of the following sequences of real numbers are fundamental?

(a) $1, 1, 1, \cdots;$
(b) $2, -2, 2, \cdots, (-1)^{n+1}2, \cdots;$
(c) $1, 1/2, 1/3, \cdots, 1/n, \cdots;$
(d) $1/2, 2/3, 3/4, \cdots, n/(n+1), \cdots;$
(e) $3 + 1, 3 - 1/2, 3 + 1/3, \cdots, 3 + (-1)^{n+1}/n, \cdots;$
(f) $a, a + d, a + 2d, \cdots, a + (n-1)d, \cdots$ where $d \neq 0$;
(g) $5, 5/3, 5/9, \cdots, 5/3^{n-1}, \cdots;$
(h) $a, ar, ar^2, \cdots, ar^{n-1}, \cdots$, where $|r| < 1$;
(i) $a, ar, ar^2, \cdots, ar^{n-1}, \cdots$, where $|r| > 1$.

Exercise (53.6). Find the limits of the fundamental sequences of of the preceding exercise.

Exercise (53.7). Prove that b is a least upper bound of the set of real numbers S if and only if

(i) $b \geq a$ for all $a \in S$,

and

(ii) if $c < b$, there exists an $a \in S$ such that $a > c$.

Exercise (53.8). Prove that a bounded monotonic nondecreasing sequence of real numbers, that is, a sequence $\{a_i\}$ such that $a_1 \leq a_2 \leq \cdots \leq a_n \leq \cdots \leq M$, is fundamental. Using the fact that every fundamental sequence of real numbers has a real limit, prove that if L is the limit of the sequence $\{a_i\}$, then $L \leq M$ and $L \geq a_i$ for every i.

Exercise (53.9). Using the result of the preceding exercise, prove the comparison test for the convergence of infinite series.

Exercise (53.10). Prove that the addition of fundamental sequences is a binary operation on S, and that S is an abelian group with respect to addition.

Exercise (53.11). If $\{a_m\}$ is a fundamental sequence of elements of R, prove that there exists an integer M such that $|a_m| < M$ for all terms a_m. [*Hint:* $|a_m| = |a_m - a_n + a_n| \leq |a_m - a_n| + |a_n|$. Thus $|a_m| < b + |a_n|$ for suitable b, n, all $m > n$.]

Exercise (53.12). Prove that the multiplication of sequences is a binary operation on S. [*Hint:* Choose N so that $|a_m| \leq M$, $|b_m| \leq M$, $|a_i - a_j| < r/2M$, $|b_i - b_j| < r/2M$ for all $i > N$, $j > N$. Then $|a_ib_i - a_jb_j| \leq |a_ib_i - a_jb_i| + |a_jb_i - a_jb_j| < r$.]

Exercise (53.13). Show that the multiplication of sequences is associative, and is distributive with respect to addition.

Exercise (53.14). Prove that the null sequences form an ideal in S.

Exercise (53.15). Prove that the residue classes $N + \{a\}$ form a subring of $S - N$ which is isomorphic to R. Define order in this subring.

Exercise (53.16). Define $\{a_m\} > 0$ in S if there exists $t > 0$ in F and an integer n such that $a_m > t$ for all $m > n$. Show that if $\{a_m\} > 0$, all sequences in $N + \{a_m\}$ are positive, and that this orders $S - N$.

Exercise (53.17). Show that if T is the set of all fundamental sequences of elements of $R^\#$, the residue class ring of T modulo the null sequences is isomorphic to $R^\#$. This means that $R^\#$ cannot be extended by this process.

Section 54. Complex Numbers

One of the consequences of the defining properties of the real numbers is that for odd n, each real number has exactly one real nth root, and for even n, each positive real number has exactly two real nth roots. However, if n is even and $a \in R^\#$ is negative, the equation $x^n = a$ has no solution in $R^\#$. For if x_1 is any element of $R^\#$, $x_1{}^n = x_1{}^{2k} = (x_1{}^k)^2 \geq 0$ by (48.3), and hence $x_1{}^n$ cannot be equal to the negative number a.

The system of complex numbers C is characterized by saying that C is the smallest field containing $R^\#$ and an element, called i, which is a solution of the equation $x^2 = -1$. We will see that this description of C implies that each complex number has n distinct complex nth roots. It may further be shown by methods involving the study of functions of a complex variable that all of the roots of a polynomial equation with coefficients in C are in C.

If F is any field containing $R^\#$ and an element i which is a solution of $x^2 = -1$, then F contains all elements of the form $a + bi$ with $a,b \in R^\#$. The algebraic identities satisfied by the operations in F imply that $(a + bi) + (c + di) = (a + c) + (b + d)i$ and $(a + bi)(c + di) = (ac - bd) + (ad + bc)i$, which are the familiar rules for the complex number operations. This indicates how to define addition and multiplication in the construction of C from $R^{\#}$ given by the following theorem.

(54.1) Theorem. The set C of all ordered pairs (a,b) of real numbers, with addition and multiplication defined by

$$(a,b) + (c,d) = (a + c,\ b + d)$$
$$(a,b) \cdot (c,d) = (ac - bd,\ ad + bc),$$

is the smallest field containing $R^{\#}$ and an element i which satisfies the equation $x^2 = -1$.

PROOF. It is routine to check that the set of pairs is a field with respect to these operations, the identities of the operations being consequences of the operational rules in $R^{\#}$. The pair $(0,0)$ is the zero element and $(1,0)$ is the identity element. The multiplicative inverse of the non-zero pair (a,b) is the pair $[a/(a^2 + b^2),\ -b/(a^2 + b^2)]$.

The subset of pairs $(a,0)$ with second component zero is a subfield of C isomorphic to $R^{\#}$ by the correspondence f defined by $f(a) = (a,0)$.

In this construction the equation $x^2 = -1$ assumes the form $(1,0)x^2 = (-1,0)$, and the element i is the pair $(0,1)$ which is seen to satisfy the equation by direct substitution.

Finally if F is any field containing $R^{\#}$ and an element i such that $i^2 = -1$, then the subset of F consisting of all elements of the form $a + bi$ with $a,b \in R^{\#}$ is isomorphic to C under the correspondence g defined by $g(a + bi) = (a,b)$. This proves that C is the smallest field with the required properties.

If we use the notation $a + bi$ for the number pair $(a,b) = (a,0) + (b,0)(0,1)$, we obtain the customary notation for the elements of the field C of complex numbers and the rules for equality, addition, and multiplication assume their familiar form. The complex numbers can be represented geometrically as the points of a plane in which we have introduced Cartesian coordinates. For there is a (1–1) correspondence between the points of a plane and pairs (a,b) of real numbers, and the number pair (a,b) is the representation of the complex number $a + bi$ given in the above construction.

This geometric representation of the complex numbers is the basis for another notation for the complex numbers which is the one most convenient to use in studying the multiplication of complex numbers. Every point $(a,b) \neq (0,0)$ has a unique pair of polar coordinates ρ and θ, $\rho > 0$ and $0 \leq \theta < 2\pi$, where $\rho = \sqrt{a^2 + b^2}$ and $\theta = \arctan b/a$. (See

Figure 4.) Since $a = \rho \cos \theta$ and $b = \rho \sin \theta$, we may write

$$a + bi = \rho(\cos \theta + i \sin \theta).$$

This, together with $0 = 0(\cos 0 + i \sin 0)$, gives every complex number a unique representation in its *trigonometric form.*

(54.2) Definition. The number $\rho = \sqrt{a^2 + b^2}$ is called the *modulus* or *absolute value* of the complex number $a + bi$ and is written $|a + bi|$. Also, $\theta = \arctan b/a$ is called the *argument* or *amplitude* of $a + bi$ and is written Amp $(a + bi)$.

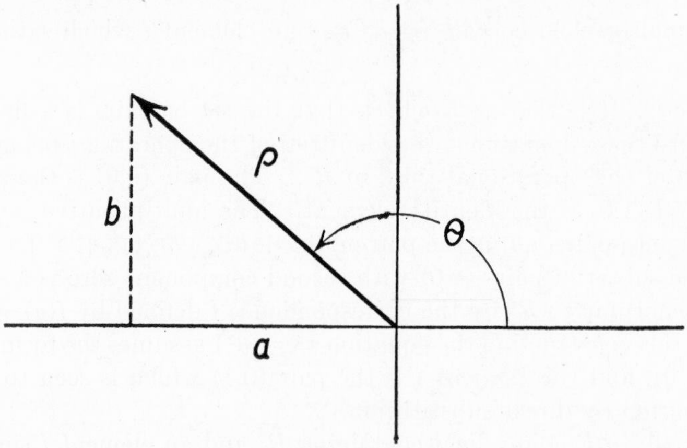

Fig. 4

The following theorem gives the rule for the multiplication of complex numbers written in trigonometric form. Let z_1 and z_2 be any two complex numbers, where $z_1 = a_1 + b_1i = \rho_1(\cos \theta_1 + i \sin \theta_1)$ and $z_2 = a_2 + b_2i = \rho_2(\cos \theta_2 + i \sin \theta_2)$.

(54.3) Theorem. $|z_1z_2| = |z_1| \cdot |z_2|$ and Amp $(z_1z_2) =$ Amp $z_1 +$ Amp z_2.

PROOF. Both properties follow from the calculation

$$\begin{aligned} z_1z_2 &= \rho_1(\cos \theta_1 + i \sin \theta_1) \cdot \rho_2(\cos \theta_2 + i \sin \theta_2) \\ &= \rho_1\rho_2[(\cos \theta_1 \cos \theta_2 - \sin \theta_1 \sin \theta_2) \\ &\qquad + i(\sin \theta_1 \cos \theta_2 + \sin \theta_2 \cos \theta_1)] \\ &= \rho_1\rho_2[\cos(\theta_1 + \theta_2) + i \sin (\theta_1 + \theta_2)]. \end{aligned}$$

(54.4) Corollary (DeMoivre's Formula). If $z = \rho(\cos \theta + i \sin \theta) \neq 0$, then $z^n = \rho^n(\cos n\theta + i \sin n\theta)$ for integral n.

PROOF. The calculation in Theorem (54.3) can be extended to any number of factors by induction. Thus if n is a positive integer,

$|z^n| = |z|^n$ and Amp $z^n = n \cdot$ Amp z, or $z^n = \rho^n(\cos n\theta + i \sin n\theta)$. If $z \neq 0$, $z^0 = 1 = \rho^0(\cos 0 + i \sin 0)$, proving the formula for $n = 0$. Finally, if $z \neq 0$, the complex number $z' = \rho^{-1}[\cos(-\theta) + i \sin(-\theta)]$ exists, and $z' = z^{-1}$ since $zz' = z'z = 1$. Therefore, if $n < 0$, $n = -m$ for $m > 0$, and $z^n = z^{-m} = (z^m)^{-1} = [\rho^m(\cos m\theta + i \sin m\theta)]^{-1} = \rho^{-m}[\cos(-m\theta) + i \sin(-m\theta)] = \rho^n(\cos n\theta + i \sin n\theta)$, proving the formula for negative integers.

In the proof of (54.3), $\theta_1 + \theta_2$ may be greater than 2π, so that z_1z_2 may not be written in its unique trigonometric form with Amp $(z_1z_2) < 2\pi$. However, $\rho[\cos(\theta + k\,2\pi) + i \sin(\theta + k\,2\pi)] = \rho(\cos\theta + i \sin\theta)$ for all integers k since the corresponding points in the plane coincide, so that multiples of 2π may be added to or subtracted from the amplitude of a complex number. This use of alternate trigonometric representations of a complex number is necessary in the consideration of the following problem.

Let r be any integer and s be a positive integer. Then $z^{r/s}$ stands for any complex number z' such that $(z')^s = z^r$. If $z = \rho(\cos\theta + i \sin\theta)$, then any complex number of the form

$$\sqrt[s]{\rho^r}\left[\cos\left(\frac{r\theta + k2\pi}{s}\right) + i \sin\left(\frac{r\theta + k2\pi}{s}\right)\right],$$

where $\sqrt[s]{\rho^r}$ is the positive real sth root of ρ^r, has the property that its sth power is equal to z^r by (54.4). Specifically, if $r = 1$, $z^{1/s}$ is called an *sth root* of z.

(54.5) Theorem. Every complex number $z \neq 0$ has s distinct sth roots.

PROOF. Consider the s numbers

$$z_k = \sqrt[s]{\rho}\left[\cos\left(\frac{\theta + k2\pi}{s}\right) + i \sin\left(\frac{\theta + k2\pi}{s}\right)\right]$$

for $k = 0, 1, 2, \cdots, s - 1$. Since $(z_k)^s = z$ for all k, each is an sth root of z. Further for $k = 0, 1, \cdots, s - 1$, the amplitudes θ/s, $(\theta + 2\pi)/s, \cdots, [\theta + (s-1)2\pi]/s$ are different, so that these are s distinct complex numbers. Now let $z' = \rho'(\cos\theta' + i \sin\theta')$ be any complex number written with $0 \leq \theta' < 2\pi$ such that $(z')^s = z$. Then $(\rho')^s = \rho$, and $\rho' = \sqrt[s]{\rho}$ since $\rho' > 0$. Also the angle $s\theta'$ must be coincident with θ, so that $s\theta' = \theta + k2\pi$ and $\theta' = (\theta + k2\pi)/s$ for some integer k. But since $0 \leq \theta' < 2\pi$, k is less than s. Therefore, $z' = z_k$ for some $k = 0, 1, \cdots, s - 1$, and every sth root of z is one of the complex numbers $z_0, z_1, \cdots, z_{s-1}$.

(54.6) Corollary. If n is a positive integer, there are n distinct nth roots of unity, given by

$$\cos\frac{k2\pi}{n} + i\sin\frac{k2\pi}{n}, \qquad \text{for } k = 0, 1, \cdots, n-1.$$

The field C of complex numbers contains a solution for every polynomial equation with coefficients in C, and we express this fact by saying that C is algebraically closed. Moreover, C is analytically closed, that is, every fundamental sequence* of complex numbers has a limit in C. Thus, the fundamental problems of both algebra and analysis are capable of solution in C, and C cannot be enlarged by either of the methods we have used in constructing C from $R^\#$ and $R^\#$ from R. For these reasons, the field C of complex numbers is the largest number field.

Exercise (54.1). Discuss the solution of the equations $ax + b = 0$ and $ax^2 + bx + c = 0$ where $a,b,c \in C$.

Exercise (54.2). Find a rule for adding complex numbers graphically. Show graphically that $|z_1 + z_2| \le |z_1| + |z_2|$.

Exercise (54.3). Compute $(1 + i)^4$ and $(3 - 7i)^3$ both by DeMoivre's formula and by the binomial theorem.

Exercise (54.4). Find $z_1^2z_2$, $1/z_2$, and $(z_1/z_2)^2$ where

(a) $z_1 = 5(\cos 273° + i \sin 273°)$, $z_2 = 3(\cos 43° + i \sin 43°)$;
(b) $z_1 = 4 - 4i$, $z_2 = 3i$;
(c) $z_1 = -2 + i$, $z_2 = 3 - i$.

Express the answers to parts (b) and (c) in the form $a + bi$.

Exercise (54.5). Find all square roots of i, $-i$, $1 + i$, and $5 - 3i$

(a) by using DeMoivre's formula;
(b) by assuming a square root $a + bi$ and determining a and b.

Exercise (54.6). Find all complex numbers z such that

(a) $z^3 = -1$, (b) $z^5 = 1 - i$, (c) $z^6 = -4 - 2i$,
(d) $z^{2/3} = 1$, (e) $z^{-3/4} = i$, (f) $z^{6/5} = -1 + i$.

Exercise (54.7). Find all third, fourth, fifth, sixth, and eighth roots of 1.

---

* We have given the definition of a fundamental sequence only in an ordered field, but it may be given in any field in which it is possible to define an absolute value.

Exercise (54.8). Prove that the points which correspond to the nth roots of a complex number lie equally spaced on a circle with center at the origin.

Exercise (54.9). Show that a positive real number cannot have more than two real nth roots.

Exercise (54.10). Prove DeMoivre's formula for rational n.

Exercise (54.11). Prove that the nth roots of unity form a cyclic group under multiplication.

Exercise (54.12). Define a fundamental sequence of complex numbers. Define a null sequence.

Exercise (54.13). Find the limit of the sequence

$$\{a_n\} = \left\{\frac{(n+1) + n^2 i}{n^3}\right\}.$$

Exercise (54.14). If $z = a + bi$ is a complex number, the complex number $\bar{z} = a - bi$ is called the *conjugate* of z. Prove that the correspondence f defined by $f(z) = \bar{z}$ is a ring-automorphism of C.

Section 55. Abstract Vector Spaces

As has been mentioned before, the only properties of a number field which were used in Chapters I, II, and III in our discussion of matrices and sequence vector spaces are the algebraic properties which are assumed for every field F in Definition (51.1). Therefore the results of Chapter III are valid for sequence vector spaces $V_n(F)$ with components in an arbitrary field F, and in this section we will refer to $V_n(F)$ and the results of Chapter III in this more general sense.

Since the operations of addition and scalar multiplication in $V_n(F)$ are the previously defined matrix operations, the algebraic properties of $V_n(F)$ are consequences of the matrix results of Chapters I and II. In the same way that we abstracted the essential properties of a group of transformations to define an abstract group in Chapter IV, we now use the sequence vector space with components in a field F as a model in defining an abstract vector space over F as a set of elements closed with respect to addition and scalar multiplication by elements of F.

(55.1) Definition. A *vector space V over a field F* is an abelian group with respect to an addition $\oplus$ for which there is a scalar multiplication $\cdot$ such that if $\alpha,\beta \in V$ and $c,d \in F$, then:

(i) $c \cdot \alpha$ is a unique element of V;
(ii) $(cd) \cdot \alpha = c \cdot (d \cdot \alpha)$;
(iii) $(c + d) \cdot \alpha = c \cdot \alpha \oplus d \cdot \alpha$;
(iv) $c \cdot (\alpha \oplus \beta) = c \cdot \alpha \oplus c \cdot \beta$;
(v) $e \cdot \alpha = \alpha$, where e is the identity of multiplication in F.

The reader should compare the properties assumed for V in this definition with the properties of $V_n(F)$ listed in (24.2). As in sequence spaces, the elements of V are called *vectors*. A *subspace* S of V is a non-empty subset of V closed with respect to the operations of addition and scalar multiplication defined for V. Again, as in $V_n(F)$, S is a subspace if and only if S is a non-empty subset of V such that $c \cdot \alpha + d \cdot \beta$ is in S for every $\alpha,\beta \in S$ and $c,d \in F$. The wide variety of examples of vector spaces is indicated by the following selection.

EXAMPLE 1. $V_n(F)$ as well as every subspace S of $V_n(F)$, is a vector space over F.

EXAMPLE 2. The set ${}_m\mathfrak{A}_n$ of all m by n matrices with elements in a field F with the matrix operations of addition and scalar multiplication is a vector space over F.

EXAMPLE 3. The set of all polynomials in a variable x with coefficients in a field F is a vector space with respect to polynomial addition and multiplication by a scalar in F.

EXAMPLE 4. The set of all real-valued functions defined at every point of the closed interval $[a,b]$ with addition $f \oplus g$ and scalar multiplication $c \cdot f$ for $c \in R^\#$ defined by

$$(f \oplus g)(x) = f(x) + g(x); \; (c \cdot f)(x) = cf(x)$$

for all $x \in [a,b]$ is a vector space over $R^\#$. The subset S of continuous functions is a subspace.

EXAMPLE 5. The elements of a field F form a vector space over F if we take the vector addition and scalar multiplication to be the operations of addition and multiplication in the field.

The definition of a finite linearly dependent set of vectors in V is the same as that given in (25.1) for $V_n(F)$. An infinite set M of vectors in V is said to be a linearly dependent set if M contains a finite subset which is a linearly dependent set. Otherwise, M is a linearly independent set. Thus M is a linearly independent set if and only if every finite subset of M is linearly independent. These definitions are necessary in an abstract vector space V, since there may exist no integer $n \geq 0$ such that every set of $n + 1$ vectors in V is linearly dependent.

In Example 3, the polynomials $1, x, x^2, \cdots, x^n, \cdots$ are linearly independent since any finite relation $c_0 + c_1x + c_2x^2 + \cdots + c_nx^n = 0$ implies that every $c_i = 0$.

We will next define basis and dimension for an abstract vector space V. We will make these definitions so that if V is a subspace of a $V_n(F)$, the new definitions will agree with the ones previously given.

(55.2) Definition. A linearly independent set M (finite or infinite) of vectors in V is a *basis* of V if every vector in V can be expressed as a finite linear combination of vectors in M.

(55.3) Definition. A vector space V has *finite dimension* $n > 0$ if V has a finite basis of n vectors. The dimension of the zero space, that is, the space consisting of the vector O alone, is zero.

It follows from Theorem (26.4) that this definition is equivalent to Definition (26.3) if V is a subspace of a $V_n(F)$. The following theorem, which is an analogue of Corollary (26.7), is often useful in deciding whether a vector space V has finite dimension.

(55.4) Theorem. If the vector space V over F is spanned by the finite set M of vectors $\alpha_1, \alpha_2, \cdots, \alpha_m$ in V, then V has finite dimension $k \leq m$.

PROOF. There exists a greatest independent subset $\alpha_{i_1}, \alpha_{i_2}, \cdots, \alpha_{i_k}$ of M where $1 \leq k \leq m$. As in the proof of Corollary (26.7), this set is a basis of V since every $\alpha \in V$ is dependent on M and every $\alpha_i \in M$ is dependent on this greatest independent subset.

In order to characterize finite-dimensional vector spaces, and in particular to show that the dimension of such a space is uniquely determined, we define the algebraic equivalence of vector spaces.

(55.5) Definition. Two vector spaces V and V' over the field F are *isomorphic* if there exists an isomorphism f between V and V' as additive groups such that $f(c \cdot \alpha) = c \cdot f(\alpha)$ for all $\alpha \in V$ and $c \in F$.

Since the two operations of addition and scalar multiplication are preserved by this correspondence, isomorphic vector spaces have the same algebraic properties and are considered to be essentially the same. For example, the set $\alpha_1, \alpha_2, \cdots, \alpha_n$ in V is a linearly independent set if and only if the image set $f(\alpha_1), f(\alpha_2), \cdots, f(\alpha_n)$ in V' is linearly independent, since $f(c_1 \cdot \alpha_1 \oplus c_2 \cdot \alpha_2 \oplus \cdots \oplus c_n \cdot \alpha_n) = c_1 \cdot f(\alpha_1) \oplus c_2 \cdot f(\alpha_2) \oplus \cdots \oplus c_n \cdot f(\alpha_n)$. From this it follows that $V_m(F)$ is not isomorphic to $V_n(F)$ if $m \neq n$.

It is a consequence of the following theorem that all results obtained for sequence spaces $V_n(F)$ are valid for finite-dimensional vector spaces.

(55.6) Theorem. If a vector space V over F has finite dimension $n > 0$, then V is isomorphic to $V_n(F)$ and V is not isomorphic to $V_m(F)$ for $m \neq n$.

PROOF. If V has dimension n, then V has a basis $\alpha_1, \alpha_2, \cdots, \alpha_n$ and every $\beta \in V$ can be expressed as $\beta = c_1 \cdot \alpha_1 \oplus c_2 \cdot \alpha_2 \oplus \cdots \oplus c_n \cdot \alpha_n$. As in the proof of Theorem (26.4), this representation of β as a linear combination of the α_i is unique. Therefore, the correspondence f defined by $f(\beta) = (c_1, c_2, \cdots, c_n)$ is a (1–1) correspondence of V onto $V_n(F)$, and it is readily checked that f is an isomorphism.

If V were isomorphic to $V_m(F)$ for $m \neq n$, then $V_m(F)$ and $V_n(F)$ would be isomorphic by the transitivity of isomorphism. But it has been remarked above that this is impossible.

(55.7) Corollary. The dimension n of a finite-dimensional vector space is unique.

PROOF. For if V had dimensions m and n with $m \neq n$, then V would be isomorphic to both $V_m(F)$ and $V_n(F)$.

(55.8) Corollary. Every subspace $S \neq O$ of $V_n(F)$ is isomorphic to $V_k(F)$ for some $k \leq n$.

PROOF. The dimension k of S is not greater than n.

(55.9) Corollary. For every integer $n \geq 0$ there exists one and, except for isomorphic spaces, only one vector space of dimension n over a given field F.

PROOF. The $V_n(F)$ exists for every n, and by (55.6) is essentially the only vector space of dimension n over F.

Exercise (55.1). Prove that every subspace of a vector space is a vector space.

Exercise (55.2). Give the dimension and find a basis for each of the following vector spaces over a field F:

(a) The n-rowed square scalar matrices with elements in F.
(b) The n-rowed square diagonal matrices with elements in F.
(c) The polynomials of degree $\leq n$ with coefficients in F.

Exercise (55.3). Give the dimension for each example in the section.

Exercise (55.4). Show that $V_3(J_p)$ has $(p^3 - 1)/(p - 1) = 1 + p + p^2$ distinct subspaces of dimension 1.

Exercise (55.5). If σ is any permutation of the integers 1, 2, $\cdots$, n, show that $(a_1, a_2, \cdots, a_n) \leftrightarrow (a_{\sigma(1)}, a_{\sigma(2)}, \cdots, a_{\sigma(n)})$ is an isomorphism of $V_n(F)$ with itself. How many isomorphisms of $V_n(F)$ of this type are there? Construct several isomorphisms of $V_n(F)$ with itself which are not of this type.

Exercise (55.6). Construct an example which shows that condition (v) of Definition (55.1) is independent of the other conditions.

Exercise (55.7). Show that $V_n(J_p)$ has p^n elements for p a prime. Write out the vectors in the subspace S of $V_5(J_3)$ spanned by $\alpha = (2,1,0,1,2)$ and $\beta = (1,1,1,2,2)$.

Exercise (55.8). Prove that $\alpha_1 = (2,1,3)$, $\alpha_2 = (1,4,2)$, and $\alpha_3 = (3,1,1)$ form a basis of $V_3(J_5)$. Find the coordinates of $\beta = (1,1,2)$ with respect to this basis.

Exercise (55.9). Let $\mathcal{L}$ be a linear mapping of $V_3(J_5)$ into $V_2(J_5)$ which maps $\epsilon_1 = (1,0,0)$ onto $(2,1)$, $\epsilon_2 = (0,1,0)$ onto $(3,2)$ and ϵ_3 onto $(1,4)$. Find bases in the two spaces with respect to which $\mathcal{L}$ has matrix D_2.

Exercise (55.10). Prove that the set M of all linear transformations of a vector space V over a field F is a vector space over F with respect to addition $\mathcal{L} * \mathcal{M}$ and scalar multiplication $c \bigcirc \mathcal{L}$ defined by

$$(\mathcal{L} * \mathcal{M})(\alpha) = \mathcal{L}(\alpha) \oplus \mathcal{M}(\alpha); \; (c \bigcirc \mathcal{L})(\alpha) = c \cdot \mathcal{L}(\alpha).$$

Prove that if V has finite dimension n, then M is isomorphic as a vector space to $\mathfrak{A}_n(F)$. What is the dimension of M in this case?

VI POLYNOMIALS AND THE ALGEBRAIC THEORY OF FIELDS

Section 56. Subdomains and Subfields Generated by a Set of Elements of a Field

The subgroup $\{S\}$ generated by any subset S of a group G is the uniquely determined smallest subgroup of G which contains S. In Chapter IV, Section 35, $\{S\}$ was described as the set of all finite power products $x_1^{i_1}x_2^{i_2} \cdots x_k^{i_k}$ with $x_j \in S$ and i_j an integer. Alternately, $\{S\}$ can be described as the intersection of all of the subgroups of G which contain S. Similarly, the subspace L of a vector space V over a field F spanned by an arbitrary set of vectors Γ in V is the set of all finite linear combinations $c_1\gamma_1 + c_2\gamma_2 + \cdots + c_k\gamma_k$ with $\gamma_j \in \Gamma$ and $c_j \in F$. Again, L is the smallest subspace of V containing Γ, and is the intersection of all of the subspaces of V containing Γ.

The above examples have been recalled because the material of this chapter is based on the similar concepts of the smallest integral domain and the smallest field containing a given set of elements of a field K. We will be interested in the situation where the given subset of K consists of a subdomain D, or a subfield F, and a subset S of K which is not contained in D. For example, if we take K to be the field C of complex numbers, the subdomain D to be the field R of rational numbers, and the set S to be the single number $\sqrt{2}\, i$, then the smallest integral domain containing R and S is the number field consisting of all numbers of the form $a + b\sqrt{2}\, i$ with $a,b \in R$.

As a second example, take K and D as above, but let S consist of the numbers $\sqrt{5}$ and π. Then the smallest integral domain containing D and S is the set M of all real numbers of the form $(a_0 + b_0\sqrt{5}) + (a_1 + b_1\sqrt{5})\pi + (a_2 + b_2\sqrt{5})\pi^2 + \cdots + (a_n + b_n\sqrt{5})\pi^n$, where n is a non-negative integer and $a_i, b_i \in R$ for $i = 0, 1, 2, \cdots, n$. Since the difference and product of two numbers in M can again be written in this form, M is a subring of K. Moreover M is a subdomain of K since M contains $1 = 1 + 0\sqrt{5}$, the identity of K [see Exercise (45.4)]. Finally, M contains R and S since it contains the elements $a = a + 0\sqrt{5}$ for all $a \in R$, $\sqrt{5} = 0 + 1 \cdot \sqrt{5}$, and $\pi = (0 + 0\sqrt{5}) +$

$(1 + 0\sqrt{5})\pi$. Since the elements of M, which are generated from D and S by the integral operations, are contained in every integral domain containing D and S, M is the smallest integral domain containing D and S.

As in the introductory paragraph, the intersection of all of the subdomains of K which contain D and S is the unique smallest integral domain $\bar{D}$ containing D and S. In the first place, there is at least one subdomain of K containing D and S, namely K itself. Further the intersection of two or more domains containing D and S is an integral domain containing D and S. The statement that $\bar{D}$ is smallest means that if D' is any subdomain of K containing D and S, then $D' \supseteq \bar{D}$. The uniqueness of $\bar{D}$ follows from the fact that if $\bar{\bar{D}}$ is any smallest domain containing D and S, then $\bar{\bar{D}} \supseteq \bar{D}$ and also $\bar{D} \supseteq \bar{\bar{D}}$, so that $\bar{\bar{D}} = \bar{D}$.

In the remainder of this section we will assume that a field K is given, that D is a subdomain of K, and that S is an arbitrary set of elements of K. The set S may or may not have elements in common with D.

(56.1) Definition. The unique smallest integral domain containing D and S is called the *domain generated by adjoining S to D*, and is denoted by $D[S]$.

In a similar way there exists a unique smallest subfield of K containing D and S.

(56.2) Definition. The unique smallest field containing D and S is called the *field generated by adjoining S to D*, and is denoted by $D(S)$.

Before discussing the structure of $D[S]$ and $D(S)$, we will give several properties of these systems. We first show the relation between $D[S]$ and $D(S)$.

(56.3) Theorem. $D \subseteq D[S] \subseteq D(S) \subseteq K$, and $D(S)$ is the quotient field of $D[S]$.

PROOF. By definition, $D \subseteq D[S] \subseteq K$ and $D \subseteq D(S) \subseteq K$. Since $D(S)$ is a field, it is an integral domain; and since $D[S]$ is the smallest integral domain containing D and S, we have that $D[S] \subseteq D(S)$. Further $D[S] \subseteq Q \subseteq D(S)$ where Q is the quotient field of $D[S]$, and therefore $Q = D(S)$ since $D(S)$ is the smallest field containing D and S.

The systems $D[S]$ and $D(S)$ are sometimes called *extensions* of D by S. If S consists of a finite set of elements $u_1, u_2, \cdots, u_k \in K$, these extensions are written as $D[u_1, u_2, \cdots, u_k]$ and $D(u_1, u_2, \cdots, u_k)$. If S consists of a single element $u \in K$, $D[u]$ and $D(u)$ are called *simple extensions* of D. The following theorem shows that an extension of D by a finite set of elements can be studied as a succession of simple extensions.

(56.4) Theorem. $D[u,v] = D[u][v] = D[v][u]$.

PROOF. Since $D[u][v]$ is an integral domain containing D and the elements u and v, $D[u][v] \supseteq D[u,v]$, since the latter domain is the smallest domain containing D, u, and v. On the other hand, $D[u,v]$ contains $D[u]$ since it contains D and u, and further $D[u,v]$ contains v. Since $D[u,v]$ is an integral domain containing $D[u]$ and v, $D[u,v] \supseteq D[u][v]$, which is the smallest domain containing $D[u]$ and v. Therefore $D[u,v] = D[u][v]$. Using this result, the proof is completed by observing that $D[v][u] = D[v,u] = D[u,v]$.

The proof of the following corollary, which can be given by induction on k, is left to the reader as an exercise.

(56.5) Corollary. $D[u_1, u_2, \cdots, u_k] = D[u_{i_1}][u_{i_2}] \cdots [u_{i_k}]$ where $i_1, i_2, \cdots, i_k$ is any ordering of $1, 2, \cdots, k$.

The description of $D[u]$ as the integral domain generated by the elements of D and u subject to the integral operations in K is made precise by the following definition and theorem.

(56.6) Definition. If $u \in K$, a *polynomial in u over D* is an expression $\sum_{i=0}^{n} c_i u^i$ with $c_i \in D$, $i = 0, 1, 2, \cdots, n$. The elements c_i are called the *coefficients* of the polynomial.

(56.7) Theorem. The simple extension $D[u]$ is the set of all polynomials in u over D.

PROOF. Let P be the set of all polynomials in u over D. Then P contains all of the "constant" polynomials, that is, expressions $\sum_{i=0}^{n} c_i u^i$ with $n = 0$, and therefore contains D. Further P contains the polynomial $eu^1 = u$, so that P contains D and u. Let $\sum_{i=0}^{n} c_i u^i$ and $\sum_{i=0}^{m} d_i u^i$ be any two elements of P where we take $m \leq n$ for definiteness. Then using the identities of addition and multiplication in K, we obtain

$$\sum_{i=0}^{n} c_i u^i - \sum_{i=0}^{m} d_i u^i = \sum_{i=0}^{m} (c_i - d_i)u^i + \sum_{i=m+1}^{n} c_i u^i \in P$$

and

$$\left(\sum_{i=0}^{n} c_iu^i\right)\left(\sum_{i=0}^{m} d_iu^i\right) = \sum_{i=0}^{m+n} (c_id_0 + c_{i-1}d_1 + \cdots + c_1d_{i-1} + c_0d_i)u^i \in P$$

where $c_j = 0$ if $j > n$ and $d_j = 0$ if $j > m$. Therefore P is a subring of K. Since P contains the identity $e \in K$, P is an integral domain containing D and u. By the definition of $D[u]$, $D[u] \subseteq P$.

Conversely, $D[u]$ is closed under addition and multiplication and consequently contains every expression of the form $\sum_{i=0}^{n} c_iu^i$ with $c_i \in D$. Thus $D[u] \supseteq P$, and this completes the proof.

(56.8) Corollary. The simple extension $D(u)$ is the set of all quotients $\sum_{i=0}^{n} c_iu^i \big/ \sum_{i=0}^{m} d_iu^i$ of polynomials in u over D, such that $\sum_{i=0}^{m} d_iu^i \neq 0 \in K$.

This follows immediately from the theorem and from Theorem (56.3). We call the elements of $D(u)$ *rational functions of u over D*.

By Theorem (56.4), the elements of $D[u,v]$ can be written as polynomials in v with coefficients in $D[u]$. Since the coefficients are themselves polynomials in u with coefficients in D, using the distributive and associative laws in K we can write the elements of $D[u,v]$ in the form $\Sigma c_{ij}u^iv^j$. Such an expression is called a polynomial in u and v over D. Since $D(u,v)$ is the quotient field of $D[u,v]$, the elements of $D(u,v)$, which are called rational functions of u and v, can be written as quotients of polynomials in u and v over D. In a similar way we can treat polynomials and rational functions in more than two elements over D.

The expression for an element of $D[u]$ as a polynomial in u may not be unique. Thus in the first example, $4 - 3(\sqrt{2}\,i) + 6(\sqrt{2}\,i)^2 = -8 - 3(\sqrt{2}\,i)$. In fact, each polynomial $c_0 + c_1(\sqrt{2}\,i) + c_2(\sqrt{2}\,i)^2 + \cdots + c_n(\sqrt{2}\,i)^n$ in the quantity $u = \sqrt{2}\,i$ can be reduced to the form $a + b\sqrt{2}\,i$, using the operations defined in C.

In the second example with $K = C$, $D = R$, and $S = \{\sqrt{5}, \pi\}$, we have that $R[\sqrt{5}, \pi] = R[\sqrt{5}][\pi]$ by Theorem (56.4). Thus the elements of $R[\sqrt{5}, \pi]$ can be written as polynomials in π with coefficients in the domain $R[\sqrt{5}]$. In this example, two polynomials in π represent the same element of $R[\sqrt{5}, \pi]$ if and only if they have the same coefficients in $R[\sqrt{5}]$. This last result is a consequence of the fact that

π satisfies no equation $c_0 + c_1x + c_2x^2 + \cdots + c_nx^n = 0$ with coefficients $c_i \in R[\sqrt{5}]$.

Exercise (56.1). Prove that if S is a set of elements in the field K, then the intersection of all integral domains in K which contain S is the smallest integral domain in K containing S.

Exercise (56.2). Prove that if S is a subset of a field K, then the smallest subfield of K containing S is $P(S)$ where P is the prime field contained in K.

Exercise (56.3). Prove that if F is a field contained in K, then $F[S]$ and $F(S)$ are vector spaces over F.

Exercise (56.4). Show that if $S \subseteq D$, then $D[S] = D$, and that if $S \subseteq Q$, the quotient field of D, then $D(S) = Q$.

Exercise (56.5). With $D = R$, $K = C$, and $S = \{\sqrt[3]{2}, \sqrt[3]{5}, \pi\}$, write $3\sqrt[3]{10}\,\pi^2 + 9\sqrt[3]{4}\,\pi^4 + 7\sqrt[3]{50}$ as

(a) a polynomial in $\sqrt[3]{5}$ with coefficients in $D[\sqrt[3]{2}, \pi]$;
(b) a polynomial in $\sqrt[3]{2}$ and π with coefficients in $D[\sqrt[3]{5}]$.

Exercise (56.6). Prove Corollary (56.5).

Exercise (56.7). Prove that $D(u,v) = D(u)(v) = D(v)(u)$.

Exercise (56.8). Prove that if Q is the quotient field in K of the integral domain D, then $D(S) = Q(S)$. Hence, using the result of the previous exercise, prove that $D[u](v) = D[v](u) = D(u,v)$. Give an example to show that $D(u)[v]$ is not necessarily equal to $D[v](u)$.

Exercise (56.9). If $D = J$ and $K = C$, find $D[S]$ for

(a) $S = \{i\}$; **(b)** $S = \{\sqrt{2}, \sqrt{3}\}$;
(c) $S = \{\sqrt{2}, \sqrt[4]{2}, \cdots, \sqrt[2^n]{2}, \cdots\}$.

Section 57. The Classification of Field Elements

The systems $F[S]$ and $F(S)$, where F is a subfield of a field K and S is an arbitrary set of elements in K, are vector spaces over F with respect to the operations of addition and multiplication in K. Let us confine our attention to the simple extension $F[u]$ for $u \in K$ and consider the dimension of $F[u]$ over F. If there exists a relation of the form

$$a_0 + a_1u + a_2u^2 + \cdots + a_nu^n = 0 \text{ with } a_i \in F \text{ and } a_n \neq 0,$$

this relation can be solved in the form $u^n = -a_n^{-1}a_0 - a_n^{-1}a_1u - \cdots - a_n^{-1}a_{n-1}u^{n-1}$ since F is a field. Using this relation, we can reduce every element of $F[u]$, which is a polynomial in u with coefficients in F by Theorem (56.7), to a polynomial in u in which no power of u higher than the $(n - 1)$st appears. This means that the elements $1, u, u^2, \cdots, u^{n-1}$ span $F[u]$, and therefore that $F[u]$ has finite dimension less than or equal to n over F.

In the example of the preceding section with $K = C$, $F = R$, and $u = \sqrt{2}\,i$, the relation $2 + u^2 = 2 + (\sqrt{2}\,i)^2 = 0$ enabled us to write each element of $R[\sqrt{2}\,i]$ in the form $a + b\sqrt{2}\,i$ with $a,b \in R$. The numbers $1, \sqrt{2}\,i$ form a basis of $R[\sqrt{2}\,i]$ over R since they span $R[\sqrt{2}\,i]$ and since any relation $a + b\sqrt{2}\,i = 0$ with $a,b \in R$ implies that $a = b = 0$.

On the other hand, if u satisfies no relation of the form $a_0 + a_1u + \cdots + a_nu^n = 0$ with $a_i \in F$ and $a_n \neq 0$, then the infinite set of elements $1, u, u^2, \cdots, u^n, \cdots$ form a linearly independent set, and $F[u]$ is not finite dimensional over F. This is the situation if we take $u = \pi$ in the above example. We are naturally led to distinguish between the two types of elements of K, for which the numbers $\sqrt{2}\,i$ and π serve as examples.

(57.1) Definition. The element $u \in K$ is called *algebraic over* F if there exists a relation of the form $c_0 + c_1u + c_2u^2 + \cdots + c_nu^n = 0$ with $c_i \in F$ for $i = 0, 1, 2, \cdots, n$, and at least one $c_i \neq 0$. Otherwise u is called *transcendental over* F.

The simple extensions $F[u]$ and $F(u)$ are called algebraic or transcendental over F according as u is algebraic or transcendental over F.

(57.2) Theorem. Let F be a subfield of K and let $u_1, u_2, \cdots, u_k \in K$. Then $F[u_1, u_2, \cdots, u_k]$ is a finite-dimensional vector space over F if and only if each u_i is algebraic over F.

PROOF. Assume first that $F[u_1, u_2, \cdots, u_k]$ is a finite-dimensional vector space over F. Then if m is the dimension of $F[u_1, u_2, \cdots, u_k]$ over F, for each i the set of $m + 1$ vectors $e, u_i, u_i^2, \cdots, u_i^m$ is linearly dependent. Thus for each i, there exists a relation $c_0 + c_1u_i + c_2u_i^2 + \cdots + c_mu_i^m = 0$ with at least one $c_i \neq 0$, and each u_i is algebraic over F by (57.1).

Conversely, assume that each u_i is algebraic over F. The elements of $F[u_1, u_2, \cdots, u_k]$ are polynomials in $u_1, u_2, \cdots, u_k$, that is, expressions of the form $\Sigma c_j u_1^{j_1}u_2^{j_2} \cdots u_k^{j_k}$ with $c_j \in F$. The relations $c_0 + c_1u_i + c_2u_i^2 + \cdots + c_{n_i}u^{n_i} = 0$ satisfied by each u_i can be used to reduce each element in $F[u_1, u_2, \cdots, u_k]$ to a polynomial in which the highest power of u_i is not greater than $n_i - 1$. Therefore the finite set of elements $u_1^{j_1}u_2^{j_2} \cdots u_k^{j_k}$ with each j_i running independently over the range $0, 1, 2, \cdots, n_i - 1$ spans $F[u_1, u_2, \cdots, u_k]$, and $F[u_1, u_2, \cdots, u_k]$ is finite-dimensional over F.

Exercise (57.1). Show that if $F(S)$ is a finite-dimensional vector space over F, then $F[S]$ is also finite-dimensional.

Exercise (57.2). Show that each element of F is algebraic over F.

Exercise (57.3). Prove that if $F(S)$ is a finite-dimensional vector space over F for a given set of elements S in K, then each element of $F(S)$ is algebraic over F. Give an example to show the converse is false.

Exercise (57.4). What is the form of $R[u,v]$ where $3 + u - u^3 = 0$ and $1 + v^2 + v^4 = 0$ in C? Express $u^4 + u^5v^5 + 4u^2v$ in its lowest form in $R[u,v]$.

Section 58. Simple Transcendental Extensions

The next several sections will be concerned with a study of the properties of the simple transcendental extensions $F[u]$ and $F(u)$, defined in the preceding section. This material is of fundamental importance in mathematics, as it is the algebraic study of polynomials and rational functions in a variable x. In particular, it is the basis for the theory of algebraic equations.

If F is a subfield of a field K and $u \in K$, then $F[u]$ is the set of all polynomials in u with coefficients in F, so that the set $e, u, u^2, \cdots, u^n, \cdots$ of all powers of u spans $F[u]$ as a vector space over F whether the element u is algebraic or transcendental over F. It is a special case of Theorem (57.2) that a finite subset of $e, u, u^2, \cdots, u^n, \cdots$ spans $F[u]$ if and only if u is algebraic over F. If u is transcendental over F, the complete set $e, u, u^2, \cdots, u^n, \cdots$ is a basis of $F[u]$, and this is the characteristic property of the simple transcendental extension $F[u]$. The following theorem gives this result.

(58.1) Theorem. If F is a subfield of a field K and $u \in K$, then $F[u]$ is a simple transcendental extension of F if and only if the expression for each element of $F[u]$ as a polynomial in u with coefficients in F is unique.

PROOF. Assume first that $F[u]$ is a transcendental extension of F, that is, that u is transcendental over F. Let $\sum_{i=0}^{n} c_i u^i$ and $\sum_{i=0}^{m} d_i u^i$ with $c_i, d_i \in F$ be any two expressions for an element $\alpha \in F[u]$. If we take $n \geq m$ for definiteness, we can write

$$\alpha = \sum_{i=0}^{n} c_i u^i = \sum_{i=0}^{n} d_i u^i \text{ where } d_{m+1} = d_{m+2} = \cdots = d_n = 0.$$

We then have that

$$0 = \alpha - \alpha = \sum_{i=0}^{n} c_i u^i - \sum_{i=0}^{n} d_i u^i = \sum_{i=0}^{n} (c_i - d_i) u^i.$$

This relation implies that $c_i - d_i = 0$, and that $c_i = d_i$, for $i = 0, 1, 2, \cdots, n$, since otherwise u would be algebraic over F, contrary to the hypothesis. Thus the two expressions for α have exactly the same coefficients in F, and the expression for each element of $F[u]$ as a polynomial in u with coefficients in F is unique.

Conversely if each element in $F[u]$ has a unique expression as a polynomial in u with coefficients in F, any relation $\sum_{i=0}^{n} c_i u^i = 0$ with $c_i \in F$ implies that $c_i = 0$ for $i = 0, 1, 2, \cdots, n$, since the element 0 has the expression $0 = 0 + 0 \cdot u + 0 \cdot u^2 + \cdots + 0 \cdot u^n$. Therefore u is transcendental over F by Definition (57.1).

It is a consequence of the above result that the structure of $F[u]$ does not depend on the particular transcendental element chosen in K. For, by the following theorem, there is essentially at most one simple transcendental extension $F[u]$ of F.

(58.2) Theorem. If u and v are transcendental over F, there exists a ring-isomorphism of $F[u]$ onto $F[v]$ by which u corresponds to v and each element of F corresponds to itself.

PROOF. Since the expressions for the elements of $F[u]$ and $F[v]$ as polynomials in u and v respectively are unique by Theorem (58.1), the correspondence f defined by $f\left(\sum_{i=0}^{n} c_i u^i\right) = \sum_{i=0}^{n} c_i v^i$ is a (1–1) correspondence of $F[u]$ onto $F[v]$. It is left to the reader as an exercise to prove that this correspondence is a ring-isomorphism with the stated properties. The rules for addition and multiplication of polynomials are given in the proof of Theorem (56.7).

(58.3) Corollary. If u and v are transcendental over F, then there exists a ring-isomorphism of $F(u)$ onto $F(v)$ by which u corresponds to v and each element of F corresponds to itself.

PROOF. It follows from the proof of Theorem (52.1) that if the integral domains $F[u]$ and $F[v]$ are isomorphic, then this isomorphism can be extended to their quotient fields $F(u)$ and $F(v)$.

The algebraic systems under consideration in the present chapter have been assumed to be subsystems of a given field K, so that the operations of addition and multiplication in these systems are the operations defined in K. We are naturally led to the question of the existence of extension fields and domains when we no longer assume the presence of the containing field K. The theorem which follows proves the existence of simple transcendental extensions $F[u]$ and $F(u)$ for an arbitrary field F.

If $F[u]$ is a simple transcendental extension of F, the elements of $F[u]$ are polynomials in u with coefficients in F by Theorem (56.7). Two polynomials in $F[u]$ are equal only if they have the same coefficients by Theorem (58.1), and the addition and multiplication of polynomials is given by the formulas stated in the proof of (56.7). We proceed to construct an integral domain which meets these conditions.

(58.4) Theorem. For every field F, there exists an integral domain D and a field K such that $F \subseteq D \subseteq K$, where D and K are simple transcendental extensions of F.

PROOF. As has been remarked before in the construction of quotient fields, it is sufficient to construct a domain D and a field K which contain a subfield isomorphic to F.

Let D consist of all distinct infinite sequences $(c_0, c_1, c_2, \cdots, c_n, \cdots)$ where the $c_i \in F$ and all but a finite number of the $c_i = 0$. Thus we have that $(c_0, c_1, c_2, \cdots, c_n, \cdots) = (d_0, d_1, d_2, \cdots, d_n, \cdots)$ if and only if $c_i = d_i$ for all i. We define addition and multiplication in D by

$$(a_0, a_1, \cdots, a_n, \cdots) + (b_0, b_1, \cdots, b_n, \cdots) = (c_0, c_1, \cdots, c_n, \cdots)$$

and

$$(a_0, a_1, \cdots, a_n, \cdots)(b_0, b_1, \cdots, b_n, \cdots) = (d_0, d_1, \cdots, d_n, \cdots),$$

where $c_i = a_i + b_i$ and $d_i = a_0b_i + a_1b_{i-1} + \cdots + a_{i-1}b_1 + a_ib_0$ for $i = 0, 1, 2, \cdots, n, \cdots$. It can be verified that these are binary operations on D, and further that D is a commutative ring with identity $(e, 0, \cdots, 0, \cdots)$ with respect to these operations.

The zero element of D is the sequence $(0, 0, \cdots, 0, \cdots)$. If $\alpha = (a_0, a_1, \cdots, a_n, \cdots)$ and $\beta = (b_0, b_1, \cdots, b_n, \cdots)$ are both different from zero, there exist unique integers $i \geq 0$ and $j \geq 0$ such that $a_0 = a_1 = \cdots = a_{i-1} = 0$ and $b_0 = b_1 = \cdots = b_{j-1} = 0$, while a_i and b_j are both different from zero. Then if $\alpha\beta = \gamma = (c_0, c_1, \cdots, c_n, \cdots)$, we have that

$$c_{i+j} = a_0b_{i+j} + a_1b_{i+j-1} + \cdots + a_{i-1}b_{j+1} + a_ib_j + a_{i+1}b_{j-1} + \cdots + a_{i+j-1}b_1 + a_{i+j}b_0 = a_ib_j \neq 0$$

since F has no divisors of zero. Therefore $\gamma \neq 0$, D has no zero-divisors, and D is an integral domain.

By (52.2), the quotient field Q of D exists and is the unique smallest field containing D. We will now show that D and $K = Q$ are simple transcendental extensions of F.

The sequences $(a, 0, \cdots, 0, \cdots)$ form a subfield F' of D which is isomorphic to F under the correspondence f defined by $f[(a, 0, 0, \cdots, 0)] = a$ for all $a \in F$. Let $x = (0, e, 0, \cdots, 0, \cdots) \in D \subseteq K$. Then $F'[x] \subseteq D$. On the other hand $D \subseteq F'[x]$. For if $\alpha = (a_0, a_1, \cdots, a_n, \cdots)$ is any element of D, there exists an integer k such that $a_{k+1} = a_{k+2} = \cdots = 0$. It may be verified by direct calculation that

$$\alpha = (a_0, a_1, \cdots, a_k, 0, \cdots) = \sum_{i=0}^{k} (a_i, 0, \cdots, 0, \cdots) \cdot (\overbrace{0, 0, \cdots, 0}^{i \text{ terms}}, e, 0, \cdots) = \sum_{i=0}^{k} (a_i, 0, \cdots, 0, \cdots)x^i.$$

Thus $\alpha \in F'[x]$, and $D = F'[x]$, a simple extension of F'. Further $K = F'(x)$, since $F'(x)$ is the quotient field of $F'[x]$ by (56.3).

Finally $x \in K$ is transcendental over F'. For if

$$\sum_{i=0}^{n} (a_i, 0, \cdots, 0, \cdots)x^i = 0,$$

then $(a_0, a_1, \cdots, a_n, 0, \cdots) = (0, 0, \cdots, 0, \cdots)$. By the definition of equality of sequences, $a_i = 0$ for $i = 0, 1, \cdots, n$.

(58.5) Corollary. For every field F there exists one, and only one, simple transcendental extension domain (field), except for isomorphic extensions.

PROOF. The existence of at least one extension of each type follows from the theorem, and the essential uniqueness of each type follows from (58.2) and (58.3).

Since in the construction given in the above theorem, F' is isomorphic to F under the correspondence f defined by $f[(a, 0, \cdots, 0, \cdots)] = a \in F$, we may replace $(a_i, 0, \cdots, 0, \cdots) \in F'$ in the polynomial $\sum_{i=0}^{n} (a_i, 0, \cdots, 0, \cdots)x^i$ by $a_i \in F$ and obtain the usual expression

$$\sum_{i=0}^{n} a_i x^i = a_0 + a_1 x + a_2 x^2 + \cdots + a_n x^n$$

for an element of $F[x]$. The transcendental element $x \in F[x]$ is often called an *indeterminate* over F, and $F[x]$ is referred to as the *domain of polynomials in the indeterminate* x with coefficients in F.

The above results hold if F is an integral domain, since the proof of Theorem (58.4) does not depend on division in F. The construction of Theorem (58.4) may further be used to obtain a ring of polynomials in an indeterminate x with coefficients in any ring R with identity. This ring is also denoted by $R[x]$, although $R[x]$ is an integral domain if and only if R is an integral domain.

Exercise (58.1). Verify that the correspondences defined in (58.2) and (58.4) are ring-isomorphisms.

Exercise (58.2). Show by an example that a vector-space isomorphism between the simple extensions $F[u]$ and $F[v]$ is not necessarily a ring-isomorphism.

Exercise (58.3). Prove that the powers $e, u, u^2, \cdots, u^n, \cdots$ of an element $u \in K$ are linearly independent over F if and only if $F[u]$ is a transcendental extension of F.

Exercise (58.4). The elements $x_1, x_2, \cdots, x_k$ in K are called *independent indeterminates* (transcendentals) over $F \subseteq K$ if a relation $\Sigma c_j x_1^{j_1} x_2^{j_2} \cdots x_k^{j_k} = 0 \in K$ with $c_j \in F$ implies that every coefficient $c_j = 0$. Prove that for every integer k there exists one, and essentially only one, extension $F[x_1, x_2, \cdots, x_k]$ and $F(x_1, x_2, \cdots, x_k)$ where $x_1, x_2, \cdots, x_k$ are independent indeterminates over F.

Exercise (58.5). Following Theorem (58.4), construct the polynomial ring $R[x]$ where R is a ring with identity. Prove that the element x commutes with every $a \in R$.

Exercise (58.6). Prove that $R[x]$ is an integral domain if and only if R is an integral domain.

Section 59. Degree of a Polynomial

We will always use the notation $F[x]$ for the integral domain of polynomials in an indeterminate x with coefficients in a field F, and we now begin a systematic study of this domain by repeating in the customary notation the defining properties of $F[x]$ which appear in the construction given in Theorem (58.4).

(59.1) Let $p(x) = \sum_{i=0}^{n} a_i x^i = a_0 + a_1 x + \cdots + a_n x^n$ and $q(x) = \sum_{i=0}^{m} b_i x^i = b_0 + b_1 x + \cdots + b_m x^m$ be any two polynomials in $F[x]$. Then $p(x) = \sum_{i=0}^{n+m} a_i x^i$ where $a_{n+1} = a_{n+2} = \cdots = a_{n+m} = 0$, $q(x) = \sum_{i=0}^{n+m} b_i x^i$ where $b_{m+1} = b_{m+2} = \cdots = b_{n+m} = 0$, and we have

(i) $p(x) = q(x)$ if and only if $a_i = b_i$ for $i = 0, 1, 2, \cdots, n + m$;

(ii) $p(x) + q(x) = \sum_{i=0}^{n+m} (a_i + b_i)x^i = \sum_{i=0}^{\max[m,n]} (a_i + b_i)x^i$;

(iii) $p(x)q(x) = \sum_{i=0}^{n+m} c_i x^i$ where $c_i = \sum_{j=0}^{i} a_j b_{i-j}$.

(59.2) Definition. If $p(x) = \sum_{i=0}^{n} a_i x^i \in F[x]$ such that not every $a_i = 0$, then the *degree* of $p(x)$ is the integer $m \geq 0$ where a_m is the last non-zero coefficient of $p(x)$. We call a_m the *leading coefficient* of $p(x)$.

Thus if we delete those terms of a polynomial which have coefficient 0, the degree is the exponent of the highest power of x. The elements of F are called constant polynomials. The non-zero constant polynomials have degree zero while the zero polynomial, that is, $0 \in F$, has no degree. The degree of a polynomial plays a role in the study of $F[x]$ analogous to that of the absolute value of an integer in the study of the domain of integers. We will use the notation deg (p) for the degree of $p(x)$.

(59.3) Theorem. If $p(x)$ and $q(x)$ are non-zero polynomials in $F[x]$, then

(i) Either $p + q = 0$, or deg $(p + q) \leq$ maximum [deg (p), deg (q)];
(ii) deg (pq) = deg (p) + deg (q).

PROOF. Since $p(x) \neq 0$ and $q(x) \neq 0$, there exist integers $n \geq 0$ and $m \geq 0$ such that $p(x) = \sum_{i=0}^{n} a_i x^i$ and $q(x) = \sum_{i=0}^{m} b_i x^i$ where $a_n \neq 0$ and $b_m \neq 0$. Thus $p(x)$ and $q(x)$ have degrees n and m respectively. The inequality (i) is evident from the formula for addition given in (59.1), the strict inequality $<$ holding only if $m = n$ and $b_m = -a_n$. By the formula for multiplication given in (59.1), the coefficient of x^{n+m} in the product $p(x)q(x)$ is $c_{n+m} = \sum_{j=0}^{n+m} a_j b_{n+m-j}$. Each term of this sum is zero except the term $a_n b_m$, and $a_n b_m \neq 0$ since $a_n \neq 0$ and $b_m \neq 0$. Thus the leading coefficient of $p(x)q(x)$ is $c_{n+m} \neq 0$, and the degree of $p(x)q(x)$ is $n + m$.

Exercise (59.1). Show that if the zero polynomial is assigned the degree $-\infty$, where the symbol $-\infty$ satisfies the conventions $-\infty < n$, $-\infty + n = n + (-\infty) = -\infty + (-\infty) = -\infty$ for all integers n, then Theorem (59.3) holds without restriction.

Section 60. The Division Algorithm. Division in $F[x]$

The result which leads to a theory of factorization in $F[x]$ analogous to that for the integers is the division algorithm, which is a precise statement of the process of dividing one polynomial by another. The reader should compare this result with the corresponding division algorithm for the integers given in the Introduction.

(60.1) Theorem. If $p(x)$ and $q(x) \neq 0$ are polynomials in $F[x]$, then there exist unique polynomials $s(x)$ and $r(x)$ in $F[x]$ such that

$$p(x) = s(x)q(x) + r(x),$$

where either $r(x) = 0$ or deg $(r) <$ deg (q).

PROOF. We first prove the existence of the polynomials $s(x)$ and $r(x)$ meeting the requirements of the theorem. Let the degree of $q(x) \neq 0$ be m so that $q(x) = b_0 + b_1 x + \cdots + b_m x^m$ with $b_m \neq 0$. If $p(x) = 0$, then $0 = 0 \cdot q(x) + 0$ is the required expression. Therefore we may assume that $p(x) \neq 0$, and that $p(x) = a_0 + a_1x + \cdots + a_nx^n$ with $a_n \neq 0$ has degree n.

If $m > n$, then $p(x) = 0 \cdot q(x) + p(x)$ gives the identity stated in the theorem.

If $m \leq n$, we write $p(x) - a_nb_m^{-1}x^{n-m} \cdot q(x) = p^*(x)$ where $p^*(x) = a_0 + a_1x + \cdots + (a_{n-m} - a_nb_m^{-1}b_0)x^{n-m} + \cdots + (a_{n-1} - a_nb_m^{-1}b_{m-1})x^{n-1}$ is either 0 or a polynomial of degree $n^* \leq n - 1$. If $p^*(x) = 0$, then $p(x) = (a_nb_m^{-1}x^{n-m})q(x) + 0$, with $s(x) = a_nb_m^{-1}x^{n-m} \in F[x]$, is the required expression. If $p^*(x) \neq 0$, then $n > n^* \geq 0$, and if we assume that for given $q(x)$ the required expression exists for all polynomials of degree less than n, we have

$$p^*(x) = s^*(x)q(x) + r(x), \qquad s^*(x) \text{ and } r(x) \in F[x],$$

where either $r(x) = 0$ or $\deg(r) < \deg(q)$. Then

$$\begin{aligned} p(x) &= a_nb_m^{-1}x^{n-m} \cdot q(x) + s^*(x)q(x) + r(x) \\ &= [a_nb_m^{-1}x^{n-m} + s^*(x)]q(x) + r(x) = s(x)q(x) + r(x), \end{aligned}$$

and the division algorithm exists for $p(x)$ of degree n.

We have yet to prove that the polynomials $s(x)$ and $r(x)$ in the expression $p(x) = s(x)q(x) + r(x)$ are unique. If $p(x) = s_1(x)q(x) + r_1(x)$ with $r_1(x)$ satisfying the requirements of the theorem, then

$$s(x)q(x) + r(x) = s_1(x)q(x) + r_1(x),$$

or

$$[s(x) - s_1(x)]q(x) = r_1(x) - r(x).$$

If $r_1(x) \neq r(x)$, then none of the polynomials $r_1(x) - r(x)$, $s(x) - s_1(x)$, and $q(x)$ is the zero polynomial, and we use Theorem (59.3) to obtain*

$$\deg(s - s_1) + \deg(q) = \deg(r_1 - r) \leq \max[\deg(r_1), \deg(r)] < \deg(q).$$

But this inequality is impossible. Therefore $r_1(x) = r(x)$, and since $q(x) \neq 0$, $s_1(x) - s(x) = 0$ and $s_1(x) = s(x)$.

The polynomials $s(x)$ and $r(x)$ of the division algorithm are called, respectively, the *quotient* and *remainder* on dividing $p(x)$ by $q(x)$.

The smallest field contained in F is its prime field P, which is isomorphic to R if F has infinite characteristic, and to J_p if F has finite characteristic p. The smallest field in F containing the coefficients of $p(x)$ and $q(x)$ is therefore the field $\bar{F} = P(a_0, a_1, \cdots, a_n, b_0, b_1, \cdots, b_m)$ of all rational functions of the a's and b's with coefficients in P. Since $p(x)$ and $q(x)$ are in $\bar{F}[x]$, by Theorem (60.1) there is a division algorithm $p(x) = s(x) \cdot q(x) + r(x)$ with $s(x)$, $r(x) \in \bar{F}[x]$. This is the

* Since $r(x) \neq r_1(x)$, at least one of these is not zero. If one is zero, max [deg (r_1), deg (r)] is the degree of the other.

unique algorithm in the domain $F[x] \supseteq \bar{F}[x]$, and the coefficients of the quotient and remainder in the division algorithm are rational functions of the coefficients of $p(x)$ and $q(x)$. For this reason we say that the division algorithm is a rational process. The division process depends only on the smallest field containing the coefficients of $p(x)$ and $q(x)$ and not on the particular field $F \supseteq \bar{F}$ in which we do the division.

Recalling the definitions in Section 46, an element $q(x)$ of the integral domain $F[x]$ is a *factor* or *divisor* of $p(x) \in F[x]$ if there exists a polynomial $h(x) \in F[x]$ such that $p(x) = h(x)q(x)$. Thus $q(x)$ is a factor of $p(x)$ if and only if the remainder $r(x)$ in the division algorithm is the zero polynomial. The units of $F[x]$ are characterized by the following theorem.

(60.2) Theorem. The polynomial $p(x)$ is a unit of $F[x]$ if and only if $p(x)$ is a non-zero element of F.

PROOF. Since the non-zero elements of F have multiplicative inverses, it follows from (46.5) that they are units of $F[x]$. Now the identity of $F[x]$ is the identity element $e \in F$, and if $p(x)$ is a unit of $F[x]$, there exists a polynomial $h(x)$ such that $p(x) \cdot h(x) = e$. By (59.3), $\deg(p) + \deg(h) = \deg(e) = 0$, which is possible only if $\deg(p) = \deg(h) = 0$. Therefore $p(x)$ is a non-zero constant polynomial, that is, $p(x) = c \neq 0 \in F$.

It follows from Theorem (60.2) that $p(x)$ and $q(x)$ are associates in $F[x]$ if and only if $p(x) = c \cdot q(x)$ where $c \neq 0 \in F$. Moreover, each polynomial $p(x) = a_0 + a_1x + \cdots + a_nx^n$ with $a_n \neq 0$ is associated with a unique polynomial $a_n^{-1}p(x)$ with leading coefficient e. A polynomial with leading coefficient e is called *monic.*

The theory of division in $F[x]$ continues to parallel that for the integers in that it is possible to prove the existence and uniqueness of the greatest common divisor $d(x)$ for every pair of polynomials $p(x)$ and $q(x)$, not both zero, in $F[x]$.

(60.3) Definition. If $p(x)$ and $q(x)$, not both zero, are polynomials in $F[x]$, then a g.c.d. of $p(x)$ and $q(x)$ is a monic polynomial $d(x)$ in $F[x]$ with the following properties:

(i) $d(x)$ is a divisor of both $p(x)$ and $q(x)$;
(ii) every polynomial which divides both $p(x)$ and $q(x)$ divides $d(x)$.

(60.4) Theorem. Every pair of polynomials $p(x)$ and $q(x) \neq 0$ in $F[x]$ has a unique g.c.d. $d(x)$ which is in $F[x]$ and which can be written in the form $d(x) = a(x)p(x) + b(x)q(x)$ for $a(x)$ and $b(x)$ in $F[x]$.

PROOF. Let S be the set of all polynomials in $F[x]$ of the form $a(x)p(x) + b(x)q(x)$ for $a(x)$, $b(x) \in F[x]$. Since $q(x) = 0 \cdot p(x) + e \cdot q(x) \neq 0 \in S$, the set of all non-zero polynomials in S is not empty. Let $d(x)$ be a polynomial of least degree in S. Since the monic associate of each polynomial in S is in S, we can choose $d(x)$ to be monic. Then it is clear that $d(x) = a(x)p(x) + b(x)q(x)$ satisfies (ii) of Definition (60.3).

Using (60.1), we can divide $p(x)$ by $d(x)$ and obtain $p(x) = s(x)d(x) + r(x)$ where either $r(x) = 0$, in which case $d(x)$ divides $p(x)$, or deg (r) $<$ deg (d). In the latter case

$$\begin{aligned} r(x) &= e \cdot p(x) - s(x) \cdot d(x) = [e - s(x)a(x)]p(x) + [-s(x)b(x)]q(x) \\ &= \bar{a}(x) \cdot p(x) + \bar{b}(x) \cdot q(x), \end{aligned}$$

with $\bar{a}(x)$, $\bar{b}(x) \in F[x]$. Therefore $r(x) \in S$, and deg (r) $<$ deg (d). But this contradicts the choice of $d(x)$ as a polynomial of least degree in S. Therefore $d(x)$ divides $p(x)$, and a similar proof shows that $d(x)$ divides $q(x)$, proving (i) of Definition (60.3). Further, $d(x)$ is of the form stated in the theorem.

If $d_1(x)$ is any other polynomial which satisfies Definition (60.3), then $d_1(x)$ divides $d(x)$ and $d(x)$ divides $d_1(x)$. Therefore $d_1(x)$ is an associate of $d(x)$, and $d_1(x) = d(x)$, since both are monic.

Two polynomials not both zero are called *relatively prime* if their g.c.d. is $e \in F$. By the theorem if $p(x)$ and $q(x)$ are relatively prime, there exist polynomials $a(x)$ and $b(x)$ in $F[x]$ with the property that $e = a(x)p(x) + b(x)q(x)$.

There is an alternate method of proving the existence of the g.c.d. of two polynomials which is used in calculating the g.c.d., $d(x)$, as well as the polynomials $a(x)$ and $b(x)$. It is called the Euclidean algorithm and is based on repeated use of the division algorithm. We will illustrate this process by an example.

Let $p(x) = x^4 - 3x^3 + 4x^2 - 12x$ and $q(x) = x^3 - 4x^2 + 4x - 3$ be polynomials in $R[x]$. Dividing $p(x)$ by $q(x)$ we obtain

$$(1) \quad x^4 - 3x^3 + 4x^2 - 12x = (x + 1)(x^3 - 4x^2 + 4x - 3) + (4x^2 - 13x + 3).$$

Now divide the original divisor $x^3 - 4x^2 + 4x - 3$ by the remainder $4x^2 - 13x + 3$:

$$(2) \quad x^3 - 4x^2 + 4x - 3 = (1/4\, x - 3/16)(4x^2 - 13x + 3) + (13/16\, x - 39/16).$$

Again, divide the divisor $4x^2 - 13x + 3$ by the remainder $13/16\,x - 39/16$:

(3) $4x^2 - 13x + 3 = (64/13\,x - 16/13)(13/16\,x - 39/16) + 0.$

By (3), $x - 3$, which is the monic associate of $13/16\,x - 39/16$, is a divisor of $4x^2 - 13x + 3$. Then by (2), $x - 3$ divides both polynomials in the right member, and therefore divides the left member $q(x)$. Finally, by (1), $x - 3$ divides both $q(x)$ and $4x^2 - 13x + 3$, so that $x - 3$ divides $p(x)$. Thus $x - 3$ is a common divisor of $p(x)$ and $q(x)$. If $d_1(x)$ is any common divisor of $p(x)$ and $q(x)$, then $d_1(x)$ divides $4x^2 - 13x + 3$ by (1). Further, $d_1(x)$ divides $13/16\,x - 39/16$ by (2), since it divides both $q(x)$ and $4x^2 - 13x + 3$. Thus $d_1(x)$ divides $x - 3$, which proves that $x - 3$ is the g.c.d. of $p(x)$ and $q(x)$.

We observe that (1) and (2) can be used to express $x - 3$ in the form $a(x)p(x) + b(x)q(x)$. By (1), $4x^2 - 13x + 3 = p(x) - (x + 1)q(x)$. Substituting in (2), we obtain

$$\begin{aligned} x - 3 &= 16/13\,q(x) - 16/13(1/4\,x - 3/16)(4x^2 - 13x + 3) \\ &= (-1/4\,x + 3/13)p(x) + (4/13\,x^2 + 1/13\,x + 1)q(x). \end{aligned}$$

It is clear that for any pair of polynomials, this process will terminate in a finite number of steps since the remainder in each step has lower degree than the remainder in the preceding step, and that the last non-zero remainder is the g.c.d. of the two polynomials. Since each step is an application of the division algorithm, the coefficients of the g.c.d. are rational functions of the coefficients of $p(x)$ and $q(x)$. Thus the g.c.d. of $p(x)$ and $q(x)$ is in $\bar{F}[x]$ where $\bar{F}$ is the smallest field containing the coefficients of $p(x)$ and $q(x)$, and the calculation of the g.c.d. does not depend on the field $F \supseteq \bar{F}$ in which we are working.

Exercise (60.1). Prove that the monic polynomials form a set of representatives for the equivalence relation of association of polynomials.

Exercise (60.2). Show that the ideal in $F[x]$ generated by two polynomials not both zero can be generated by a single polynomial.

Exercise (60.3). Define the g.c.d. of a set of k polynomials, and generalize Theorem (60.4).

Exercise (60.4). Where does the well-ordering principle enter into the proof of Theorem (60.4)?

Exercise (60.5). Find $d(x)$ and an expression $d(x) = a(x)p(x) + b(x)q(x)$ for

(a) $p(x) = x^3 - 8$, $q(x) = x^3 + x - 2$;
(b) $p(x) = x^6 - x^5 + 2x^4 - 3x^3 + x^2 - 2x + 2$,
$q(x) = x^5 - x^3 - x^2 + 1$.

Exercise (60.6). Show that $a(x)$ and $b(x)$ in the expression $d(x) = a(x)p(x) + b(x)q(x)$ are not unique.

Exercise (60.7). Show that there exist polynomials $a(x)$ and $b(x)$ such that $e = a(x)p(x) + b(x)q(x)$ if and only if $p(x)$ and $q(x)$ are relatively prime.

Exercise (60.8). Discuss the Euclidean algorithm for the integers.

Exercise (60.9). We call the monic polynomial $m(x)$ the least common multiple (l.c.m.) of $p(x)$ and $q(x)$ if $m(x)$ is a common multiple of $p(x)$ and $q(x)$, and if every common multiple of $p(x)$ and $q(x)$ is a multiple of $m(x)$. Prove that $m(x)$ exists and is an associate of $p(x)q(x)/d(x)$ where $d(x)$ is the g.c.d. of $p(x)$ and $q(x)$.

Section 61. The Factorization of Polynomials

The smallest field containing the coefficients of the polynomials $p(x) = x^5 - 1/2\,x^4 - x^3 + 1/2\,x^2 - 2x + 1$ and $q(x) = x^4 - 2x^3 + 4x - 4$ is the field R of rational numbers. Thus $p(x)$ and $q(x)$ are elements of $F[x]$ where F is any field containing R. We saw in the preceding section that whatever F we choose for the study of $p(x)$ and $q(x)$, the g.c.d., $d(x)$, of $p(x)$ and $q(x)$ is in $R[x]$, that is, $d(x)$ is independent of the choice of $F \supseteq R$. In this example, $d(x) = x^2 - 2$. However, if we are asked to factor the polynomials $p(x)$ and $q(x)$ in $F[x]$, our result depends upon the particular choice of $F \supseteq R$. In $R[x]$ we have $p(x) = (x^2 + 1)(x^2 - 2)(x - 1/2)$ and $q(x) = (x^2 - 2x + 2)(x^2 - 2)$. In $R^{\#}[x]$, $p(x) = (x^2 + 1)(x - \sqrt{2})(x + \sqrt{2})(x - 1/2)$ and $q(x) = (x^2 - 2x + 2)(x - \sqrt{2})(x + \sqrt{2})$. In $C[x]$, $p(x) = (x - i)(x + i)(x - \sqrt{2})(x + \sqrt{2})(x - 1/2)$ and $q(x) = (x - 1 + i)(x - 1 - i)(x - \sqrt{2})(x + \sqrt{2})$. The factors in each case are irreducible in the particular polynomial domain considered.

(61.1) Definition. A nonconstant polynomial $f(x) \in F[x]$ is called *irreducible in* $F[x]$ if its only divisors in $F[x]$ are its associates and the units. Otherwise $f(x)$ is called *reducible*.

This is in accord with Definition (46.6), since the constant polynomials are the zero and the units in $F[x]$. Thus the factorization theory in $F[x]$ concerns only polynomials of degree $n \geq 1$.

If the polynomial $f(x)$ is reducible in $F[x]$, there exists at least one pair of nonconstant polynomials $g(x)$, $h(x) \in F[x]$ such that $f(x) = g(x) \cdot h(x)$. Thus a linear polynomial $ax + b$ is irreducible in $F[x]$ where F is any field which contains a and b.

If $p(x)$ is irreducible in $F[x]$ and $q(x)$ is any polynomial in $F[x]$, then either $p(x)$ and $q(x)$ are relatively prime, or else their g.c.d. is the monic associate of $p(x)$. For their g.c.d. is a divisor of $p(x)$, and the only divisors of $p(x)$ are the associates of $p(x)$ and the units, that is, the non-zero constants in F.

(61.2) Theorem. If $p(x)$ is an irreducible polynomial in $F[x]$ which divides the product $g(x)h(x)$ in $F[x]$, then either $p(x)$ divides $g(x)$ or $p(x)$ divides $h(x)$.

PROOF. If the g.c.d. of $p(x)$ and $g(x)$ is an associate of $p(x)$, then $p(x)$ divides $g(x)$. Otherwise $p(x)$ and $g(x)$ are relatively prime, and there exist polynomials $a(x)$ and $b(x)$ such that $a(x)p(x) + b(x)g(x) = e \in F$. Then $a(x)p(x)h(x) + b(x)[g(x)h(x)] = h(x)$. Since $p(x)$ divides $g(x)h(x)$ by hypothesis, $p(x)$ divides each term in the left member of the last equality and hence divides the right member $h(x)$.

(61.3) Corollary. If $p(x)$ is an irreducible polynomial in $F[x]$ which divides the product $g_1(x)g_2(x) \cdots g_s(x)$ in $F[x]$, then $p(x)$ divides some $g_i(x)$.

(61.4) Corollary. If $p(x)$ and $g(x)$ are relatively prime polynomials in $F[x]$ such that $p(x)$ divides the product $g(x)h(x)$ in $F[x]$, then $p(x)$ divides $h(x)$.

The proof of these corollaries is left to the reader as an exercise.

(61.5) Theorem. Each polynomial $f(x) \neq 0$ in $F[x]$ can be written in the form $f(x) = c f_1(x)f_2(x) \cdots f_r(x)$ where $c \neq 0$ is in F and $f_i(x)$ is a monic irreducible polynomial in $F[x]$ for $i = 1, 2, \cdots, r$. This factorization is unique except for the order of the factors $f_i(x)$.

PROOF. If $f(x)$ has degree zero, then $f(x) = c \neq 0 \in F$. Assume that polynomials of degree less than n can be written in the form stated in the theorem, and let $f(x)$ have degree $n > 0$. If $f(x)$ is irreducible, then $f(x) = c f_1(x)$ where $f_1(x)$ is the monic associate of $f(x)$. If $f(x)$ is reducible, then $f(x) = g(x)h(x)$ where $0 < \deg (g) < n$ and $0 < \deg (h) < n$. By the induction assumption, $g(x) = c_1 g_1(x) \cdots g_s(x)$ and $h(x) = c_2 h_1(x) \cdots h_t(x)$ where c_1 and c_2 are in F and the $g_i(x)$ and $h_j(x)$ are monic irreducible polynomials. Thus $f(x) = (c_1c_2)g_1(x) \cdots g_s(x)h_1(x) \cdots h_t(x)$ has the desired form.

We again use induction to prove the uniqueness of factorization.

There is nothing to prove if $f(x)$ has degree zero. Assume the uniqueness of factorization for polynomials of degree less than n, and let

$$f(x) = c f_1(x) \cdots f_r(x) = d g_1(x) \cdots g_s(x)$$

be any two factorizations of $f(x)$ of degree $n > 0$ in the stated form. Then since the $f_i(x)$ and $g_j(x)$ are monic, $c = d$. Furthermore, $f_1(x)$ divides the product $g_1(x) \cdots g_s(x)$, and hence by Corollary (61.3), $f_1(x)$ divides some $g_j(x)$. But since both $f_1(x)$ and $g_j(x)$ are monic irreducible polynomials, $f_1(x) = g_j(x)$. Therefore

$$f_2(x) \cdots f_r(x) = g_1(x) \cdots g_{j-1}(x) g_{j+1}(x) \cdots g_s(x),$$

and we have two factorizations of a polynomial of degree less than n. By the induction assumption, $r = s$ and the $f_i(x)$ are the $g_k(x)$ in some order. This completes the proof of the theorem.

By collecting the repeated factors $f_i(x)$ in the factorization of $f(x)$, we may write

$$f(x) = c f_1(x)^{\alpha_1} f_2(x)^{\alpha_2} \cdots f_t(x)^{\alpha_t}$$

where $f_1(x), f_2(x), \cdots, f_t(x)$ are the distinct irreducible factors of $f(x)$ and $\alpha_1, \alpha_2, \cdots, \alpha_t$ are positive integers. The exponents α_i and the factors $c, f_1(x), f_2(x), \cdots, f_t(x)$ are uniquely determined by $f(x)$, and a polynomial $g(x)$ is a factor of $f(x)$ if and only if $g(x) = d f_1(x)^{\beta_1} f_2(x)^{\beta_2} \cdots f_t(x)^{\beta_t}$ with $0 \leq \beta_i \leq \alpha_i$ for $i = 1, 2, \cdots, t$. The set of all products of the form $p_1(x)^{n_1} p_2(x)^{n_2} \cdots p_k(x)^{n_k}$, where the $p_i(x)$ are relatively prime irreducible monic polynomials, is a set of canonical forms for the equivalence relation of association in $F[x]$ which is particularly useful in discussing factorization in $F[x]$.

There is no general algorithm, such as the Euclidean algorithm for computing the g.c.d. of two polynomials, which enables us to find in a finite number of steps the canonical factorization of a polynomial in $F[x]$. Given a certain type of polynomial or a specific coefficient field, there are methods* available for factoring the polynomial or, what is more important, for telling whether or not the polynomial is reducible in the domain $F[x]$. Several of these results will be suggested by the exercises.

Exercise (61.1). Prove Corollaries (61.3) and (61.4).

Exercise (61.2). List all monic polynomials which divide

$$f(x) = (x + 3)(x - 2)^3(x - 7).$$

---

* See B. L. van der Waerden, *Modern Algebra*, (New York, 1949), I, Secs. 24 and 25.

Exercise (61.3). Factor $x^4 - 3x^2 + 2$ in $R[x]$ and in $C[x]$. What is the smallest field F contained in C such that the polynomial factors into linear factors in $F[x]$?

Exercise (61.4). Find all fields $J_p[x]$ such that $x^2 + 5$ is a factor of $x^5 - 4x + 42$ in $J_p[x]$.

Exercise (61.5). List all monic polynomials in $J_3[x]$ of degree less than three, and write each in its canonical form. List all irreducible polynomials of second degree in $J_3[x]$.

Exercise (61.6). Prove that the following polynomials are irreducible in $J_3[x]$ by showing that any proper factorization is impossible:

(a) $x^3 + 2x + 1$;
(b) $x^4 + x^3 + x^2 + 1$.

Exercise (61.7). What are the units of $J[x]$ where J is the domain of integers? What are the irreducible elements? Give a set of canonical forms for association in $J[x]$. Factor $6x^3 - 10x$ in $J[x]$ and in $R[x]$.

Exercise (61.8). Show that if $f(x)$ is a monic reducible polynomial in $J[x]$, it is reducible in $J_p[x]$ for all primes p. Using this, show that $x^5 - x^2 + 11$ is irreducible in $J[x]$ by showing it irreducible in $J_2[x]$.

Exercise (61.9). Prove that $f(x) = x^4 + 4x^3 + 17x^2 + 3x + 1$ is irreducible in $J[x]$ by showing that

(i) $x^3 + 2x + 1$ is a factor in $J_3[x]$; [*Note:* Since $x^3 + 2x + 1$ is irreducible in $J_3[x]$ [see Exercise (61.6 a)], if $f(x)$ reduces in $J[x]$, it must reduce as a linear factor multiplied by a cubic factor.]
(ii) $f(x)$ has no linear factors in $J_5[x]$.

Exercise (61.10) Prove that $f(x) = \sum_{i=0}^{n} a_i x^i \in J[x]$ is irreducible in $J[x]$ except for factors in J if there exists a prime $p \in J$ which divides all a_i except a_n, but such that p^2 does not divide a_0. [*Note:* Assume $f(x) = (\Sigma b_i x^i)(\Sigma c_i x^i)$ with $c_i, d_i \in J$ where p divides b_0 but not c_0 and arrive at a contradiction.] This is known as *Eisenstein's Theorem*.

Exercise (61.11). Using the above test, prove that the following polynomials have no nonconstant proper factors in $J[x]$:

(a) $x^3 + 3x^2 + 9x + 6$;
(b) $x^n - p$ for p a prime;
(c) $x^2 + 1$. [*Note:* $\Sigma a_i x^i$ reduces if and only if $\Sigma a_i (x + a)^i$ reduces for $a \in J$.]

Section 62. Multiple Factors of a Polynomial

The exponents α_i in the canonical form $f(x) = cf_1(x)^{\alpha_1}f_2(x)^{\alpha_2} \cdots f_r(x)^{\alpha_r}$ of a polynomial in $F[x]$ count the multiplicity of each irreducible factor of $f(x)$. However, it is usually difficult, even if methods are available, to obtain this canonical factorization of a given polynomial. In this section we discuss a constructive method for finding the multiple factors of a polynomial which is often useful as the first step in factoring the polynomial. We begin with the definition of the derivative of a polynomial, which is the basis of this discussion.

(62.1) Definition. If $f(x) = \sum_{i=0}^{n} a_ix^i \in F[x]$ is a nonconstant polynomial, the polynomial $\sum_{i=1}^{n} ia_ix^{i-1}$ is called the *derivative* of $f(x)$ and is denoted by $f'(x)$. The derivative of a constant polynomial is zero.

The coefficient ia_i is, of course, the sum of the element a_i with itself i times. Since every element of $F[x]$ has a unique representation as a polynomial in the indeterminate x with coefficients in F, every element of $F[x]$ has a uniquely defined derivative in $F[x]$ and the coefficients of $f'(x)$ depend rationally upon the coefficients of $f(x)$. For polynomials, the derivative as defined above in a purely algebraic manner is the same as the derivative defined by limit processes in the calculus. Moreover it is possible to derive directly from Definition (62.1) the following properties of the derivative which we will need in our calculations:

(i) If $f(x) = g(x) + h(x)$ for $g(x), h(x) \in F[x]$, then
$$f'(x) = g'(x) + h'(x).$$
(ii) If $f(x) = g(x)h(x)$ for $g(x), h(x) \in F[x]$, then
$$f'(x) = g'(x)h(x) + g(x)h'(x).$$
(iii) If $f(x) = [g(x)]^n$ for $g(x) \in F[x]$ and n a positive integer, then
$$f'(x) = n[g(x)]^{n-1}g'(x).$$

The proof of these properties is left to the reader as an exercise.

(iv) If $f(x) \in F[x]$ where F has infinite characteristic, then $f'(x) = 0$ if and only if $f(x)$ is a constant in F.

PROOF. Let $f(x) = \sum_{i=0}^{n} a_ix^i \in F[x]$, so that $f'(x) = \sum_{i=1}^{n} ia_ix^{i-1} \in F[x]$. Then $f'(x) = 0$ if and only if $ia_i = 0$ for all $i = 1, 2, \cdots, n$, and since F has infinite characteristic, $ia_i = (ie)a_i = 0$ for $i > 0$ if and only if $a_i = 0$. Thus $f'(x) = 0$ if and only if $f(x) = a_0 \in F$.

This property is not true if F has finite characteristic. For example, if F has characteristic five, the derivative of $x^{10} + 2x^5 + 3$ is zero. See Exercise (62.6) for the theorem concerning these fields.

(62.2) Definition. The polynomial $\Phi(x) \in F[x]$ is an *r-fold factor* $(r > 0)$ of the polynomial $f(x) \in F[x]$ if $f(x) = [\Phi(x)]^r g(x)$ where $g(x) \in F[x]$ is not divisible by $\Phi(x)$.

Thus $\Phi(x)$ is an r-fold factor of $f(x)$ if $[\Phi(x)]^r$ is a factor of $f(x)$ while $[\Phi(x)]^{r+1}$ is not. To say that $\Phi(x)$ is a 0-fold factor of $f(x)$ means that $\Phi(x)$ is not a factor of $f(x)$. Since the factorization of $f(x)$ in $F[x]$ is unique, every factor of $f(x)$ has a uniquely defined multiplicity $r \geq 1$. The multiple factors of $f(x)$ are those with $r \geq 2$. If $\Phi(x)$ is a multiple factor of $f(x)$, then the derivative of $f(x) = [\Phi(x)]^r g(x)$ is

(62.3) $$f'(x) = [\Phi(x)]^{r-1}\{r\Phi'(x)g(x) + \Phi(x)g'(x)\}.$$

This implies that every multiple factor of $f(x)$ is a factor of $f'(x)$.

(62.4) Theorem. Let $f(x) \in F[x]$ where F has infinite characteristic, and let $\Phi(x)$ be any factor of $f(x)$ in $F[x]$ such that $\Phi(x)$ is relatively prime to its derivative. Then $\Phi(x)$ is an r-fold factor $(r \geq 1)$ of $f(x)$ if and only if $\Phi(x)$ is an $(r - 1)$-fold factor of $f'(x)$.

PROOF. Assume first that $\Phi(x)$ is an r-fold factor of $f(x)$. Then $f(x) = [\Phi(x)]^r g(x)$ where $\Phi(x)$ is not a factor of $g(x)$. By (62.3), $[\Phi(x)]^{r-1}$ is a factor of $f'(x)$. If $[\Phi(x)]^r$ is a factor of $f'(x)$, then $\Phi(x)$ is a factor of $r\Phi'(x)g(x) + \Phi(x)g'(x)$ and therefore of $r\Phi'(x)g(x) = (re)\Phi'(x)g(x)$. Since F has infinite characteristic and $r \geq 1$, $\Phi(x)$ is a factor of $\Phi'(x)g(x)$. Since $\Phi(x)$ is relatively prime to $\Phi'(x)$, $\Phi(x)$ is a factor of $g(x)$ by (61.4). But $\Phi(x)$ is not a factor of $g(x)$, so that $[\Phi(x)]^r$ is not a factor of $f'(x)$, and therefore $\Phi(x)$ is an $(r - 1)$-fold factor of $f'(x)$.

Conversely, assume that $\Phi(x)$ is an $(r - 1)$-fold factor of $f'(x)$. By hypothesis $\Phi(x)$ is a factor of $f(x)$. Assume that $\Phi(x)$ is an s-fold factor $(s \geq 1)$ of $f(x)$. Then by the above argument, $\Phi(x)$ is an $(s - 1)$-fold factor of $f'(x)$, so that $s - 1 = r - 1$ and $s = r$.

The following theorem shows that Theorem (62.4) can be applied if $\Phi(x)$ is a factor of $f(x)$ which is irreducible in $F[x]$.

(62.5) Theorem. If $f(x)$ is an irreducible polynomial in $F[x]$ where F has infinite characteristic, then $f(x)$ is relatively prime to its derivative.

PROOF. Since $f(x)$ is irreducible, $f(x) = \sum_{i=0}^{n} a_i x^i$ has degree $n \geq 1$. Then the highest power of x which appears in $f'(x) = \sum_{i=1}^{n} i a_i x^{i-1}$ is x^{n-1}, and its coefficient is $na_n = (ne)a_n$ which is not equal to zero since $a_n \neq 0$ and F has infinite characteristic. Thus $f'(x)$ has degree $n - 1 \geq 0$, and the g.c.d. of $f(x)$ and $f'(x)$ has degree $\leq n - 1$. Then the irreducibility of $f(x)$ implies that the degree of the g.c.d. is zero, so that it is $e \in F$.

(62.6) Corollary. Let $f(x) \in F[x]$ where F has infinite characteristic. Then $f(x)$ has multiple factors in $F[x]$ if and only if the g.c.d., $d(x)$, of $f(x)$ and $f'(x)$ is not $e \in F$.

PROOF. By (62.3) every multiple factor of $f(x)$ is a factor of $f'(x)$ and therefore of $d(x)$. Conversely, assume that $d(x) \neq e \in F$. Let $\Phi(x)$ be any factor of $d(x)$ which is irreducible in $F[x]$. Then $\Phi(x)$ is a factor of $f(x)$ which is relatively prime to its derivative by (62.5), and $\Phi(x)$ divides $f'(x)$. Applying (62.4) to $\Phi(x)$, we see that $\Phi(x)$ is at least a twofold factor of $f(x)$.

This corollary shows that the existence of multiple factors of $f(x)$ in $F[x]$ depends only on $\bar{F}$, the smallest subfield of F containing the coefficients of $f(x)$. For $f'(x)$ and therefore $d(x)$ are polynomials in $\bar{F}[x]$. This means that $f(x)$ has multiple factors in $F[x]$ if and only if it has multiple factors in $\bar{F}[x]$. In particular, we have the following consequence of the above results, the proof of which is left to the reader as an exercise.

(62.7) Theorem. If $f(x)$ is irreducible in $F[x]$ where F has infinite characteristic, it has no multiple factors in $K[x]$ where K is any field containing the coefficients of $f(x)$.

Given a polynomial $f(x) \in F[x]$, let $d_1(x)$ be the g.c.d. of $f(x)$ and $f'(x)$. If $d_1(x) = e \in F$, $f(x)$ has no multiple factors and the above theorems are of no help in factoring $f(x)$ in $F[x]$. Otherwise, let $d_2(x)$ be the g.c.d. of $d_1(x)$ and $d_1'(x)$, $d_3(x)$ the g.c.d. of $d_2(x)$ and $d_2'(x)$, and so on. Since $\deg d_1(x) > \deg d_2(x) > \cdots \geq 0$, there must exist an integer $i \geq 1$ such that $d_i(x)$ is not constant, while $d_{i+1} = e \in F$. Then $d_i(x)$ is relatively prime to its derivative, and since $d_i(x)$ is a factor of $d_{i-1}(x)$ and its derivative, $d_i(x)$ is a twofold factor of $d_{i-1}(x)$ by Theorem (62.4). Similarly by (62.4), $d_i(x)$ is a threefold factor of $d_{i-2}(x)$, $\cdots$, an i-fold factor of $d_1(x)$, and an $(i + 1)$-fold factor of $f(x)$. Therefore $f(x) = [d_i(x)]^{i+1} \cdot g(x)$ in $F[x]$. Closer examination of the above sequence of polynomials will show that $g(x)$ has no factors in common with $d_i(x)$ and no factors of multiplicity greater than i. We may then find the multiple factors of $g(x)$ by using the same procedure.

EXAMPLE 1. If $f(x) = x^8 - x^6 - 12x^5 - x^4 - 37x^2 + 12x + 36 \in R[x]$, then $d_1(x) = x^3 - x - 6$ and $d_2(x) = 1$. Therefore $f(x) = (x^3 - x - 6)^2(x^2 + 1)$, where $x^3 - x - 6$ and $x^2 + 1$ have no multiple factors and no factors in common. This factorization is valid in $F[x]$ for any $F \supseteq R$. Thus to find the canonical factorization of $f(x)$ in $F[x]$ we have only to solve the simpler problems of obtaining the canonical factorizations of $x^3 - x - 6$ and $x^2 + 1$ in $F[x]$.

EXAMPLE 2. If $f(x) = x^7 + 7x^6 + 14x^5 + 14x^4 + 49x^3 + 63x^2 + 108 \in R[x]$, then $d_1(x) = x^4 + 5x^3 + 5x^2 + 3x + 18$, $d_2(x) = x + 3$ and $d_3(x) = 1$. Thus $x + 3$ is a threefold factor of $f(x)$, and $f(x) = (x + 3)^3 (x^4 - 2x^3 + 5x^2 - 4x + 4)$ and $d_1(x) = (x + 3)^2(x^2 - x + 2)$. Now $x^2 - x + 2$ is a twofold factor of $f(x)$ since it is a factor of $d_1(x)$ which is relatively prime to its derivative. Thus $f(x) = (x + 3)^3(x^2 - x + 2)^2$. Since $x^2 - x + 2 = (x - 1/2 + \sqrt{7}/2\, i)(x - 1/2 - \sqrt{7}/2\, i)$ in $C[x]$, $f(x)$ has a further factorization in $F[x]$ if and only if F is a number field containing $\sqrt{7}\, i$.

Exercise (62.1). Prove properties (i), (ii), and (iii) of derivatives given after Definition (62.1).

Exercise (62.2). Prove Theorem (62.7).

Exercise (62.3). Factor the following completely in $R[x]$ using Theorem (62.4):

(a) $x^4 - x^3 - 3x^2 + 5x - 2$;
(b) $x^4 - 10x^3 + 33x^2 - 40x + 16$;
(c) $x^4 - 15x^2 - 28x - 12$;
(d) $x^4 + 12x^3 + 54x^2 + 108x + 81$;
(e) $x^4 - 2x^3 - 2x^2 + 6x + 5$.

Exercise (62.4). Show that $\Phi(x) = x^3 - x^2$ is a twofold factor of both $f(x) = x^8 - 3x^7 + 3x^6 - x^5$ and its derivative. Does this contradict Theorem (62.4)?

Exercise (62.5). Factor completely in $R^{\#}[x]$ using Theorem (62.4):

(a) $x^4 - 2\sqrt[5]{2}\, x^3 + 2\sqrt[5]{8}\, x - \sqrt[5]{16}$;
(b) $x^4 + (3 - 2\sqrt{3})x^3 + (6 - 6\sqrt{3})x^2 + (9 - 6\sqrt{3})x + 9$.

Exercise (62.6). Let F be a field of characteristic p. Prove that $f'(x) = 0$ if and only if $f(x) = g(x^p)$ for $g(x) \in F[x]$.

Exercise (62.7). If F has characteristic 7, show that $f(x) = x^7 - 1 \in F[x]$ is the g.c.d. of $f(x)$ and its derivative. Factor $f(x)$ in $F[x]$ Does this contradict Theorem (62.4)?

Section 63. The Zeros of a Polynomial

Let $p(x) = \sum_{i=0}^{n} c_i x^i$ be a polynomial in $F[x]$. For $a \in F$, we denote by $p(a)$ the element $\sum_{i=0}^{n} c_i a^i \in F$, and we call $p(a)$ the *value of* $p(x)$ *when* x *equals* a. Since two polynomials are equal in $F[x]$ only if they have the same coefficients in F, it follows that $p(x) = q(x)$ in $F[x]$ implies that their values $p(a) = q(a)$ in F for all $a \in F$.

The theory of equations is concerned with the problem of finding all $a \in F$ such that $p(a) = 0$. Using the division algorithm in $F[x]$ we can relate this problem to the factorization of a polynomial, which was discussed in the preceding sections.

(63.1) Definition. The element $a \in F$ is called a *zero of the polynomial* $p(x) \in F[x]$, or a root of the equation $p(x) = 0$, if $p(a) = 0$.

If $c \neq 0$ is in F, then $c \cdot p(a) = 0$ if and only if $p(a) = 0$, so that the zeros of $p(x)$ are unchanged if $p(x)$ is multiplied by a non-zero constant in F.

(63.2) Theorem (Remainder Theorem). If $p(x) \in F[x]$ and $a \in F$, then $p(a)$ is the remainder on dividing $p(x)$ by $x - a$.

PROOF. By the division algorithm, $p(x) = s(x) \cdot (x - a) + r(x)$ where either $r(x) = 0$ or deg $(r) <$ deg $(x - a) = 1$. In either case $r(x) = r$, a constant in F. Finding the values of these expressions when x equals a, we have that

$$p(a) = s(a) \cdot (a - a) + r = r.$$

(63.3) Theorem (Factor Theorem). The element $a \in F$ is a zero of the polynomial $p(x) \in F[x]$ if and only if $x - a$ is a factor of $p(x)$.

PROOF. By the division algorithm, $x - a$ is a factor of $p(x)$ if and only if the remainder on dividing $p(x)$ by $x - a$ is zero, and this remainder is $p(a)$ by the Remainder Theorem.

(63.4) Corollary. Let $a_1, a_2, \cdots, a_k$ be distinct elements of F. Then $a_1, a_2, \cdots, a_k$ are zeros of $p(x) \in F[x]$ if and only if $p(x)$ is divisible by $(x - a_1)(x - a_2) \cdots (x - a_k)$.

PROOF. If $p(x) = (x - a_1)(x - a_2) \cdots (x - a_k) \cdot q(x)$, then $p(a_i) = 0$ for $i = 1, 2, \cdots, k$ by direct substitution. Conversely, the Factor Theorem gives the result for $k = 1$. Assume that if $p(x)$ has $k - 1$ distinct zeros, $a_1, a_2, \cdots, a_{k-1}$, then $p(x) = (x - a_1)(x - a_2) \cdots (x - a_{k-1})t(x)$. Now if $p(x)$ has an additional zero a_k, we have that

$$p(a_k) = (a_k - a_1)(a_k - a_2) \cdots (a_k - a_{k-1})t(a_k) = 0.$$

Since a_k is distinct from $a_1, a_2, \cdots, a_{k-1}$, the product $(a_k - a_1)(a_k - a_2) \cdots (a_k - a_{k-1}) \neq 0$, and therefore $t(a_k) = 0$. Again by the Factor Theorem, $t(x) = (x - a_k)q(x)$, so that

$$p(x) = (x - a_1)(x - a_2) \cdots (x - a_{k-1})(x - a_k) \cdot q(x).$$

(63.5) Corollary. A polynomial $p(x) \in F[x]$ of degree n has at most n distinct zeros in F.

PROOF. By Corollary (63.4), if $p(x)$ has k distinct zeros, then $p(x) = (x - a_1)(x - a_2) \cdots (x - a_k)q(x)$, and $n = \deg(p) = k + \deg(q)$. Thus $k = n - \deg(q) \leq n$.

If $a_1, a_2, \cdots, a_k$ are distinct zeros of $p(x)$, then the monic irreducible linear factors $(x - a_i)$ for $i = 1, 2, \cdots, k$ appear in the canonical factorization of $p(x)$ so that

$$p(x) = c(x - a_1)^{\alpha_1}(x - a_2)^{\alpha_2} \cdots (x - a_k)^{\alpha_k}p_{k+1}(x)^{\alpha_{k+1}} \cdots p_t(x)^{\alpha_t}.$$

The exponent α_i, which gives the multiplicity of the factor $(x - a_i)$, is also called the *multiplicity of the zero* a_i of $p(x)$. If $\alpha_i = 1$, a_i is called a *simple zero* of $p(x)$, and if $\alpha_i > 1$, a_i is called an *α_i-fold zero* of $p(x)$. The methods of the preceding section may be used to obtain information about the multiple zeros of $p(x)$. For example, consider $p(x) = x^5 - 3/2\, x^4 + 7/4\, x^3 - 13/8\, x^2 + 3/4\, x - 1/8$ in $R[x]$. Then $p'(x) = 5x^4 - 6x^3 + 21/4\, x^2 - 13/4\, x + 3/4$, and using the Euclidean algorithm, we find that the g.c.d. of $p(x)$ and $p'(x)$ is $d(x) = x^2 - x + 1/4 = (x - 1/2)^2$. Since $1/2$ is a double zero of $d(x)$, $1/2$ is a triple zero of $p(x)$ by Theorem (62.4). Dividing $p(x)$ by $(x - 1/2)^3$ we have $p(x) = (x - 1/2)^3(x^2 + 1)$. Since $x^2 + 1$ is irreducible in $R[x]$, $p(x)$ has only the triple zero $1/2$ in R.

It was remarked at the beginning of the section that if $p(x) = q(x) \in F[x]$, their values $p(a) = q(a) \in F$ for all $a \in F$. The converse of this statement is also true if the field F contains enough elements.

(63.6) Theorem. Let $p(x)$ and $q(x)$ be polynomials in $F[x]$ of degrees n and m respectively where $n \geq m$. If $p(a_i) = q(a_i)$ for at least $n + 1$ distinct elements $a_1, a_2, \cdots, a_{n+1} \in F$, then $p(x) = q(x)$ in $F[x]$.

PROOF. Let $s(x) = p(x) - q(x)$. Then if $s(x) \neq 0$, $s(x)$ has degree $\leq n$. But $s(a_i) = p(a_i) - q(a_i) = 0$ for the distinct elements $a_1, a_2, \cdots, a_{n+1} \in F$. This contradicts Corollary (63.5), so that $s(x) = p(x) - q(x) = 0$ and $p(x) = q(x)$.

There are various methods for constructing a polynomial $p(x)$ of degree $\leq n$ which has preassigned values $p(a_i) \in F$ for distinct $a_i \in F$, $i = 1, 2, \cdots, n+1$ [see Exercise (63.1)]. The above theorem proves the uniqueness of such a polynomial.

The correspondence $a \to p(a)$, where $p(a)$ is the value of the polynomial $p(x)$ when x equals a, is a transformation of the field F into itself. Such a transformation is called a *polynomial function*, and every polynomial in $F[x]$ defines a polynomial function of F into itself.

Recalling the definition of equality of transformations, two polynomial functions are equal (that is, are identical functions) if and only if $p(a) = q(a)$ for all $a \in F$. If F is an infinite field and if $p(a) = q(a)$ for all $a \in F$, then the hypotheses of Theorem (63.6) are satisfied and the polynomials $p(x)$ and $q(x)$ which define the functions are equal in $F[x]$. Thus in most cases, for example, for fields of infinite characteristic and in particular for number fields, the identity of polynomial functions coincides with the equality of polynomials in $F[x]$.

Exercise (63.1). Show that the expression

$$P(x) = \sum_{i=0}^{n} \frac{(x - a_0) \cdots (x - a_{i-1})(x - a_{i+1}) \cdots (x - a_n)}{(a_i - a_0) \cdots (a_i - a_{i-1})(a_i - a_{i+1}) \cdots (a_i - a_n)} c_i$$

is a polynomial in $F[x]$ of degree $\leq n$ which takes on preassigned values $c_0, c_1, \cdots, c_n$ in F when x is equal to the distinct values $a_0, a_1, \cdots, a_n \in F$. This is called Lagrange's interpolation formula.

Exercise (63.2). Find a polynomial $p(x)$ which has the property that

(a) $p(-2) = -41, p(-1) = -10, p(1) = -2, p(2) = -13;$
(b) $p(-4) = 46, p(-2) = 6, p(2) = -2, p(4) = 30;$
(c) $p(-3) = 0, p(0) = 0, p(3) = 8, p(6) = 0.$

Exercise (63.3). Give an example of a non-zero polynomial $p(x) \in J_5[x]$ such that $p(a) = 0$ for all $a \in J_5$. Hence find two non-zero polynomials $p(x) \neq q(x)$ in $J_5[x]$ such that $p(a) = q(a)$ for all $a \in J_5$.

Exercise (63.4). Find the condition on the coefficients such that $x^3 + ax + b$ has no multiple zeros.

Exercise (63.5). Derive Taylor's formula $f(x) = \sum_{i=0}^{n} \frac{f^{(i)}(h)}{i!} (x - h)^i$ for $h \in F$, and show that a is an r-fold zero of $f(x)$ if and only if $f(a) = f'(a) = \cdots = f^{(r-1)}(a) = 0$, $f^{(r)}(a) \neq 0$. Show how to obtain $f^{(i)}(a)$ using the division algorithm.

Section 64. The Fundamental Theorem of Algebra

It has already been mentioned in Section 54 that the field C of complex numbers is algebraically closed. This result, known as the Fundamental Theorem of Algebra, may now be stated in its usual form using the terminology of the present chapter.

(64.1) Theorem. If $p(x) \in C[x]$ has degree $n \geq 1$, then $p(x)$ has at least one zero in C.

We will accept this theorem without proof since, as has been mentioned before, the known proofs involve some knowledge of the theory of functions of a complex variable. The proof of the following corollary is left to the reader as an exercise.

(64.2) Corollary. If $p(x) \in C[x]$ has degree $n \geq 1$, then $p(x)$ factors into n linear factors in $C[x]$.

Although this corollary gives no information about how to obtain the factorization of a polynomial, it does have theoretical importance. We may use it to obtain the form of the factorization in $R^{\#}[x]$ as a corollary to the following theorem.

(64.3) Theorem. If $p(x) \in R^{\#}[x]$ and if $a + bi \in C$ is a zero of $p(x)$, then $a - bi$ is also a zero.

PROOF. If $p(x) = \sum_{i=0}^{n} a_i x^i \in R^{\#}[x]$ and α is any complex number, then $p(\alpha) = \sum_{i=0}^{n} a_i \alpha^i$. Since the correspondence $\alpha = a + bi \rightarrow \bar{\alpha} = a - bi$ is a field-automorphism of C, the conjugate of a sum or product of complex numbers is respectively the sum or product of the conjugates of the factors. Thus

$$\overline{p(\alpha)} = \overline{\sum_{i=0}^{n} a_i \alpha^i} = \sum_{i=0}^{n} \overline{a_i \alpha^i} = \sum_{i=0}^{n} a_i \bar{\alpha}^i = p(\bar{\alpha})$$

since a_i is real for $i = 0, 1, 2, \cdots, n$. In particular, if $p(a + bi) = 0$, then $p(a - bi) = \overline{p(a + bi)} = \bar{0} = 0$ and $a - bi$ is also a zero.

(64.4) Corollary. If $p(x) \in R^{\#}[x]$ has degree $n \geq 1$, then $p(x)$ factors into linear and irreducible quadratic factors in $R^{\#}[x]$.

PROOF. By Corollary (64.2), $p(x)$ factors as a product of linear factors $x - \alpha_i$ in $C[x]$. If $\alpha_i \in R^{\#}$, $x - \alpha_i \in R^{\#}[x]$. If $\alpha_i = a + bi \in C$ with $a,b \neq 0$ in $R^{\#}$, then by the theorem $x - \overline{\alpha_i}$ is also a factor of

$p(x)$. But $(x - \alpha_i)(x - \overline{\alpha_i}) = (x - a - bi)(x - a + bi) = x^2 - 2ax + (a^2 + b^2)$ is in $R^\#[x]$. This polynomial is irreducible in $R^\#[x]$ since any factorization in $R^\#[x]$ is valid in $C[x]$, and $(x - \alpha_i)(x - \overline{\alpha_i})$ is the unique factorization in $C[x]$.

(64.5) Corollary. If $p(x) \in R^\#[x]$ has odd degree, $p(x)$ has at least one real zero.

The proof of this corollary is left to the reader as an exercise.

We will close this section with a discussion of a relationship between the coefficients and zeros of a polynomial. Let D be any integral domain and let $k_1, k_2, \cdots, k_n$ be any set of elements in D. We define polynomials $\sigma_i(k) = \sigma_i(k_1, k_2, \cdots, k_n)$ for $i = 0, 1, 2, \cdots, n$ by

$$\begin{aligned}
\sigma_0(k) &= e \\
\sigma_1(k) &= k_1 + k_2 + \cdots + k_n \\
\sigma_2(k) &= k_1k_2 + k_1k_3 + \cdots + k_1k_n + k_2k_3 + \cdots + k_{n-1}k_n \\
&\cdots \\
\sigma_n(k) &= k_1k_2 \cdots k_n,
\end{aligned}$$

where in general $\sigma_i(k)$ is the sum of all products of the elements $k_1, k_2, \cdots, k_n$ taken i at a time. These polynomials in D are called the *elementary symmetric functions* of $k_1, k_2, \cdots, k_n$, and they are left unchanged by any permutation of the elements $k_1, k_2, \cdots, k_n$.

Let $p(x) = \sum_{i=0}^{n} a_ix^i \in F[x]$ and assume that there exists a field $K \supseteq F$ such that $p(x)$ factors into linear factors in the domain $K[x]$. Then in $K[x]$

$$p(x) = \sum_{i=0}^{n} a_ix^i = a_n \prod_{i=1}^{n} (x - r_i) = a_n \sum_{i=0}^{n} (-1)^{n-i}\sigma_{n-i}x^i$$

where $\sigma_i = \sigma_i(r)$ is the ith elementary symmetric function of the zeros $r_1, r_2, \cdots, r_n$. But since the coefficients of $p(x)$ in K are unique, this implies that

(64.6) $$a_i = (-1)^{n-i}a_n\sigma_{n-i} \qquad \text{for } i = 0, 1, 2, \cdots, n.$$

The above relationships are useful in the study of the form of a polynomial which has zeros with preassigned properties. The ideas discussed above can be used for any polynomial, for it can be proved that given any field F, there exists at least one algebraically closed field $K \supseteq F$, that is, a field $K \supseteq F$ such that every polynomial with coefficients in F factors into linear factors in $K[x]$. In particular, if F is a number field, K may be taken to be the field C by Corollary (64.2).

EXAMPLE 1. To construct a monic polynomial in $R[x]$ with $r_1 = 3$ and $r_3 = 3r_2$. Then $a_3 = 1$, $a_2 = -(3 + 4r_2)$, $a_1 = 12r_2 + 3r_2^2$, and $a_0 = -9r_2^2$, so that $p(x)$ has the form $x^3 - (3 + 4k)x^2 + (12k + 3k^2)x - 9k^2$ where k is any rational number.

EXAMPLE 2. To determine h and k in $x^4 - 7x^3 + hx^2 + kx - 48 = 0$ so that two of its roots are 3 and -2. Let the roots be $r_1 = 3, r_2 = -2$, r_3, and r_4. Then $1 + r_3 + r_4 = 7$ and $-6r_3r_4 = -48$. This shows that $r_3 = 2$, $r_4 = 4$, and therefore that $h = 8$ and $k = 28$.

Exercise (64.1). Prove Corollary (64.2).

Exercise (64.2). Prove that if $a + bi$ is a zero of $p(x) \in R^{\#}[x]$, the multiplicity of $a - bi$ is the same as that of $a + bi$.

Exercise (64.3). Construct a monic polynomial in $R[x]$, using (64.6),

(a) with zeros 2, -1, and 4;
(b) with zeros i and $1 + i$;
(c) with zeros r_1, $r_2 = r_1 + 1$, and $r_3 = r_1 + 2$;
(d) with zeros r_1, r_2, and $r_3 = r_1r_2$.

Exercise (64.4). Find the conditions on the coefficients so that

(a) 1 is a double zero of $x^4 + hx^3 - x^2 + kx + 4$;
(b) one zero of $x^3 + hx + k$ is the reciprocal of a second;
(c) the zeros of $x^4 + hx^3 + kx^2 + ax + b$ are 1, -1, r, and $-r$.

Exercise (64.5). Prove that $\sigma_i = s_i + k_n s_{i-1}$, where σ_i is the ith elementary symmetric function of $k_1, k_2, \cdots, k_n$, where s_i is the ith elementary symmetric function of $k_1, k_2, \cdots, k_{n-1}$, and where $s_n = 0$.

Exercise (64.6). Using the previous exercise, prove by induction on n that

$$\prod_{i=1}^{n} (x - r_i) = \sum_{i=0}^{n} (-1)^{n-i}\sigma_{n-i}(r)x^i.$$

Section 65. The Theory of Equations in $R[x]$ and $R^{\#}[x]$

Since the problem of finding the zeros in F of a polynomial $p(x) \in F[x]$ is the same as that of finding the linear factors of $p(x)$ in $F[x]$, the methods employed to solve the equation $p(x) = 0$ depend upon special properties of the field F. We will include in this section some important results about the theory of equations in $R[x]$ and $R^{\#}[x]$.

The problem of finding the zeros in R of a polynomial $p(x)$ in $R[x]$ is very easily solved. Let m be the l.c.m. of the denominators of the coefficients of $p(x)$. Then $mp(x)$ is a polynomial with integral coefficients which has the same zeros in R as $p(x)$. Thus the problem of finding the rational zeros of a polynomial with rational coefficients is reduced to that of finding the rational zeros of a polynomial with integral coefficients.

(65.1) Theorem. Let $p(x) = \sum_{i=0}^{n} a_i x^i \in J[x]$ and let $r = s/t \in R$ where s and t are relatively prime integers. Then r is a zero of $p(x)$ only if s divides a_0 and t divides a_n.

PROOF. If $r = s/t$ is a zero of $p(x)$, then $\sum_{i=0}^{n} a_i(s/t)^i = a_0 + a_1(s/t) + a_2(s/t)^2 + \cdots + a_{n-1}(s/t)^{n-1} + a_n(s/t)^n = 0$. Multiplying this by t^n, we have that

$$a_0t^n = s(-a_1t^{n-1} - a_2st^{n-2} - \cdots - a_{n-1}s^{n-2}t - a_ns^{n-1})$$

and that

$$(a_0t^{n-1} + a_1st^{n-2} + a_2s^2t^{n-3} + \cdots + a_{n-1}s^{n-1})t = -a_ns^n.$$

The first of these equalities shows that s divides a_0t^n and the second that t divides a_ns^n. Since s and t are relatively prime, we obtain the desired result using (0.10) of the Introduction.

Using this theorem we may obtain in a finite number of steps all the rational roots of an equation with rational coefficients. For the problem is reduced to that of examining all factors of an integer, and every integer has a finite number of factors. Thus, given the equation $x^4 - 2x^3 - 7x^2 - 11/3\, x - 4/3 = 0$, we can replace it by the equation $3x^4 - 6x^3 - 21x^2 - 11x - 4 = 0$ for the purpose of finding its roots. Since the divisors of 4 are 1, 2, and 4 and the divisors of 3 are 1 and 3, the only possible rational roots are ± 1, ± 2, ± 4, and $\pm 1/3$, $\pm 2/3$, $\pm 4/3$. Direct substitution shows that 4 is the only rational root of the given equation.

The property of polynomials in $R^\#[x]$ which is basic for the study of real zeros is that the polynomial function defined by $p(x) \in R^\#[x]$ is a continuous function of $R^\#$ into itself. For if $a \in R^\#$ and if $a_1, a_2, \cdots, a_n, \cdots$ is any fundamental sequence of real numbers with a as its limit, it can be verified that $p(a_1), p(a_2), \cdots, p(a_n), \cdots$ is a fundamental sequence of real numbers with limit $p(a)$.

(65.2) Theorem. If there exist real numbers $a < b$ such that $p(a)$ and $p(b)$ have opposite signs for $p(x) \in R^\#[x]$, then $p(x)$ has a real zero r such that $a < r < b$.

This theorem is known as the Location Principle and is valid for all continuous functions of $R^{\#}$. Since the proof of this theorem is best presented using the least upper bound characterization of the real numbers, which was only briefly discussed in Section 53, we will only sketch its proof.* If we let S be the set of all real numbers c such that $a < c < b$ and such that $p(c)$ has the same sign as $p(a)$, then S will have a real number r as its least upper bound, and it can be proved, using the continuity of $p(x)$, that $p(r) = 0$.

The problem of finding the real roots of a polynomial equation $p(x) = 0$ with real coefficients is solved by finding rational numbers which approximate the real roots. For, by definition, a real number is a limit of a fundamental sequence of rational numbers. The Location Principle (65.2) is basic for the two aspects of the solution of this problem which may be described as follows. First, the number of distinct real roots of $p(x) = 0$ is counted and each real root r is isolated between two rational numbers; and second, a fundamental sequence of rational numbers is constructed which has r as its limit. The reader is familiar with some of the techniques employed in the solution of this problem from college algebra, and is referred to a text on the Theory of Equations for a detailed account of the methods involved. The following examples illustrate the use of some of these methods.

EXAMPLE 1. Let $p(x) = x^3 - \sqrt{3}\,x^2 + 7x - 5$. Since $p(x)$ has odd degree, it has either one or three real zeros by (64.4). Since $p(0) = -5 < 0$ and $p(a) > 0$ if a is large enough, $p(x)$ has at least one real zero by (65.2). Rolle's Theorem from differential calculus, which is valid for polynomial functions, states that between two real zeros of $p(x)$, there is at least one zero of $p'(x)$. In this example, $p'(x) = 3x^2 - 2\sqrt{3}\,x + 7$ is a quadratic polynomial with a negative discriminant, and therefore has no real zeros. Then by Rolle's Theorem, $p(x)$ cannot have two distinct real zeros. Thus $p(x)$ has exactly one real zero r and $0 < r < 1$, since $p(1) = 3 - \sqrt{3} > 0$, completing the first part of the problem.

To construct a fundamental sequence of rational numbers with r as its limit, we can use the Location Principle to locate r between successive tenths, hundredths, thousandths, and so forth. This procedure is systematized and the calculations are shortened by Horner's Method. In this example, $.7 < r < .8$, $.79 < r < .80$, and so on, so that a fundamental sequence of rational numbers with r as its limit is $0, .7, .79, \cdots$.

* See B. L. van der Waerden, *Modern Algebra* (New York, 1949), I, 218.

EXAMPLE 2. Let $p(x) = x^4 - 3x^3 + 7x^2 + 1$. Descartes's Rule of Signs states that the number of positive zeros of a polynomial $p(x)$ is equal to the number of variations in sign of the coefficients minus a non-negative even integer. Using this, $p(x)$ has two positive zeros or none. But since $p'(x) = 4x^3 - 9x^2 + 14x = x(4x^2 - 9x + 14)$ has no positive zeros, $p(x)$ has no positive double zeros by (62.4), and $p(x)$ cannot have two distinct positive zeros by Rolle's Theorem. Thus $p(x)$ has no positive zeros. Since the negative zeros of $p(x)$ are the positive zeros of $p(-x) = x^4 + 3x^3 + 7x^2 + 1$, we can again use Descartes' Rule to show that $p(x)$ has no negative zeros. Since $p(0) \neq 0$, $p(x)$ has no real zeros.

EXAMPLE 3. Let $p(x) = x^5 - 5x^2 + 1$. Then $p'(x) = 5x^4 - 10x = 5x(x - \sqrt[3]{2})(x^2 + \sqrt[3]{2}\,x + \sqrt[3]{4})$ has only two real zeros so that $p(x)$ has at most three distinct real zeros. Since $p(-1) < 0$, $p(0) > 0$, $p(1) < 0$, and $p(2) > 0$, $p(x)$ has exactly three real zeros r_1, r_2, r_3 such that $-1 < r_1 < 0$, $0 < r_2 < 1$, and $1 < r_3 < 2$.

Exercise (65.1). Show that if a_0 and a_n have different signs, $p(x) \in R^{\#}[x]$ has at least one positive real zero. Why is there no corresponding theorem in $C[x]$?

Exercise (65.2). Find all rational zeros of

(a) $3x^4 - 7/2\,x^2 + 2/5\,x - 1$;
(b) $x^4 - 64x^3 + 3x^2 + 2/27\,x + 2$;
(c) $3x^4 + 47/15\,x^3 + 12/5\,x^2 - 3/5\,x - 8/15$;
(d) $4x^3 - 20x^2 + 36x - 48$.

Exercise (65.3). Find a set of canonical forms in $J[x]$ for the polynomials in $R[x]$ under the equivalence relation of association.

Exercise (65.4). Discuss the real zeros of

(a) $6x^4 - 9x^2 + 5$;
(b) $5x^4 - 7x + 1$;
(c) $x^4 - x^3 + 7$;
(d) $x^4 - x^3 - x^2 + 4x + 4$;
(e) $x^5 - 3x^3 - 7x$;
(f) $x^2 + ax + b$ where $a, b \in R^{\#}$;
(g) $x^n - a$ for n a positive integer and $a \in R^{\#}$.

Exercise (65.5). Prove that $a_1, a_2, \cdots, a_n, \cdots$ is a fundamental sequence of rational numbers if $a_i \leq a_{i+1} < a_i + 10^{-i}$ for all i.

Exercise (65.6). Prove that $p(x) = ax^n$ defines a continuous function of $R^{\#}$, where n is a positive integer. Since a sum of continuous functions is continuous, this proves that a polynomial function is continuous.

Section 66. Polynomials in Several Indeterminates

The proof of the existence of the polynomial domain $F[x]$ given in Theorem (58.4) depended on the properties of F as an integral domain. Therefore the same construction may be used to obtain an integral domain $F[x][y]$ where y is an indeterminate over $F[x]$. By Theorem (56.4), $F[x][y] = F[y][x] = F[x, y]$, and it may be shown that x and y are independent indeterminates over F [see Exercise (58.4) for the definition of independent indeterminates]. We may use induction to establish the existence of an integral domain $F[x_1, x_2, \cdots, x_n]$ where $x_1, x_2, \cdots, x_n$ are independent indeterminates over the field F.

The elements of $F[x_1, x_2, \cdots, x_n]$ are polynomials in $x_1, x_2, \cdots, x_n$ with coefficients in F, that is, they are finite sums of the form $p(x_1, x_2, \cdots, x_n) = \Sigma c_j x_1^{j_1} x_2^{j_2} \cdots x_n^{j_n}$ where $c_j \in F$ and each j_k is a non-negative integer. The expression $\Sigma c_j x_1^{j_1} x_2^{j_2} \cdots x_n^{j_n}$ is written so that there is only one term with a given set of exponents $j_1, j_2, \cdots, j_n$. Then by the fact that $x_1, x_2, \cdots, x_n$ are independent indeterminates over F, $p(x_1, x_2, \cdots, x_n) = 0$ if and only if each coefficient $c_j = 0$, and it follows that $q(x_1, x_2, \cdots, x_n) = p(x_1, x_2, \cdots, x_n)$ if and only if p and q have the same coefficients in F.

The degree of a single non-zero term $c_j x_1^{j_1} x_2^{j_2} \cdots x_n^{j_n}$ of $p(x_1, x_2, \cdots, x_n)$ is the integer $\sum_{k=1}^{n} j_k \geq 0$, and the degree of $p(x_1, x_2, \cdots, x_n)$ is the maximum of the degrees of its terms. For example, the polynomial $p(x_1, x_2, x_3) = 7 + 2x_1^2x_2 - 1/3\, x_1x_2x_3 + 5x_1^4 - 6x_2^3x_3$ has degree 4. It has terms of degree 4, 3, and 0.

Of particular interest because of their relation to groups of matrix transformations are those polynomials in which all terms have the same degree.

(66.1) Definition. A polynomial $p(x_1, x_2, \cdots, x_n) \in F[x_1, x_2, \cdots, x_n]$ is called a *form* or a *homogeneous polynomial* if all terms have the same degree. The zero polynomial is called the *zero form.*

Thus $\sum_{i=1}^{n} c_i x_i = c_1x_1 + c_2x_2 + \cdots + c_nx_n$ is called a linear form,

and $\sum_{i=1}^{n} \sum_{j=i}^{n} c_{ij}x_ix_j = \sum_{j=1}^{n} c_{1j}x_1x_j + \sum_{j=2}^{n} c_{2j}x_2x_j + \cdots + \sum_{j=n}^{n} c_{nj}x_nx_j = c_{11}x_1^2$

$+ c_{12}x_1x_2 + \cdots + c_{1n}x_1x_n + c_{22}x_2^2 + c_{23}x_2x_3 + \cdots + c_{n-1n}x_{n-1}x_n + c_{nn}x_n^2$ is called a quadratic form.

It is clear that each polynomial in $F[x_1, x_2, \cdots, x_n]$ can be written as a sum of forms

$$p(x_1, x_2, \cdots, x_n) = \sum_{i=0}^{m} f_i(x_1, x_2, \cdots, x_n),$$

where either $f_i(x_1, x_2, \cdots, x_n) = 0$ or $f_i(x_1, x_2, \cdots, x_n)$ is a form of degree i. In the example given earlier, $p(x_1, x_2, x_3) = f_0(x_1, x_2, x_3) + f_3(x_1, x_2, x_3) + f_4(x_1, x_2, x_3)$ where $f_0 = 7$, $f_3 = 2x_1^2x_2 - 1/3\, x_1x_2x_3$, and $f_4 = 5x_1^4 - 6x_2^3x_3$.

After verifying that the product of two forms of degrees s and t respectively is a form of degree $s + t$, we obtain a generalization of Theorem (59.3) for polynomials in n indeterminates.

(66.2) Theorem. If $p(x_1, x_2, \cdots, x_n)$ and $q(x_1, x_2, \cdots, x_n)$ are polynomials of degree s and t respectively, then:

(i) $p(x_1, x_2, \cdots, x_n) \pm q(x_1, x_2, \cdots, x_n)$ is either the zero polynomial or is a polynomial with degree $\leq \max [s,t]$.
(ii) $p(x_1, x_2, \cdots, x_n) \cdot q(x_1, x_2, \cdots, x_n)$ has degree $s + t$.

We conclude this section with a discussion of those forms which will be considered in detail in Chapter VIII.

In the quadratic form $\sum_{i=1}^{n} \sum_{j=i}^{n} c_{ij}x_ix_j$, writing* $c_{ij}x_ix_j$ for $i \neq j$, as $d_{ij}x_ix_j + d_{ji}x_jx_i$ where $d_{ij} = d_{ji} = 1/2\, c_{ij}$, and writing $d_{ii} = c_{ii}$, the form becomes $\sum_{i=1}^{n} \sum_{j=1}^{n} x_id_{ij}x_j$ where $D = (d_{ij})$ is an n-rowed square symmetric matrix, called the matrix of the form. In matrix notation with $X = (x_1, x_2, \cdots, x_n)$, the form is written XDX'.

A principle of considerable importance in discussing polynomials in $F[x_1, x_2, \cdots, x_n]$, is that they may be regarded as polynomials in $x_{k+1}, x_{k+2}, \cdots, x_n$ with coefficients in $F[x_1, x_2, \cdots, x_k]$. We use it here to describe a special quadratic form called a bilinear form. Let the indeterminates $x_1, x_2, \cdots, x_n$ be separated into two sets $x_1, x_2, \cdots, x_k$ and $x_{k+1}, x_{k+2}, \cdots, x_n$, where for convenience we denote $x_{k+1}, x_{k+2}, \cdots, x_n$ by $y_1, y_2, \cdots, y_m$, respectively. A *bilinear form* is a quadratic form with coefficients in F in the complete set of indeterminates

* For this discussion, we assume that the characteristic of F is not 2.

$x_1, x_2, \cdots, x_k, y_1, y_2, \cdots, y_m$ which is a linear form in each set $x_1, x_2, \cdots, x_k$ and $y_1, y_2, \cdots, y_m$ with coefficients in $F[y_1, y_2, \cdots, y_m]$ and $F[x_1, x_2, \cdots, x_k]$ respectively. For example, $p(x_1, x_2, x_3, y_1, y_2) = 3x_1y_1 + 1/2\, x_2y_1 - 5x_3y_2$ is a bilinear form in x_1, x_2, x_3 and y_1, y_2 with coefficients in R. Thus, any bilinear form has the expression $\sum_{i=1}^{k} \sum_{j=1}^{m} x_i c_{ij} y_j$. In matrix notation, with $X = (x_1, x_2, \cdots, x_k)$ and $Y = (y_1, y_2, \cdots, y_m)$, the form is written XCY' where $C = (c_{ij})$ is a k by m matrix called the matrix of the form. Bilinear forms have a theory of reduction to canonical form which coincides with the reduction of rectangular matrices to canonical form by equivalence transformations, as was proved in Section 29.

Exercise (66.1). Show that if $p(x_1, x_2, \cdots, x_n)$ is a form of degree m, then $p(tx_1, tx_2, \cdots, tx_n) = t^m p(x_1, x_2, \cdots, x_n)$.

Exercise (66.2). Prove that the set of all linear forms $c_1x_1 + c_2x_2 + \cdots + c_nx_n$ plus the zero form in $F[x_1, x_2, \cdots, x_n]$ is a vector space over F isomorphic to $V_n(F)$.

Exercise (66.3). Prove that the set of all forms of degree s plus the zero form in $F[x_1, x_2, \cdots, x_n]$ is a finite-dimensional vector space over F. What is the dimension of this space?

Exercise (66.4). Write the following polynomials in $R[x_1, x_2, x_3, x_4]$ as a sum of forms:

(a) $5x_1^2x_2x_4 - 1/2\, x_1^3 + 2x_1x_2x_3^2x_4 - x_4^4 + 5x_2^3x_3^2 - 4x_1 + 2x_2 + 10$;

(b) $x_1x_2x_3x_4 - 2x_1^2x_3 + 5x_1x_4^2 + 7x_3^2x_4 + 2x_1x_2 + 1/3\, x_2^2$.

Find the product of these two polynomials.

Exercise (66.5). Write the following quadratic forms in $R[x_1, x_2, x_3]$ in matrix notation with a symmetric matrix:

(a) $x_1^2 + 3x_1x_2 - 5x_1x_3 + x_3^2$;

(b) $1/3\, x_1x_2 + x_2^2 - x_2x_3 - x_3^2$;

(c) $x_1^2 + x_2^2 + x_3^2 + x_1x_2 + x_1x_3 + x_2x_3$.

Exercise (66.6). What are the units of $F[x_1, x_2, \cdots, x_n]$? Prove that the following polynomials are irreducible in $R[x_1, x_2]$:

(a) $x_1^2x_2 - x_1x_2 + x_1^2 - 2x_1 + 3$;

(b) $x_1^2 + x_2^2 + x_1x_2$.

Section 67. Algebraic Elements over F

We now turn to a study of algebraic elements over a field F and of the structure of the simple algebraic extensions $F[u]$ and $F(u)$. We assume as we did at the beginning of this chapter that the field F is contained in a field K and that $u \in K$, so that $F[u]$ and $F(u)$ are respectively the smallest subdomain and smallest subfield of K containing F and u. The study of algebraic elements over F is an extension of the theory of equations in the polynomial domain $F[x]$. For if u is algebraic over F, there is a relation $c_0 + c_1u + c_2u^2 + \cdots + c_nu^n = 0$ with coefficients $c_i \in F$ not all zero. Moreover some $c_i \neq 0$ for $i \geq 1$, for otherwise every $c_i = 0$. Thus u is a zero of the nonconstant polynomial $p(x) = c_0 + c_1x + c_2x^2 + \cdots + c_nx^n \in F[x] \subseteq K[x]$. We have seen in Section 57 that the simple algebraic extension $F[u]$ is a finite-dimensional vector space over F. The exact nature $F[u]$ as a vector space over F is a consequence of the following theorem.

(67.1) Theorem. If K is a field containing F, and if $u \in K$ is algebraic over F, then there exists a unique monic irreducible polynomial $\varphi(x) \in F[x] \subseteq K[x]$ such that u is a zero of $\varphi(x)$. Moreover, $\varphi(x)$ is a factor of every polynomial $p(x) \in F[x]$ of which u is a zero.

PROOF. Since u is algebraic over F, u is a zero of some monic polynomial $p(x) \in F[x]$ of degree $n \geq 1$. Let $\varphi(x)$ of degree m be a monic polynomial of least degree in $F[x]$ such that $\varphi(u) = 0$. Then u is not a zero of any polynomial $f(x)$ in $F[x]$ of degree less than m. For if it were, u would be a zero of the monic associate of $f(x)$, contrary to the choice of $\varphi(x)$.

Now $\varphi(x)$ is irreducible in $F[x]$. For if $\varphi(x)$ has a proper factorization $\varphi(x) = g(x) \cdot h(x)$ in $F[x]$, then $\varphi(u) = g(u)h(u) = 0$ in K. But since $g(u)$ and $h(u)$ are elements of the field K, this implies that either $g(u) = 0$ or $h(u) = 0$ and therefore that u is a zero of a polynomial in $F[x]$ of degree less than m, which is a contradiction.

If $p(x) \in F[x]$, then by the division algorithm $p(x) = q(x)\varphi(x) + r(x)$ where either $r(x) = 0$ or $r(x)$ has degree less than m. If u is a zero of $p(x)$, we have $0 = p(u) = q(u)\varphi(u) + r(u) = r(u)$. If $r(x) \neq 0$, then u is a zero of $r(x)$, again contradicting the choice of $\varphi(x)$. Therefore $r(x) = 0$, $p(x) = q(x)\varphi(x)$, and $\varphi(x)$ is a factor of $p(x)$.

Finally, if u is a zero of a monic irreducible polynomial $\bar{\varphi}(x) \in F[x]$, then by the above paragraph, $\varphi(x)$ is a factor of $\bar{\varphi}(x)$. Since $\bar{\varphi}(x)$ is irreducible, $\bar{\varphi}(x) = c \cdot \varphi(x)$ where $c \in F$, and since both $\bar{\varphi}(x)$ and $\varphi(x)$ are monic, $c = e \in F$. Therefore $\bar{\varphi}(x) = \varphi(x)$ and $\varphi(x)$ is the unique polynomial with the stated properties.

(67.2) Definition. The irreducible polynomial $\varphi(x)$ of Theorem (67.1) is called the *minimum polynomial of the element u*. The degree m of $\varphi(x)$ is called the *degree of the algebraic element u* over F.

As an example, consider the number fields $R \subset C$ and the element $u = \sqrt{3} + i \in C$. Then $u^2 = 2 + 2\sqrt{3}\,i$ and $(u^2 - 2)^2 = -12$, so that $u^4 - 4u^2 + 16 = 0$. Thus u is a zero of $p(x) = x^4 - 4x^2 + 16 \in R[x]$, and u is algebraic over R. The canonical factorization of $p(x)$ in $C[x]$ is

$$p(x) = (x - \sqrt{3} - i)(x - \sqrt{3} + i)(x + \sqrt{3} - i)(x + \sqrt{3} + i),$$

which shows that $p(x)$ can have no linear or quadratic factor in $R[x] \subset C[x]$. Therefore, $p(x)$ is irreducible in $R[x]$, $p(x) = \varphi(x)$ is the minimum polynomial of $u = \sqrt{3} + i$, and the element u has degree 4 over R. Since u is a zero of the polynomial $x^2 + 2\sqrt{3}\,x + 4$ which is irreducible in $R^\#[x]$, u has degree 2 over $R^\#$. The following theorem shows that the simple algebraic extension $R[u]$ is a vector space over R of dimension 4 with the elements 1, $u = \sqrt{3} + i$, $u^2 = 2 + 2\sqrt{3}\,i$, and $u^3 = 8i$ as a basis.

(67.3) Theorem. The simple algebraic extension $F[u]$ is a vector space of dimension m over F where m is the degree of the algebraic element u over F. The elements $e, u, u^2, \cdots, u^{m-1}$ are a basis of $F[u]$ over F.

PROOF. The minimum polynomial $\varphi(x)$ of u has degree m so that $\varphi(u) = c_0 + c_1u + c_2u^2 + \cdots + c_{m-1}u^{m-1} + u^m = 0$ with $c_i \in F$ for $i = 0, 1, 2, \cdots, m - 1$. Thus $u^m = -c_0e - c_1u - c_2u^2 - \cdots - c_{m-1}u^{m-1}$, and we can express u^m and each higher power of u as a linear combination of $e, u, u^2, \cdots, u^{m-1}$ with coefficients in F. Since the elements of $F[u]$ are polynomials in u with coefficients in F, each element of $F[u]$ may be expressed as a linear combination of $e, u, u^2, \cdots, u^{m-1}$ with coefficients in F, so that this set spans $F[u]$ as a vector space over F. Moreover the set is a linearly independent set over F. For if not, there exist $a_i \in F$, not all zero, such that $a_0e + a_1u + a_2u^2 + \cdots + a_{m-1}u^{m-1} = 0$. Since $a_0e \neq 0$ if $a_0 \neq 0$, some $a_i \neq 0$ with $i \geq 1$. This means that u is a zero of the nonconstant polynomial $a_0 + a_1x + a_2x^2 + \cdots + a_{m-1}x^{m-1} \in F[x]$ of degree less than m, which is impossible by Theorem (67.1). Therefore the m elements $e, u, u^2, \cdots, u^{m-1}$ are a basis of $F[u]$ over F, and this completes the proof of the theorem.

As a consequence of the above theorem, $F[u]$ is isomorphic as a vector space to $V_m(F)$, and using Theorem (26.2), we have that each element of $F[u]$ has a unique expression $f(u) = a_0 + a_1u + \cdots$

$+ a_{m-1}u^{m-1}$ as a polynomial in u with coefficients in F. If the elements of $F[u]$ are written in this unique form, addition in $F[u]$ is vector addition. With $g(u) = b_0 + b_1u + \cdots + b_{m-1}u^{m-1}$, we have

$$f(u) \pm g(u) = (a_0 \pm b_0) + (a_1 \pm b_1)u + \cdots + (a_{m-1} \pm b_{m-1})u^{m-1}.$$

In addition to the description of $F[u]$ as a vector space over F, $F[u]$ is an integral domain. The product of two elements $f(u)$ and $g(u)$ in $F[u]$ can be obtained in the following way. We first compute $f(x) \cdot g(x)$ in the polynomial domain $F[x]$. By the division algorithm in $F[x]$,

$$f(x) \cdot g(x) = q(x) \cdot \varphi(x) + r(x)$$

where $\varphi(x)$ of degree m is the minimum polynomial of u and either $r(x) = 0$ or $r(x)$ has degree less than m. We then have $f(u) \cdot g(u) = q(u) \cdot \varphi(u) + r(u) = r(u)$ since $\varphi(u) = 0$, and thus the product $f(u) \cdot g(u) = r(u)$ is written in its unique form as a polynomial in u with coefficients in F.

To continue the earlier example of $R[u] = R[\sqrt{3} + i]$, consider the elements $\alpha = f(u) = 1 + u - 1/2\, u^3$ and $\beta = g(u) = 2 - 3u^2$ in $R[u]$. Then $\alpha + \beta = 3 + u - 3u^2 - 1/2\, u^3$. To compute $\alpha\beta$,

$$\begin{aligned} f(x)g(x) &= 2 + 2x - 3x^2 - 4x^3 + 3/2\, x^5 \\ &= (3/2\, x)(16 - 4x^2 + x^4) + (2 - 22x - 3x^2 + 2x^3) \end{aligned}$$

and $\alpha\beta = f(u) \cdot g(u) = 2 - 22u - 3u^2 + 2u^3$.

We defined $F(u)$ to be the smallest subfield of $K \supseteq F$ which contains F and $u \in K$, and we proved that $F(u)$ is the quotient field of $F[u]$, whether u is algebraic or transcendental over F. If u is algebraic, we find that the integral domain $F[u]$ is itself a field, so that $F[u] = F(u)$.

(67.4) Theorem. The simple algebraic extension $F[u]$ is a field. Further, $F[u] = F(u)$ if and only if u is algebraic over F.

PROOF. We will show that if u is algebraic over F, each non-zero element of the integral domain $F[u]$ has an inverse in $F[u]$. If the minimum polynomial $\varphi(x)$ of u has degree m, and $\alpha \neq 0$ is in $F[u]$, then

$$\alpha = f(u) = a_0 + a_1u + \cdots + a_{m-1}u^{m-1}$$

with not every $a_i = 0$. The polynomial $f(x) \neq 0 \in F[x]$ is relatively prime to $\varphi(x)$ since $\varphi(x)$ is irreducible and $f(x)$ has degree less than m. Then by (60.4), there exist polynomials $s(x)$ and $t(x)$ in $F[x]$ such that

$$s(x)\varphi(x) + t(x)f(x) = e,$$

and consequently

$$s(u)\varphi(u) + t(u)f(u) = t(u)f(u) = e.$$

Therefore $t(u) \in F[u]$ is the inverse of $\alpha = f(u)$.

We have shown that $F[u] = F(u)$ if u is algebraic over F. Conversely, if u is transcendental over F, $F[u]$ is isomorphic to the polynomial domain $F[x]$, and it follows from (60.2) that no polynomial of degree $n \geq 1$ has an inverse in $F[u]$. Therefore $F[u] \neq F(u)$.

Using the same elements $\alpha = f(u) = 1 + u - 1/2\, u^3$ and $\beta = g(u) = 2 - 3u^2$ in $R[u] = R[\sqrt{3} + i]$ as before, we will compute the quotient $\alpha/\beta = \alpha \cdot (1/\beta) \in R[u] = R(u)$ by the method of the theorem. We find that

$$(-5/62 + 3/124\, x^2)\, g(x) + (9/124)\, \varphi(x) = 1,$$

and therefore that $(-5/62 + 3/124\, u^2)g(u) = 1$. Thus $1/\beta = -5/62 + 3/124\, u^2$ and $\alpha/\beta = -5/62 + 7/62\, u + 3/124\, u^2 + 1/62\, u^3$.

The above results show that computation in the simple algebraic extension $F(u)$ is accomplished by operating with polynomials in the polynomial domain $F[x]$. The relation of the structure of $F(u)$ to that of $F[x]$ will be explained in the next section where the question of the existence of a simple algebraic extension of a field F is considered.

Exercise (67.1). Show that the following elements of C are algebraic over R and find their minimum polynomials:

(a) $\sqrt[3]{5}$, (b) $-1/2 + \sqrt{2}\, i$, (c) $i/\sqrt{3}$, (d) $a + bi$ where $a,b \in R$.

Exercise (67.2). Find $1/u$ and $1/u^2$ in $R(u) = R(\sqrt{3} + i)$. If $\alpha = u + u^3$ and $\beta = 3 + 2u^2 + 3u^3$, find $3\alpha - 4\beta$, α^2, and $(\alpha + u)/(\beta - u)$.

Exercise (67.3). Prove that $R(\sqrt{3} + i) = R(\sqrt{3}, i) = R(\sqrt{3})(i)$. Find other bases of $R(\sqrt{3} + i)$ over R.

Exercise (67.4). Find the smallest number field which contains the zeros of $a_0 + a_1x + a_2x^2 \in C[x]$.

Exercise (67.5). Find the field $R(u)$ if $u = \sqrt[3]{5}$, and find $1/u$ in this field.

Exercise (67.6). Find the field $R(u)$ if $u = \sqrt[4]{-1}$.

Exercise (67.7). Prove that if $u \in K$ is algebraic over $F \subseteq K$, then u is algebraic over every field H such that $F \subseteq H \subseteq K$.

Exercise (67.8). Prove that if K is any field containing F which as a vector space over F is finite-dimensional, then every element of K

is algebraic over F. In particular, if u is algebraic over F, every element of $F(u)$ is algebraic over F.

Exercise (67.9). If $F \subseteq K$ and $u \in K$, prove that $u \in F$ if and only if u is an algebraic element of degree 1 over F.

Section 68. The Structure of a Simple Algebraic Extension

The simple extension $F[u]$ is the set of all polynomials in u with coefficients in F by Theorem (56.7) whether u is transcendental or algebraic over F. In either case, it is possible to define a correspondence from the polynomial domain $F[x]$, which is a simple transcendental extension of F, to the simple extension $F[u]$. The obvious correspondence is given by

(68.1) $$p(x) = \sum_{i=0}^{n} a_i x^i \to \sum_{i=0}^{n} a_i u^i = p(u).$$

It is left as an exercise for the reader to check that this correspondence is a ring-homomorphism of $F[x]$ onto $F[u]$.

If u is transcendental over F, then two polynomials in u are the same element of $F[u]$ only if they have the same coefficients in F, and the correspondence (68.1) is an isomorphism, as we have already seen in Theorem (58.2). However, if u is algebraic over F with minimum polynomial $\varphi(x)$ of degree m in $F[x]$, then all polynomials $h(x) \cdot \varphi(x)$, with $\varphi(x)$ as a factor, are mapped onto $h(u)\varphi(u) = 0$ by the correspondence (68.1). By Theorem (67.1), all polynomials $p(x) \in F[x]$ such that $p(u) = 0$, have $\varphi(x)$ as a factor, so that this set of polynomials is just the subset of $F[x]$ which is mapped onto zero by the correspondence (68.1). Therefore by (44.7), the multiples of $\varphi(x)$ form an ideal in $F[x]$, denoted by $I_{\varphi(x)}$, and $F[u] = F(u)$ is isomorphic to the residue class ring $F[x] - I_{\varphi(x)}$. In this isomorphism, each element $f(u) = \sum_{i=0}^{m-1} c_i u^i \in F(u)$ corresponds to the residue class $I_{\varphi(x)} + f(x)$.

As an example, each element of $R(\sqrt{2})$ has the form $a + b\sqrt{2}$ with $a,b \in R$ and corresponds to the residue class

$$I_{x^2-2} + a + bx \in R[x] - I_{x^2-2}.$$

The isomorphism $F(u) \cong F[x] - I_{\varphi(x)}$ explains the method of computing sums and products in $F(u)$. For, since $\varphi(x)$ has degree m, the polynomials of degree less than m form a canonical set of representatives of the residue classes of $F[x]$ modulo the ideal $I_{\varphi(x)}$, and computation in

$F(u)$ corresponds to computation with these representatives in $F[x]$ modulo $I_{\varphi(x)}$.

If u and v in the field $K \supseteq F$ are algebraic elements over F with the same minimum polynomial $\varphi(x)$, then it follows from the above discussion that $F(u)$ and $F(v)$ are isomorphic, since each is isomorphic to $F[x] - I_{\varphi(x)}$. This result is included in the following theorem which corresponds to Corollary (58.3) for simple transcendental extensions.

(68.2) Theorem. Let u and v be algebraic over F. There exists an isomorphism of $F(u)$ onto $F(v)$, in which u corresponds to v and each element of F corresponds to itself, if and only if u and v have the same minimum polynomial $\varphi(x) \in F[x]$.

PROOF. Assume first that there is an isomorphism between $F(u)$ and $F(v)$ with the properties stated in the theorem, and let $\varphi(x) \in F[x]$ be the minimum polynomial of u. Then $\varphi(u) = \sum_{i=0}^{m} a_i u^i = 0$, and by the isomorphism $\varphi(u) = 0$ corresponds to $\sum_{i=0}^{m} a_i v^i = \varphi(v) = 0$. Therefore v is a zero of the monic irreducible polynomial $\varphi(x) \in F[x]$, and by Theorem (67.1), $\varphi(x)$ is the minimum polynomial of v.

Conversely, if u and v have the same minimum polynomial $\varphi(x)$ of degree m in $F[x]$, then by the chain of isomorphisms

$$F(u) \cong F[x] - I_{\varphi(x)} \cong F(v),$$

each element $\sum_{i=0}^{m-1} c_i u^i \in F(u)$ corresponds to the element $\sum_{i=0}^{m-1} c_i v^i \in F(v)$.

Just as the complex numbers $2 + 3i$ and $2 - 3i$, which are zeros of the same irreducible polynomial $x^2 - 4x + 13$ in $R^{\#}[x]$, are called conjugates, the zeros in $K \supseteq F$ of an irreducible polynomial $\varphi(x) \in F[x]$ are called *conjugate over* F. Thus $\sqrt{2}$ and $-\sqrt{2}$, as zeros of $x^2 - 2 \in R[x]$, are conjugate over R. In the example $R(\sqrt{3} + i)$ given in the preceding section, the zeros $\sqrt{3} + i$, $\sqrt{3} - i$, $-\sqrt{3} + i$, and $-\sqrt{3} - i$ of $x^4 - 4x^2 + 16$ are conjugates over R. Over $R^{\#}$ or $R(\sqrt{3})$, $\sqrt{3} + i$ and $\sqrt{3} - i$ are conjugates satisfying $x^2 - 2\sqrt{3}\,x + 4 = 0$. By Theorem (68.2), the simple extensions $R(\sqrt{3} + i)$, $R(\sqrt{3} - i)$, $R(-\sqrt{3} + i)$ and $R(-\sqrt{3} - i)$ are algebraically equivalent. It is easy to show that these four extensions are actually the same subfield of C, so that in this case the isomorphisms of Theorem (68.2) are automorphisms of $R(\sqrt{3} + i)$.

Under the assumption made at the beginning of Section 67 that F is a subfield of a field K and that $u \in K$ is algebraic over F, we have completed our study of the simple algebraic extension $F(u)$. For we have given a unique form for the elements of $F(u)$, we have described the two operations in $F(u)$ in terms of the operations in the polynomial domain $F[x]$, and we have given the condition that two simple algebraic extensions be the same algebraically. These facts depend upon the irreducible monic polynomial $\varphi(x)$ in $F[x]$ satisfied by u and on the isomorphism between $F(u)$ and $F[x] - I_{\varphi(x)}$.

We will now discuss algebraic extension fields from a different standpoint. Let $\varphi(x)$ be any irreducible polynomial in $F[x]$. If there exists a field $K \supseteq F$ which contains a zero u of $\varphi(x)$, then $\varphi(x)$ is the minimum polynomial of u and $F(u)$ is completely described by the previous theorems. In particular, if F is a number field, we may take the field C of complex numbers as the field K, since every polynomial in $F[x]$ has a zero in C. Thus C is always available as a field containing the number field F and a zero u of a polynomial $p(x) \in F[x]$, and we have completely determined the structure of $F(u)$ as a subfield of C.

The question arises as to what can be proved without assuming the existence of the field K. Thus, if $\varphi(x)$ is a polynomial which is irreducible in $F[x]$, does there exist a field $K \supseteq F$ which contains a zero u of $\varphi(x)$? The existence of such a field is proved by constructing a field $K = F(u)$. It may be proved directly that the set $I_{\varphi(x)}$ of all multiples of $\varphi(x)$ is an ideal in $F[x]$ and that the residue class ring $F[x] - I_{\varphi(x)}$ is a field. The construction of this field from F is possible by (58.4) and (44.5). It may further be proved that the set of residue classes $I_{\varphi(x)} + a$ for $a \in F$ is a subfield F' isomorphic to F, that the residue class $u = I_{\varphi(x)} + x$ is a zero of the polynomial with coefficients in F' which corresponds to $\varphi(x)$, and that $F[x] - I_{\varphi(x)} = F'(u)$. This gives the construction in the usual algebraic sense of a simple algebraic extension $K = F(u)$ of F where $u \in K$ is a zero of the irreducible polynomial $\varphi(x) \in F[x]$. The details of this construction are suggested in the following example.

Consider the polynomial $\varphi(x) = x^3 + x + 1 \in J_5[x]$. Since none of the elements 0, 1, 2, 3, 4 of J_5 are zeros of $x^3 + x + 1$, $\varphi(x)$ has no linear factors in $J_5[x]$ and is therefore irreducible. For every $p(x) \in J_5[x]$, by the division algorithm there is a unique polynomial $ax^2 + bx + c \in J_5[x]$ such that $p(x) = q(x) \cdot (x^3 + x + 1) + ax^2 + bx + c$. Thus the elements of $J_5[x] - I_{\varphi(x)}$ are the residue classes $I_{\varphi(x)} + (ax^2 + bx + c)$, and the residue class ring is finite with $5^3 = 125$ elements. Since $J_5[x]$ is commutative with identity element 1, $K = J_5[x] - I_{\varphi(x)}$ is commutative with identity $I_{\varphi(x)} + 1$. Thus to prove that K is a field, we need only find the inverse of each non-zero element, and this can be done, using (60.4). For example, since $(2x^2 + 2x + 2)(x^2 + 3x + 2) + (3x + 2)(x^3 + x + 1) = 1$ in $J_5[x]$, the class $I_{\varphi(x)} + (2x^2 + 2x + 2)$ is the inverse of the class $I_{\varphi(x)} + (x^2 + 3x + 2)$. The classes $I_{\varphi(x)} + c$ for $c = 0, 1, 2, 3, 4$ form a subfield of K isomorphic to J_5, and the element $u = I_{\varphi(x)} + x$ is a zero of the polynomial which corresponds to $\varphi(x)$ since

$$\begin{aligned} u^3 + u + [I_{\varphi(x)} + 1] &= [I_{\varphi(x)} + x]^3 + [I_{\varphi(x)} + x] + [I_{\varphi(x)} + 1] \\ &= [I_{\varphi(x)} + x^3] + [I_{\varphi(x)} + x] + [I_{\varphi(x)} + 1] \\ &= I_{\varphi(x)} + (x^3 + x + 1) \\ &= I_{\varphi(x)}. \end{aligned}$$

Exercise (68.1). Prove that the correspondence (68.1) is a ring-homomorphism of $F[x]$ onto $F[u]$.

Exercise (68.2). Show that $R(\sqrt{2})$ is not ring-isomorphic to $R(\sqrt{3})$, although they are isomorphic as vector spaces over R.

Exercise (68.3). List the sets of conjugate elements in C among the zeros of $x^8 - 1 \in R[x]$.

Exercise (68.4). Discuss $R(u)$ where u is a zero of $x^7 - x^3 + 1$. Exhibit some typical calculations in this field.

Exercise (68.5). If u_1, u_2, and u_3 are the distinct zeros in C of $x^3 - 2$, show that $R(u_1)$, $R(u_2)$, and $R(u_3)$ are distinct fields.

Exercise (68.6). In the example $J_5[x] - I_{x^3+x+1}$ in the text, find the inverse of $I_{x^3+x+1} + 2$ and of $I_{x^3+x+1} + (x + 3)$.

Exercise (68.7). Construct fields containing 8, 9, and 16 elements.

Exercise (68.8). Prove that the set of all multiples of a polynomial $p(x) \in F[x]$ is an ideal $I_{p(x)}$ in $F[x]$.

Exercise (68.9). Prove that if $p(x)$ is irreducible in $F[x]$, then $K = F[x] - I_{p(x)}$ is a field. [*Hint:* K is commutative with an identity since F has these properties. To find the inverse of $f(x)$ use (60.4).]

Section 69. Algebraic Extension Fields

In the preceding section we indicated how to construct a simple algebraic extension $F(u)$ where u is a zero of an irreducible polynomial $\varphi(x) \in F[x]$. This result and Theorem (68.2) tell us that there exists one and essentially only one such extension field of F for each irreducible polynomial $\varphi(x) \in F[x]$. In that section we discussed $J_5(u)$ where u is a zero of the polynomial $x^3 + x + 1 \in J_5[x]$. This is a finite field with

$5^3 = 125$ elements of the form $a_0 + a_1u + a_2u^2$ with $a_i \in J_5$. Since u is a zero of $x^3 + x + 1$ in $J_5(u)$, $x - u$ is a factor of $x^3 + x + 1$ in $J_5(u)[x]$. Factoring $x^3 + x + 1$ in $J_5(u)[x]$ we find that

$$\begin{aligned} x^3 + x + 1 &= (x - u)(x^2 + ux + 1 + u^2) \\ &= (x - u)(x - [1 + u + 4u^2])(x - [4 + 3u + u^2]), \end{aligned}$$

so that $x^3 + x + 1$ factors into linear factors and has the three zeros u, $1 + u + 4u^2$, and $4 + 3u + u^2$ in $J_5(u) = J_5(u, 1 + u + 4u^2, 4 + 3u + u^2)$.

On the other hand, if u is a zero of the irreducible polynomial $x^3 - 5 \in R[x]$, then in $R(u)[x]$ we have

$$x^3 - 5 = (x - u)(x^2 + ux + u^2),$$

and it can be shown that $x^2 + ux + u^2$ is irreducible in $R(u)[x]$. Therefore, in order to factor $x^3 - 5$ into linear factors it is necessary to further enlarge the coefficient field. We can do this by constructing $R(u)(v) = R(u,v)$ where v is a zero of $x^2 + ux + u^2$. Then in $R(u,v)[x]$ we find that

$$x^3 - 5 = (x - u)(x - v)(x + u + v),$$

and $R(u,v) = R(u,v,-u-v)$ is the smallest field containing the zeros u, v, and $-u - v$ of $x^3 - 5$.

It can be proved by induction that given any field F and any polynomial $p(x) \in F[x]$, there exists one and essentially only one field $K = F(u_1, u_2, \cdots, u_n)$ such that

$$p(x) = (x - u_1)(x - u_2) \cdots (x - u_n)$$

in $K[x]$. The construction of the preceding section can be used to obtain a field containing a zero of any irreducible factor of $p(x)$. If we assume that we have constructed a field $H = F(u_1, u_2, \cdots, u_r)$ containing r zeros of $p(x)$, and if

$$p(x) = (x - u_1)(x - u_2) \cdots (x - u_r)\varphi_1(x)\varphi_2(x) \cdots \varphi_r(x)$$

in $H[x]$ where each $\varphi_i(x)$ is an irreducible polynomial of degree ≥ 2 in $H[x]$, then constructing a simple algebraic extension of H by adjoining a zero of $\varphi_1(x)$, we obtain the field $H(u_{r+1})$ containing at least one more zero of $p(x)$. Thus K can be constructed in a finite number of steps. The argument given in (68.2) can be extended to show that K is unique except for isomorphic extensions of F.

This smallest field K containing F and the zeros of $p(x) \in F[x]$ is called the *decomposition field* of $p(x)$. It is the algebraic closure of F with respect to the single polynomial $p(x) \in F[x]$, and is basic in a further study of algebraic extension fields which leads to the Galois theory of equations. If F is a number field, we may always take the decomposition field of $p(x) \in F[x]$ to be a subfield of C. For $p(x)$ factors in $C[x]$ into linear factors and the decomposition field of $p(x)$ is the subfield K of C generated by F and the zeros in C of $p(x)$. For example, the zeros of $x^3 - 5$ in C are $\sqrt[3]{5}$, $\sqrt[3]{5}\,\omega$, and $\sqrt[3]{5}\,\omega^2$ where $\sqrt[3]{5} \in R^\#$ and $\omega = -1/2 + \sqrt{3}/2\; i$, so that $R(\sqrt[3]{5}, \sqrt[3]{5}\,\omega, \sqrt[3]{5}\,\omega^2) = R(\sqrt[3]{5}, \sqrt{-3})$ is the decomposition field of $x^3 - 5$. This field and the previously constructed $R(u, v, -u - v)$ are algebraically equivalent extensions of R, for there is an isomorphism f between them in which $f(\sqrt[3]{5}) = u$, $f(\sqrt[3]{5}\,\omega) = v$, $f(\sqrt[3]{5}\,\omega^2) = -u - v$, and $f(r) = r$ for all $r \in R$.

By Exercise (67.8) if a field $K \supseteq F$ is a finite-dimensional vector space over F, then every element of K is algebraic over F. In particular, every element of the simple algebraic extension $F[u] = F(u)$ is algebraic over F. This is an example of what we mean by an algebraic extension.

(69.1) Definition. If $K \supseteq F$ are fields, then K is an *algebraic extension* of F if every element of K is algebraic over F.

Another example of an algebraic extension of F is the decomposition field of a polynomial. Let u and v be algebraic elements over F. We have already proved in Theorem (67.4) that $F[u] = F(u)$, and in (56.5) that $F[u,v] = F[u][v]$. Using the fact that if v is algebraic over the field F, then v is algebraic over the larger field $F(u)$, we have that

$$F[u,v] = F[u][v] = F(u)[v] = F(u)(v).$$

This proves that the integral domain $F[u,v]$ is a field $F(u)(v)$, and is therefore identical with its quotient field, which is $F(u,v)$ by (56.3). In the same way we may prove by induction that $F[u_1, u_2, \cdots, u_k] = F(u_1, u_2, \cdots, u_k)$ if each u_i is algebraic over F. Now by (57.2) $F[u_1, u_2, \cdots, u_k] = F(u_1, u_2, \cdots, u_k)$ is a finite-dimensional vector space over F, so that again using Exercise (67.8), every element of $F(u_1, u_2, \cdots, u_k)$ is algebraic over F. Thus we have shown that any extension of F by a finite number of algebraic elements is an algebraic extension of F. A decomposition field is such an extension.

We want to prove next that if H is an algebraic extension of F and K is an algebraic extension of H, then K is an algebraic extension of F. In order to prove this theorem we first prove the corresponding theorem where each extension is finite-dimensional.

In the example of the decomposition field of $x^3 - 5 \in R[x]$, each element of $R(u,v) = R(u)(v)$ has the unique form $c_0 + c_1 v$ where c_0 and c_1 are in $R(u)$, and each element of $R(u)$ has the unique form $a_0 + a_1 u$

$+ a_2u^2$ where a_0, a_1, and a_2 are in R. Hence each element of $R(u,v)$ has the unique expression

$$(a_0 + a_1u + a_2u^2) + (b_0 + b_1u + b_2u^2)v = a_0e + a_1u + a_2u^2 + b_0v + b_1uv + b_2u^2v$$

where a_i and b_j are in R for $i, j = 0, 1, 2$. Therefore the elements e, u, u^2, v, uv, u^2v are a basis of $R(u,v)$ over R, and $R(u,v)$ is a vector space of dimension 6 over R. Since $R(u,v)$ has dimension 2 over $R(u)$ and $R(u)$ has dimension 3 over R, we have the relation

$$\underbrace{\overbrace{R \subseteq R(u)}^{\text{dim } 3} \subseteq \overbrace{R(u,v)}^{\text{dim } 2}}_{\text{dim } 6},$$

which is an example of the following theorem.

(69.2) Theorem. If $F \subseteq H \subseteq K$ are fields such that H is a vector space of dimension r over F, and K is a vector space of dimension s over H, then K is a vector space of dimension rs over F.

PROOF. Let $u_1,u_2, \cdots, u_r$ be a basis of H over F and $v_1,v_2, \cdots, v_s$ be a basis of K over H. Then each element of K can be written as $\sum_{i=1}^{s} c_iv_i$ with $c_i \in H$, and each $c_i \in H$ can be written as $c_i = \sum_{j=1}^{r} b_{ij}u_j$ with $b_{ij} \in F$. Therefore each element of K has the form

$$\sum_{i=1}^{s} \left(\sum_{j=1}^{r} b_{ij}u_j \right) v_i = \sum_{i=1}^{s} \sum_{j=1}^{r} b_{ij}u_jv_i,$$

and the rs elements u_jv_i span K over F. Further, any relation

$$\sum_{i=1}^{s} \sum_{j=1}^{r} d_{ij}u_jv_i = 0$$

with $d_{ij} \in F$ implies that $\sum_{j=1}^{r} d_{ij}u_j = 0$ for $i = 1, 2, \cdots, s$ since $v_1, v_2, \cdots, v_s$ are linearly independent over H, and each relation $\sum_{j=1}^{r} d_{ij}u_j = 0$ implies that $d_{ij} = 0$ for $j = 1, 2, \cdots, r$ since $u_1, u_2, \cdots u_r$ are linearly independent over F. Therefore $d_{ij} = 0$ for all i,j, and the rs elements u_jv_i are linearly independent over F so that these elements form a basis of K over F.

In the following proof we need only the result that if H is finite-dimensional over F, and K is finite-dimensional over H, then K is finite-dimensional over F, and we do not need the exact dimension relation between the three fields given in Theorem (69.2).

(69.3) Theorem. If $F \subseteq H \subseteq K$ are fields such that H is an algebraic extension of F and K is an algebraic extension of H, then K is an algebraic extension of F.

PROOF. If α is any element of K, then α is a zero of an irreducible polynomial $a_0 + a_1x + a_2x^2 + \cdots + a_nx^n \in H[x]$. Thus α is algebraic over $F(a_0, a_1, \cdots, a_n)$ and the simple algebraic extension $F(a_0, a_1, \cdots, a_n)(\alpha)$ is a finite-dimensional vector space over $F(a_0, a_1, \cdots, a_n)$. Since each a_i is in H, each a_i is algebraic over F, so that $F(a_0, a_1, \cdots, a_n) = F[a_0, a_1 \cdots, a_n]$ is a finite-dimensional vector space over F by (57.2). Therefore by (69.2), $F(a_0, a_1, \cdots, a_n)(\alpha) = F(a_0, a_1, \cdots, a_n, \alpha)$ is a finite-dimensional vector space over F, so that α is algebraic over F. Thus K is an algebraic extension of F by Definition (69.1).

(69.4) Corollary. If $F \subseteq H \subseteq K$ are fields such that H is an algebraic extension of F, and if $u \in K$ is algebraic over H, then u is algebraic over F.

(69.5) Corollary. If $K = F(u_1, u_2, \cdots, u_k)$ where u_1 is algebraic over F and u_i is algebraic over $F(u_1, u_2, \cdots, u_{i-1})$ for $i = 2, 3, \cdots, k$, then K is an algebraic extension of F.

The proof of these corollaries is left to the reader as an exercise.

The following theorem may be used to obtain examples of algebraic extensions of a field F which are not finite-dimensional vector spaces over F.

(69.6) Theorem. If $K \supseteq F$ are fields, then the subset $A \subseteq K$ of all elements of K which are algebraic over F is an algebraic extension of F.

PROOF. Since $A \supseteq F$, A contains at least two elements of K. If $u,v \in A$, then as proved above, $F(u,v)$ is an algebraic extension of F, so that the elements $u \pm v$, uv, and u/v if $v \neq 0$, which are in $F(u,v)$, are algebraic over F and are therefore in A. Thus A is closed with respect to the rational operations in K and is a subfield of K. Since by hypothesis each element of A is algebraic over F, A is an algebraic extension of F.

The most important special case of this theorem is obtained when we take the fields K and F to be the number fields C and R respectively. In this example A is called the *field of algebraic numbers*. This field is algebraically closed and is called the algebraic closure of R since it is the smallest algebraically closed number field. For if $p(x)$ is a polynomial in $A[x]$, then $p(x)$ has a zero $u \in C$ and $A(u)$ is an algebraic extension of R by (69.3). Thus u is algebraic over R and hence is in A. This proves that A is algebraically closed. Further, if B is any algebraically closed number field, then $A \subseteq B$ since every element of A is a zero of a polynomial in $R[x] \subseteq B[x]$, and B contains the zeros of every polynomial in $B[x]$.

This field A of algebraic numbers is not the whole field C of complex numbers since there exist numbers in C like π and e which are transcendental over R. Further A is not a finite-dimensional vector space over R. For if it were of finite dimension n, each element of A would be a zero of an irreducible polynomial of degree $\leq n$ with rational coefficients. But in particular, A would have to contain a zero of $x^{2n} + 1$ of degree $2n$, and this polynomial is irreducible in $R[x]$ by (65.1).

If F is any field, we have called the field $F(x)$, where x is an indeterminate over F, the field of rational functions of x with coefficients in F. An important example of an algebraic extension is given by a field K which is an algebraic extension of $F(x)$. Such a field K is called a *field of algebraic functions of x over F*. Each element of K is a zero u of a polynomial $p(y) \in F(x)[y]$, where y is an indeterminate over $F(x)$. For example, consider the field $R(x)$ and the polynomial $y^2 - x \in R(x)[y]$. Now $y^2 - x$ is irreducible, for if it had a linear factor in $R(x)[y]$, it would have a zero $s(x)/r(x) \in R(x)$. But $[s(x)/r(x)]^2 - x = 0$ implies $[s(x)]^2 = x[r(x)]^2$ in $R[x]$, which is impossible since the two members of the last equality cannot have the same degree. Thus, we can construct the simple algebraic extension $R(x)(u)$ of dimension 2 over $R(x)$ where u is a zero of $y^2 - x$. Adopting the obvious notation $u = \sqrt{x}$, the field $R(x)(\sqrt{x}) = R(x, \sqrt{x}) = R(\sqrt{x})$ is a field of algebraic functions of x over R and is just the set of all rational functions of $\sqrt{x}$ with rational coefficients.

Exercise (69.1). Find the decomposition field in C of the following polynomials in $R[x]$:

(a) $x^5 - 1$; (b) $x^3 - 2x^2 - 5x + 6$;
(c) $x^3 - 3$; (d) $x^8 - 1$.

What is the dimension of each over R?

Exercise (69.2). Find a decomposition field of $x^3 + 2x + 1 \in J_3[x]$. What is its dimension over J_3?

Exercise (69.3). Prove that $x^2 + ux + u^2$ is irreducible in $R(u)[x]$ where u is a zero of $x^3 - 5$ in $R[x]$.

Exercise (69.4). Let $H \supseteq F$ be the decomposition field of $p_1(x) \in F[x]$ and $K \supseteq H$ be the decomposition field of $p_2(x) \in F[x] \subseteq H[x]$. Prove that K is the decomposition field of $p(x) = p_1(x)p_2(x) \in F[x]$.

Exercise (69.5). What are the dimensions of the following extensions of R?

$$R(\sqrt{2}, \sqrt{3});\ R(\sqrt{2}, \sqrt[3]{2});\ R(\sqrt{2}, \sqrt[4]{2});\ R(\sqrt{3} + i, i).$$

Give a basis over R for each extension.

Exercise (69.6). Prove that if $K \supseteq H \supseteq F$ are fields such that K is a finite-dimensional vector space over F, then K is a finite-dimensional vector space over H.

Exercise (69.7). Prove Corollaries (69.4) and (69.5).

Exercise (69.8). If $f(x) \in F[x]$ is of degree n, what are the possible dimensions of its decomposition field over F?

Exercise (69.9). Prove that if $K \supseteq F$ are fields such that K is a vector space of dimension n over F, then:

(a) Every $u \in K$ is a zero of an irreducible polynomial in $F[x]$ of degree m where m divides n.
(b) If $u \in K$ is a zero of an irreducible polynomial in $F[x]$ of degree n, then $K = F(u)$.

Exercise (69.10). Prove that if $K \supseteq F$ are fields such that K is a vector space of dimension n over F and if $p(x)$ is an irreducible polynomial of degree m in $F[x]$ where m is relatively prime to n, then $p(x)$ has no zeros in K.

Exercise (69.11). Discuss the field of algebraic functions of x over R defined by $y^2 + xy + x^2$. Also discuss the field over C.

Exercise (69.12). Prove that $y^3 + xy + x^2/(x + 1)$ is irreducible as a polynomial in y with coefficients in $R(x)$. [*Hint:* Use the method of Theorem (65.1).]

Exercise (69.13). Prove that the only elements in $R(\sqrt{x})$ which are algebraic over R are the elements of R.

VII | MATRICES WITH POLYNOMIAL ELEMENTS

Section 70. Introduction

This and the final chapter of this book, together with Chapters I, II, and III, are intended to present to those readers primarily interested in applications, an introduction to the algebra of matrices and their reduction to canonical form. These five chapters are therefore, as much as possible, self-contained. For a study of the present chapter, only the material in the first three chapters and a knowledge of the basic properties of polynomials are needed. In order to shorten the exposition and to avoid repetition for those who have read the intervening chapters, we will refer to the results which we need about polynomials by their numbers in Chapter VI. All of those results are confined to Sections 59 through 66 in Chapter VI and, except for certain explanatory paragraphs, these sections can be read independently* if "field F" is read as "number field F."

The reader is familiar from college algebra with the definition of a polynomial in a variable or indeterminate x as an expression of the form $p(x) = \sum_{i=0}^{n} a_i x^i = a_0 + a_1 x + a_2 x^2 + \cdots + a_n x^n$, where the coefficients a_i are in some number field F. The set of all polynomials in x with coefficients in F is denoted by $F[x]$, and the formulas given in (59.1) may be used as definitions of equality, addition, and multiplication of polynomials in $F[x]$. It may be proved from (59.1) that the set $F[x]$ of polynomials with coefficients in F has the same algebraic properties with regard to the operations of addition and multiplication as does the number field F itself, with the exception that an element $p(x) \in F[x]$ has a multiplicative inverse in $F[x]$ if and only if $p(x)$ is a non-zero constant in F. For an inverse of $p(x)$ is any polynomial $q(x)$ in $F[x]$ such that $p(x)q(x) = 1$, and by (59.3), $p(x)q(x) = 1$ if and only if both $p(x)$ and $q(x)$ have degree zero, that is, are constants in F. It

* The reader may use (60.2) as a definition of the term *unit* and the statement immediately following this theorem as a definition of *associate*. The identity e of the field F may be read as the integer 1 of the number field F. All results of Section 62 are valid for number fields.

is a further consequence of (59.3) that the product of non-zero polynomials in $F[x]$ is a non-zero polynomial.

An m by n matrix $A = (a_{ij})$ is said to be a *matrix in* $F[x]$ if $a_{ij} = p_{ij}(x)$ is a polynomial in $F[x]$ for all pairs i,j. The following matrices are examples of matrices in $R[x]$.

$$\begin{pmatrix} x^2+x+1 & 1/2\,x & 6x^3-1/2 \\ 25 & 2x^2-4 & 1/3 \end{pmatrix}, \quad \begin{pmatrix} x-2 & 1/2 & 0 \\ -3 & x-4 & 1 \\ -1 & -5 & x \end{pmatrix}, \quad (1, 3, -6).$$

Using the properties of $F[x]$, we see that with a single exception, the matrices in $F[x]$ are closed under the matrix operations defined in Chapter I, and that the determinant of a square matrix in $F[x]$ is a polynomial in $F[x]$. The exception referred to is the process of inverting a nonsingular matrix, since in general a nonsingular matrix in $F[x]$ does not have an inverse in $F[x]$.

(70.1) Theorem. An n-rowed square matrix A in $F[x]$ has an inverse in $F[x]$ if and only if $|A|$ is a non-zero constant in F.

PROOF. If there exists a matrix $B \in F[x]$ such that either $AB = I$ or $BA = I$, then $|A| \cdot |B| = |I| = 1$. By the above remarks, this implies that $|A|$ and $|B|$, which are polynomials in $F[x]$, are non-zero constants in F.

Conversely, if $|A|$ is a non-zero constant in F, the matrix $A^{-1} = 1/|A| \cdot \operatorname{adj} A$ is in $F[x]$, and as it may be verified that Theorem (11.4) of Chapter I is valid for matrices in $F[x]$, we have $AA^{-1} = A^{-1}A = I$.

For example, the matrix

$$A = \begin{pmatrix} -x^2+1 & 3 & -1/2\,x^2+1/2 \\ 4 & x^2-2 & 5 \\ 2 & 0 & 1 \end{pmatrix}$$

has $|A| = 18$, so that

$$A^{-1} = 1/18 \begin{pmatrix} x^2-2 & -3 & 1/2\,x^4 - 3/2\,x^2 + 16 \\ 6 & 0 & 3x^2-3 \\ -2x^2+4 & 6 & -x^4+3x^2-14 \end{pmatrix}.$$

On the other hand, the matrix $B = \begin{pmatrix} -x^2+1 & 2x \\ x^2 & 5 \end{pmatrix}$ has $|B| = -2x^3 - 5x^2 + 5$, so that B has no inverse in $R[x]$. However, there does exist a matrix

$$C = 1/|B| \cdot \operatorname{adj} B = \begin{pmatrix} \dfrac{5}{-2x^3-5x^2+5} & \dfrac{-2x}{-2x^3-5x^2+5} \\ \dfrac{-x^2}{-2x^3-5x^2+5} & \dfrac{-x^2+1}{-2x^3-5x^2+5} \end{pmatrix}$$

which satisfies $BC = CB = 1$, but C is not a matrix in $R[x]$ since its elements are rational functions of x and not polynomials.

Exercise (70.1). Find $A - 2B$ and $[(x^2 + 1)A + 3xB]'$ where

$$A = \begin{pmatrix} 2x - 5 & 4x + 2 & x - 1 \\ 3x^2 & x & 1 \end{pmatrix} \quad \text{and} \quad B = \begin{pmatrix} 0 & 2x + 2 & 5 \\ x^2 - 1 & 4x^2 - 3x & 3x \end{pmatrix}.$$

Exercise (70.2). Compute all possible products of two of the following matrices:

$$A = \begin{pmatrix} x^2 + 3x & 3 & 5x + 2 \\ 2x & 0 & -2x \\ x & x & 0 \end{pmatrix}; \; B = \begin{pmatrix} 3 & -x \\ 0 & x^2 \\ 3 & 2x \end{pmatrix}; \; C = \begin{pmatrix} 2x & 4x + 2 & 3 \\ x^2 & x - 1 & x \end{pmatrix}.$$

Exercise (70.3). Find the determinant of each of the following matrices, and find the inverse of each when it exists in $F[x]$:

$$A = (-4x + 3); \; B = \begin{pmatrix} 2x^2 & 4x \\ x^2 & 2x + 1 \end{pmatrix}; \; C = \begin{pmatrix} 2x - 3 & 3 & 0 \\ x^2 & 0 & 1 \\ 2x^2 - 3x + 5 & 3x & 0 \end{pmatrix};$$

$$D = \begin{pmatrix} x + 1 & x & 1 \\ -x^2 + 5 & -x^2 - x + 5 & x \\ -x & 0 & -x \end{pmatrix}.$$

Exercise (70.4). Show that if $f(x)A = f(x)B$, where A and B are m by n matrices with elements in $F[x]$ and $f(x) \neq 0$ is a polynomial in $F[x]$, then $A = B$.

Section 71. Equivalence of Matrices in $F[x]$

In this and the next section we will give a theory of equivalence of rectangular matrices with polynomial elements which is similar to that developed in Chapter II for matrices with elements in a number field F. The difference in the theories comes from the fact that in order to obtain a group of equivalence transformations $T_{P,Q}$ where P and Q are matrices in $F[x]$, it is necessary by Theorem (70.1) to restrict P and Q to be matrices with non-zero constant determinants.

Let ${}_m\mathfrak{A}_n(F[x])$ denote the set of all m by n matrices with elements in $F[x]$.

(71.1) Definition. The transformation $T_{P,Q}$ of ${}_m\mathfrak{A}_n(F[x])$, defined by

$$T_{P,Q}(A) = PAQ \qquad \text{for all } A \in {}_m\mathfrak{A}_n(F[x]),$$

where P and Q are m- and n-rowed square matrices respectively in

$F[x]$ with non-zero constant determinants, is called an *equivalence transformation* of ${}_m\mathfrak{A}_n(F[x])$.

As in Section 18, it can be proved that the set of all equivalence transformations of ${}_m\mathfrak{A}_n(F[x])$ is a group of transformations, with T_{I_m,I_n} the identity transformation, and with the formulas $T_{P,Q}T_{R,S} = T_{PR,SQ}$ and $(T_{P,Q})^{-1} = T_{P^{-1},Q^{-1}}$ remaining valid. This group, of course, induces an equivalence relation on ${}_m\mathfrak{A}_n(F[x])$, and two matrices A and B in ${}_m\mathfrak{A}_n(F[x])$ are said to be *equivalent over* F if there exists an equivalence transformation $T_{P,Q}$ such that $T_{P,Q}(A) = B$.

The description of the elementary transformation matrices U of type I and the corresponding elementary transformations $T_{U,I}$ and $T_{I,U}$ remains the same as in Section 19. The same is true for matrices V of type II and the corresponding transformations $T_{V,I}$ and $T_{I,V}$, except that now the set of scalars is the set of all polynomials, $F[x]$. In order that the type III matrices W shall have inverses in $F[x]$, they are formed by multiplying a row or column of the identity matrix $I = (\delta_{ij})$ by a non-zero constant $c \in F$. Thus the type III elementary transformations $T_{W,I}$ and $T_{I,W}$ of a matrix A are restricted to multiplying a row or column of A by a non-zero constant $c \in F$. By the above definitions, the elementary transformation matrices in $F[x]$ have non-zero constant determinants and have inverses which are elementary transformation matrices in $F[x]$ of the same type. This means that the elementary transformations are equivalence transformations of ${}_m\mathfrak{A}_n(F[x])$.

Our present goal is to obtain a set of canonical forms for the group of equivalence transformations of ${}_m\mathfrak{A}_n(F[x])$. As in Chapter II, this will be accomplished by first studying the effect of the elementary transformations and then by showing that each equivalence transformation is equal to a product of elementary transformations.

We will see that if the matrices A and B with polynomial elements are equivalent over F, they have the same rank. However, the concept of rank alone is not sufficient to characterize the equivalence of such matrices, as the following example shows: Let $A = \begin{pmatrix} 1 & 0 \\ 0 & 1 \end{pmatrix}$ and $B = \begin{pmatrix} 1 & 0 \\ 0 & x \end{pmatrix}$, so that each matrix has rank 2. If A and B were equivalent, then $B = PAQ$ where $|P|$ and $|Q|$ are non-zero constants. But $|PAQ| = |P| \cdot |A| \cdot |Q| = |P| \cdot |Q|$ is a constant, while $|B| = x$ is not. The remainder of this section is devoted to that property of an elementary transformation which is the basis of a complete description of the equivalence of matrices in ${}_m\mathfrak{A}_n(F[x])$.

If $f_1(x), f_2(x), \cdots, f_s(x)$ is a set of polynomials in $F[x]$, then a linear combination of these polynomials is an expression $\sum_{i=1}^{s} h_i(x)f_i(x)$ where $h_i(x) \in F[x]$ for $i = 1, 2, \cdots, s$.

(71.2) Lemma. Let $f_1(x), f_2(x), \cdots, f_s(x)$ and $g_1(x), g_2(x), \cdots, g_t(x)$ be sets of polynomials in $F[x]$ where at least one polynomial in each set is not zero. If each $f_i(x)$ is a linear combination of $g_1(x), g_2(x), \cdots, g_t(x)$ and if each $g_j(x)$ is a linear combination of $f_1(x), f_2(x), \cdots, f_s(x)$, then the two sets of polynomials have the same greatest common divisor.

PROOF. Let $d_1(x)$ be the g.c.d. of $f_1(x), f_2(x), \cdots, f_s(x)$ and $d_2(x)$ be the g.c.d. of $g_1(x), g_2(x), \cdots, g_t(x)$. Since $d_1(x)$ divides every $f_i(x)$ and since each $g_j(x) = \sum_{i=1}^{s} h_{ij}(x)f_i(x)$, $d_1(x)$ divides $g_j(x)$ for $j = 1, 2, \cdots, t$. Thus $d_1(x)$ divides $d_2(x)$, the g.c.d. of the $g_j(x)$. Similarly $d_2(x)$ divides $d_1(x)$, and hence $d_1(x) = d_2(x)$ since they are associated monic polynomials.

(71.3) Theorem. If $A \in {}_m\mathfrak{A}_n(F[x])$ has rank r, and if T is an elementary transformation, then the matrix $B = T(A)$ has rank r, and the g.c.d. of all k-rowed minors of B $(k \leq r)$ is the same as the g.c.d. of all k-rowed minors of A.

PROOF. A repetition of the argument of Lemma (21.2) shows that if B_1 is any t-rowed square submatrix of B, then either $|B_1| = \pm|A_1|$, $|B_1| = |A_1| + g(x)\,|A_2|$ or $|B_1| = c|A_1|$, according as T is of type I, II, or III, and where A_1 and A_2 are t-rowed square submatrices of A. Thus each t-rowed minor of B is a linear combination of the set of all t-rowed minors of A. Similarly, since T^{-1} is an elementary transformation and $T^{-1}(B) = A$, each t-rowed minor of A is a linear combination of the set of all t-rowed minors of B. This means that if $t > r$, all t-rowed minors of B are zero, and if $t \leq r$, B has at least one non-zero t-rowed minor. Thus A and B have the same rank r, and if $k \leq r$, the k-rowed minors of each matrix have the same g.c.d. by Lemma (71.2).

Exercise (71.1). Prove that the set of all equivalence transformations of ${}_m\mathfrak{A}_n(F[x])$ is a group of transformations.

Exercise (71.2). Construct elementary transformation matrices which define the following elementary transformations of

$$A = \begin{pmatrix} x^2 - 1 & x^2 + x + 1 & -x + 3 \\ x + 1 & x^2 + x & 2x \end{pmatrix}:$$

(a) interchange columns 1 and 3;
(b) add to the elements of row 1 the elements of row 2 multiplied by $-x+1$;
(c) multiply column 2 by 5/3.

Find a single equivalence transformation $T_{P,Q}$ which performs all three operations.

Exercise (71.3). (a) Find $B = T_{P,Q}(A)$ if

$$A = \begin{pmatrix} x^3+2x^2+x & -x^3+x & 0 \\ 0 & 1/2\,x^2+1/2\,x & x^3+x^2 \\ 3x^2+3x & 0 & 0 \end{pmatrix},$$

$$P = \begin{pmatrix} 0 & 0 & 1 \\ 0 & 1 & 0 \\ 1 & 0 & -1/3\,(x+1) \end{pmatrix}, \quad Q = \begin{pmatrix} 1/3 & 0 & 0 \\ 0 & 1 & -2x \\ 0 & 0 & 1 \end{pmatrix}.$$

Find the g.c.d. of all 1, 2, and 3-rowed minors of A and of B.

(b) Similarly treat $C = T_{R,S}\,(A)$ where

$$R = \begin{pmatrix} 0 & 0 & 1 \\ 0 & 2 & 0 \\ 1 & 2x-2 & -1/3\,(x+1) \end{pmatrix}, \quad S = \begin{pmatrix} 1/3 & 0 & 0 \\ 0 & 1 & x \\ 0 & 0 & -1/2 \end{pmatrix}.$$

Exercise (71.4). Find the rank of each of the following matrices by applying elementary transformations to simplify the matrix:

$$A = \begin{pmatrix} 4 & 2x & 4 \\ 0 & -1 & x+2 \\ 2 & 0 & x^2+2x \end{pmatrix}, \quad B = \begin{pmatrix} x-3 & 3x-7 & -7x+11 \\ -x+4 & 2x & -3x-4 \\ x+2 & x+4 & -3x-10 \end{pmatrix},$$

$$C = \begin{pmatrix} -x^2+2x & 4x \\ 3x & -2 \\ x+2 & 3 \end{pmatrix}.$$

Exercise (71.5). Find the g.c.d. of $f(x)$ and $g(x)$ by applying suitable elementary transformations to the matrix $(f(x), g(x))$:

(a) $f(x) = 2x^4+5x^3-6x^2-15x$, $g(x) = 3x^4+2x^3-9x^2-6x$;
(b) $f(x) = 6x^3-10x^2+4x-2$, $g(x) = 4x^3-12x-6$;
(c) $f(x) = x^4+2x^2+x+2$, $g(x) = 3x^4-4x^3+9x^2-4x+4$.

Section 72. The Rational Canonical Form for Matrices in $F[x]$

In this section we will obtain a set of canonical forms for the set of matrices ${}_m\mathfrak{A}_n(F[x])$ under the group of equivalence transformations.

The first step in reducing a matrix to its canonical form is given in the following lemma.

(72.1) Lemma. If A is a non-zero matrix in ${}_m\mathfrak{A}_n(F[x])$ and if $a_{ij}(x) \neq 0$ is an element of A of minimum degree t, then either $a_{ij}(x)$ divides all elements of A, or else there exists an equivalence transformation T, which is a product of elementary transformations, such that $T(A) = B$ has an element $b_{rs}(x) \neq 0$ of degree less than t.

PROOF. Since any element of A can be carried to the (1,1) position by at most two elementary transformations of type I, we suppose that $a_{11}(x) \neq 0$ has minimum degree t. Assume that $a_{11}(x)$ does not divide every element of A.

If $a_{11}(x)$ does not divide some element $a_{k1}(x)$ in column 1, then by the division algorithm (60.1) there exist $q(x)$ and $r(x) \neq 0$ in $F[x]$ such that $a_{k1} = q \cdot a_{11} + r$ with $\deg r(x) < t$. By applying the type II transformation which adds to the elements of row k the elements of row 1 multiplied by $-q(x)$, we obtain a matrix B which has the element $r(x)$ in the $(k,1)$ position. A similar procedure will yield a matrix $B = (b_{ij})$ with $\deg b_{1l}(x)$ less than t if the element $a_{11}(x)$ does not divide the element $a_{1l}(x)$ in row 1.

Assume finally that $a_{11}(x)$ divides every element of row 1 and column 1, but that $a_{11}(x)$ does not divide the element $a_{ij}(x)$. Let $a(x)$, $b(x)$, $q(x)$, and $r(x) \neq 0$ be the polynomials in $F[x]$ such that $a_{i1} = a \cdot a_{11}$, $a_{1j} = b \cdot a_{11}$, and $a_{ij} = q \cdot a_{11} + r$ where $\deg r(x) < t$. Then applying the type II transformation which adds to the elements of row i the elements of row 1 multiplied by $1 - a(x)$, we obtain a matrix B_1 which has the element

$$a_{i1} + (1 - a)a_{11} = a \cdot a_{11} + a_{11} - a \cdot a_{11} = a_{11}$$

in the $(i, 1)$ position and the element

$$\begin{aligned} a_{ij} + (1 - a)a_{1j} &= q \cdot a_{11} + r + (1 - a)b \cdot a_{11} \\ &= \{q + (1 - a)b\}a_{11} + r \end{aligned}$$

in the (i,j) position. A type II transformation which adds to the elements of column j the elements of column 1 multiplied by the polynomial $-\{q + (1 - a)b\}$ will then give a matrix B with the element $r(x)$ in the (i,j) position.

In every case we have described elementary transformations of A which give an equivalent matrix B in ${}_m\mathfrak{A}_n(F[x])$ with an element of degree less than t if the element $a_{ij}(x) \neq 0$ of A of minimum degree t does not divide every element of A. This completes the proof of the lemma.

If $A \neq 0$ is any matrix in ${}_m\mathfrak{A}_n(F[x])$, we can by repeated use of the above lemma obtain an equivalent matrix B with an element $b_{rs}(x) \neq 0$ which divides every element of B. For if the element $a_{ij}(x) \neq 0$ of A of minimum degree t does not divide every element of A, we can obtain an equivalent matrix A_1 with a non-zero element of degree less than or equal to $t - 1$. We can repeat this process with A_1. Since the minimum degree is lowered each time and since we can lower the degree only a finite number of times, we can obtain the desired matrix B by a finite number of elementary transformations. In particular, if at any stage we obtain a matrix with an element of degree zero, that is, a constant $c \in F$, this element is a unit and divides every element of B since it divides every polynomial in $F[x]$.

EXAMPLE 1. Given

$$A = \begin{pmatrix} x^3 + 2x^2 + 5x + 9 & x^4 - x^3 + 2x^2 + 4x \\ x^2 + 4 & x^3 + 2x \end{pmatrix}.$$

The element $x^2 + 4$ has minimum degree, and since $x^3 + 2x^2 + 5x + 9 = (x + 2)(x^2 + 4) + (x + 1)$, A is equivalent to

$$B = \begin{pmatrix} x + 1 & -3x^2 \\ x^2 + 4 & x^3 + 2x \end{pmatrix}.$$

Since $x^2 + 4 = (x - 1)(x + 1) + 5$, B is equivalent to

$$C = \begin{pmatrix} x + 1 & -3x^2 \\ 5 & 4x^3 - 3x^2 + 2x \end{pmatrix}.$$

The element $5 \in R$ divides all elements of C.

The complete reduction procedure is given in the following theorem.

(72.2) Theorem. For every matrix $A \in {}_m\mathfrak{A}_n(F[x])$, there exists an equivalence transformation T which is a product of elementary transformations such that

$$T(A) = D = \left(\begin{array}{ccccc|c} d_1(x) & & & & & \\ & d_2(x) & & & 0 & \\ & & \cdot & & & \\ & & & \cdot & & 0 \\ & 0 & & & \cdot & \\ & & & & d_r(x) & \\ \hline & & 0 & & & 0 \end{array}\right)$$

where the diagonal matrix $D \in {}_m\mathfrak{A}_n(F[x])$ has the following properties:

(i) each $d_i(x)$ is a monic polynomial;
(ii) $d_i(x)$ divides $d_{i+1}(x)$ for $i = 1, 2, \cdots, r-1$;
(iii) the number r of non-zero $d_i(x)$ is the rank of A;
(iv) the product $e_k(x) = d_1(x)d_2(x) \cdots d_k(x)$ is the g.c.d. of all k-rowed minors of A for $k = 1, 2, \cdots, r$.

PROOF. If A is the zero matrix, it is already in the desired form with $r = 0$, and we can take T to be the identity transformation. Therefore we will assume that $A \neq 0$. By the remarks following Lemma (72.1), we can obtain an equivalent matrix $B = (b_{ij})$ with an element $b_{st}(x) \neq 0$, which divides every element of B, by a finite sequence of elementary transformations. A type III transformation which multiplies the elements of row s by $1/c$, where $c \neq 0$ is the leading coefficient of $b_{st}(x)$, will transform B into a matrix B_1 with the element $d_1(x) = (1/c)b_{st}(x)$, a monic polynomial in $F[x]$, in the (s,t) position. Not more than two type I transformations are required to transform B_1 into a matrix B_2 with the monic polynomial $d_1(x)$ in the (1,1) position, where $d_1(x)$ divides every element of B_2.

We next apply a finite sequence of type II transformations to B_2 to obtain a matrix

$$C_1 = \left(\begin{array}{c|c} d_1(x) & 0 \\ \hline 0 & C_1^* \end{array}\right).$$

For example, if $b_{i1} = q_{i1}d_1 \neq 0$ is an element of B_2, we can get a zero in the $(i,1)$ position by adding to the elements of row i the elements of row 1 multiplied by $-q_{i1}(x)$. Since the elements of C_1^* are linear combinations of the elements of B_2, $d_1(x)$ divides every element of C_1^*.

By applying a similar sequence of elementary transformations to C_1^* if $C_1^* \neq 0$, we obtain a matrix

$$C_2 = \left(\begin{array}{cc|c} d_1(x) & 0 & \\ 0 & d_2(x) & 0 \\ \hline \multicolumn{2}{c|}{0} & C_2^* \end{array}\right).$$

The transformations applied to the block C_1^* do not affect the first row or column of C_1, and $d_1(x)$ divides $d_2(x)$ since $d_2(x)$ is a linear combination of the elements of C_1^*, all of which are multiples of $d_1(x)$. We may continue in this fashion until, after a finite number of steps, we either run out of rows or columns, or else we obtain a block $C_r^* = 0$. Then $C_r = D$ has the desired form.

Conditions (i) and (ii) of the theorem are satisfied by the construction of D, and conditions (iii) and (iv) follow from (71.3) since, by inspection, the rank of D is r and the g.c.d. of the k-rowed minors of D is $e_k(x) = d_1(x)d_2(x) \cdots d_k(x)$.

EXAMPLE 2. The following is an outline of the reduction of the matrix

$$A = \begin{pmatrix} x^3 + x^2 - x - 2 & x^2 - 1 & x^2 - 1 \\ x^2 - 1 & -x^3 + x^2 + x - 1 & -x^3 + x^2 + x - 1 \\ x^3 + x^2 - x - 2 & x^2 - 1 & 2x^2 - 2 \end{pmatrix}.$$

1. The element $x^2 - 1$ in the (2,1) position has minimum degree. Since it does not divide $a_{11}(x)$ and since $x^3 + x^2 - x - 2 = (x + 1)(x^2 - 1) - 1$, we may add to the elements of row 1 the elements of row 2 multiplied by $-(x + 1)$ to get

$$B = \begin{pmatrix} -1 & x^4 - x^2 & x^4 - x^2 \\ x^2 - 1 & -x^3 + x^2 + x - 1 & -x^3 + x^2 + x - 1 \\ x^3 + x^2 - x - 2 & x^2 - 1 & 2x^2 - 2 \end{pmatrix}.$$

Multiplying the first row of B by -1 gives a matrix B_1 with $b_{11} = 1$. This element is a monic polynomial which divides every element of B_1.

2. Clearing the first row and first column of B_1 by suitable type II transformations, we obtain

$$C_1 = \left(\begin{array}{c|c} 1 & 0 \\ \hline 0 & C_1^* \end{array}\right) =$$

$$\begin{pmatrix} 1 & 0 & 0 \\ 0 & x^6 - 2x^4 - x^3 + 2x^2 + x - 1 & x^6 - 2x^4 - x^3 + 2x^2 + x - 1 \\ 0 & x^7 + x^6 - 2x^5 - 3x^4 + x^3 + 3x^2 - 1 & x^7 + x^6 - 2x^5 - 3x^4 + x^3 + 4x^2 - 2 \end{pmatrix}.$$

3. We now reduce C_1^*. Rather than following strictly the procedure of the theorem, it is now convenient to subtract column 2 of C_1^* from column 1 to obtain

$$C_1^{**} = \begin{pmatrix} 0 & x^6 - 2x^4 - x^3 + 2x^2 + x - 1 \\ -x^2 + 1 & x^7 + x^6 - 2x^5 - 3x^4 + x^3 + 4x^2 - 2 \end{pmatrix}.$$

4. The element $-x^2 + 1$ divides all elements of C_1^{**}. We first multiply row 2 of C_1^{**} by -1, then interchange rows 1 and 2, and finally get a zero in the (1,2) position by a type II column transformation. This gives

$$C_2^* = \begin{pmatrix} x^2 - 1 & 0 \\ 0 & x^6 - 2x^4 - x^3 + 2x^2 + x - 1 \end{pmatrix}$$

$$= \begin{pmatrix} x^2 - 1 & 0 \\ 0 & (x^2 - 1)(x^4 - x^2 - x + 1) \end{pmatrix}.$$

5. Therefore A is equivalent to

$$C_2 = D = \begin{pmatrix} 1 & 0 & 0 \\ 0 & x^2 - 1 & 0 \\ 0 & 0 & (x^2-1)(x^4 - x^2 - x + 1) \end{pmatrix}$$
$$= \begin{pmatrix} 1 & 0 & 0 \\ 0 & (x-1)(x+1) & 0 \\ 0 & 0 & (x-1)^2(x+1)(x^3 + x^2 - 1) \end{pmatrix}.$$

If A is a matrix of rank r, the polynomials $e_1(x), e_2(x), \cdots, e_r(x)$, which are the g.c.d.'s of the 1-, 2-, $\cdots$, r-rowed minors of A respectively, are uniquely determined by the matrix A, and so are the polynomials $d_1(x) = e_1(x)$, $d_2(x) = e_2(x)/e_1(x)$, $\cdots$, $d_r(x) = e_r(x)/e_{r-1}(x)$ which appear in the diagonal form D of Theorem (72.2). By Theorem (71.3), the set of polynomials $d_1(x), d_2(x), \cdots, d_r(x)$ associated with the matrix A is left invariant when A is transformed by an elementary transformation. It is a consequence of the corollary to the following theorem that this set of polynomials is left unchanged by any transformation of the equivalence group.

(72.3) Theorem. An m-rowed square matrix A in $F[x]$ has a non-zero constant determinant in F if and only if A is a product of elementary transformation matrices in $F[x]$.

PROOF. If $A = P_1P_2 \cdots P_s$ where the P_i are elementary transformation matrices, then since $|A| = |P_1||P_2| \cdots |P_s|$ and since each $|P_i|$ is a non-zero constant in F, $|A|$ is a non-zero constant in F. Conversely, by Theorem (72.2), for each matrix A in $F[x]$, there exists an equivalence transformation $T_{P,Q}$, where P and Q are products of elementary transformation matrices in $F[x]$, such that $T_{P,Q}(A) = PAQ = D$, a diagonal matrix. If $|A| = c \neq 0$ in F, then $|D| = |P||A||Q|$ is a non-zero constant in F. Since $|D| = d_1(x)d_2(x) \cdots d_m(x)$, and since each $d_i(x)$ is a monic polynomial, each $d_i(x) = 1$, so that $D = I_m$. Thus $PAQ = I_m$ and $A = P^{-1}Q^{-1}$ where P^{-1} and Q^{-1} are products of elementary transformation matrices in $F[x]$. [Compare with the proof of (20.3).]

(72.4) Corollary. T is an equivalence transformation of ${}_m\mathfrak{A}_n(F[x])$ if and only if T is a product of elementary transformations.

The proof of (72.4) is left to the reader as an exercise.

Now by (72.4) the polynomials $d_1(x) = e_1(x)$, $d_2(x) = e_2(x)/e_1(x)$, $\cdots$, $d_r(x) = e_r(x)/e_{r-1}(x)$ in $F[x]$, which are uniquely determined by the matrix A in $F[x]$, are left invariant by every equivalence transformation. They are called the *invariant factors* of A. By Theorem (72.2) each matrix A in $F[x]$ is equivalent to a diagonal matrix D in $F[x]$ which exhibits these invariant factors. The following theorem completes the argument that this set of diagonal matrices D is a set of canonical forms for the group of equivalence transformations of ${}_m\mathfrak{A}_n(F[x])$.

(72.5) Theorem. Two matrices A and B in ${}_m\mathfrak{A}_n(F[x])$ are equivalent over F if and only if they have the same invariant factors.

PROOF. If $B = T_{P,Q}(A)$ where $T_{P,Q}$ is an equivalence transformation, then A and B have the same invariant factors by Theorem (71.3) and (72.4). Conversely, if A and B have the same invariant factors, they are both equivalent to the same diagonal matrix D by Theorem (72.2) and therefore are equivalent to each other.

An alternate statement of this theorem is that two matrices A and B in ${}_m\mathfrak{A}_n(F[x])$ are equivalent over F if and only if they are equivalent to the same diagonal matrix D of (72.2). Thus, these diagonal matrices in $F[x]$ are a set of canonical forms for the equivalence group over F and are called the *rational canonical forms* of this group.

The g.c.d. of a set of polynomials in $F[x]$ is in $F[x]$ and is unchanged if the coefficient field F is enlarged (see Section 60). Therefore the invariant factors of a matrix A in $F[x]$, which are quotients of such g.c.d.'s, have this same property. In particular, if $\bar{F}$ is the smallest number field which contains the coefficients of the elements of A, the invariant factors of A are in $\bar{F}[x]$ and do not depend on the number field $F \supseteq \bar{F}$ in which we are discussing equivalence. It is for this reason that the diagonal matrices D of (72.2) are called rational canonical forms. Further, it is a consequence of Theorem (72.5) that if A and B are matrices in ${}_m\mathfrak{A}_n(F[x])$ and if K is any number field containing F, then A and B are equivalent over K if and only if they are equivalent over F. This fact permits us to speak of the equivalence of polynomial matrices without reference to a specific number field F containing their elements.

Exercise (72.1). Find the rational canonical form of each of the following matrices:

(a) $$\begin{pmatrix} 6x^3 + 7x^2 + 4x & 2x^3 + 2x^2 + x \\ -6x^3 - x^2 & -3x^2 \end{pmatrix};$$

(b) $$\begin{pmatrix} x + 1 & 3x - 4 & x \\ -x & -3x + 4 & -x + 1 \\ 2x + 1 & 6x - 7 & 2x - 1 \end{pmatrix};$$

(c) $$\begin{pmatrix} x^2 - x & -4x & -2x^2 + 4x \\ 2x & 4x & -6x \\ x^2 + x & 0 & -2x^2 - 2x \end{pmatrix};$$

(d) $\begin{pmatrix} -6x^2 & -2x^2+1 & -2x^3-2x^2-x+1 & 4x^2+1 \\ 3x & x & x^2+x+1 & -2x \\ 4x^2+2x+1 & x^2 & x^3+x^2+x & -3x^2-2x-1 \end{pmatrix}$;

(e) $\begin{pmatrix} x^2+2x+1 & x & x^2+x \\ 2x+2 & x+1 & x+1 \\ x^2+4x+3 & 2x+1 & 2x^2+2x \end{pmatrix}$;

(f) $\begin{pmatrix} x^3+2x^2-4x-8 & x^3+3x^2-4x-12 & x^3+2x^2-5x-6 \\ -x^3-x^2+3x+6 & -x^3-2x^2+4x+8 & -x^3-x^2+4x+4 \\ x^3+2x^2-3x-10 & x^3+3x^2-3x-14 & x^3+2x^2-4x-8 \end{pmatrix}$.

Exercise (72.2). Express each of the following as a product of elementary transformation matrices:

(a) $\begin{pmatrix} 4x^3-14x^2-16x+18 & 2x^2-8x+4 & 4x^2-20x+12 \\ 4x^2-14x-28 & 2x-8 & 4x-20 \\ 4x^3+2x^2-9x-7 & 2x^2-2x-4 & 4x^2-4x-5 \end{pmatrix}$;

(b) $\begin{pmatrix} 4x-7 & 2x-4 & 2x-5 \\ 6x-11 & 3x-4 & 3x-10 \\ -2x+1 & -x & -x+2 \end{pmatrix}$.

Exercise (72.3). Write out all possible rational canonical forms for 3 by 3 matrices in $F[x]$ which have one or more of the polynomials $1, x, x^2, (x+1), x(x+1)$, as invariant factors.

Section 73. Matric Polynomials

An m by n matrix $A = (a_{ij}(x))$ with polynomial elements in $F[x]$ can be written as a polynomial in x with coefficients which are m by n matrices with elements in F as in the following example:

$$\begin{pmatrix} 5x^3-x^2 & -3x^2 & 2x^3 \\ 2 & 4x & x^3+x^2 \end{pmatrix} = \begin{pmatrix} 5 & 0 & 2 \\ 0 & 0 & 1 \end{pmatrix} x^3 + \begin{pmatrix} -1 & -3 & 0 \\ 0 & 0 & 1 \end{pmatrix} x^2 + \begin{pmatrix} 0 & 0 & 0 \\ 0 & 4 & 0 \end{pmatrix} x + \begin{pmatrix} 0 & 0 & 0 \\ 2 & 0 & 0 \end{pmatrix}.$$

Since the operations in this process are reversible, it is seen that the two concepts of a matrix with polynomial elements and a polynomial with constant matrix coefficients are interchangeable. In this section, we develop several properties of square matrices in $F[x]$ from this alternate point of view.

Let $A = (a_{ij}(x)) \neq 0$ be an n-rowed square matrix in $F[x]$ and let r be the maximum degree of the polynomials $a_{ij}(x)$. Then we have

$$A = (a_{ij}(x)) = A_0 + A_1x + \cdots + A_rx^r = \sum_{i=0}^{r} A_ix^i,$$

where the A_i are n-rowed square matrices in F. The expression $\sum_{i=0}^{r} A_i x^i$ is called a *square matric polynomial* of *degree* r. The matrix $A_r \neq 0$ is called the *leading coefficient.* We first obtain a theorem like (59.3) for matric polynomials.

(73.1) Theorem. Let $A = \sum_{i=0}^{r} A_i x^i$ and $B = \sum_{i=0}^{s} B_i x^i$ be n-rowed square matric polynomials in $F[x]$ of degrees r and s respectively. Then

(i) either $A + B = 0$ or $\deg (A + B) \leq \max [r,s]$;
(ii) either $AB = 0$ or $\deg (AB) \leq r + s$;
(iii) if either leading coefficient A_r or B_s is nonsingular, then $\deg (AB) = r + s$.

PROOF. For the discussion of addition, assume that $r \geq s$ and write $B = \sum_{i=0}^{r} B_i x^i$ where $B_{s+1} = B_{s+2} = \cdots = B_r = 0$. Then using the properties of matrix addition and scalar multiplication, we have

$$A + B = \sum_{i=0}^{r} A_i x^i + \sum_{i=0}^{r} B_i x^i = \sum_{i=0}^{r} (A_i + B_i) x^i$$

where either $B_i = -A_i$ for $i = 0, 1, \cdots, r$ and $A + B = 0$, or $\deg (A + B) \leq r = \max [r,s]$.

For the discussion of multiplication, we use the original form of A and B and the distributive law of matrix multiplication with respect to addition to obtain

$$AB = \left(\sum_{i=0}^{r} A_i x^i\right)\left(\sum_{i=0}^{s} B_i x^i\right)$$
$$= A_0 B_0 + (A_0 B_1 + A_1 B_0)x + \cdots + A_r B_s x^{r+s}.$$

The product $A_r B_s$ may be zero even though $A_r \neq 0$ and $B_s \neq 0$, so that the best result on the degree of the product is given by (ii). However, if A_r is nonsingular, $A_r B_s$ has the rank of B_s which is positive since $B_s \neq 0$. Similarly, if B_s is nonsingular, $A_r B_s$ has positive rank. Thus in either case $A_r B_s \neq 0$ and $\deg (AB) = r + s$.

For square matric polynomials, we continue to parallel the theory of polynomials with coefficients in a number field by proving a division algorithm. However, since the multiplication of matrices is not commutative, we obtain both right and left quotients and remainders.

(73.2) Theorem. If A and B are n-rowed square matric polynomials in $F[x]$ such that $B \neq 0$ has degree s and has a nonsingular leading coefficient, then there exist unique n-rowed square matric polynomials Q_1, Q_2, R_r, and R_l in $F[x]$ such that

$$A = Q_1B + R_r \text{ and } A = BQ_2 + R_l,$$

where either $R_r = 0$ or deg $R_r < s$ and either $R_l = 0$ or deg $R_l < s$.

PROOF. An inductive proof follows exactly as for the proof of the division algorithm (60.1) for polynomials in $F[x]$. The only nontrivial case is where $A \neq 0$ has degree $r \geq s$. Let $A = \sum_{i=0}^{r} A_ix^i$ and $B = \sum_{i=0}^{s} B_ix^i$. Then since B_s is a nonsingular matrix with constant elements, B_s^{-1} exists and the matric polynomials

$$A - (A_rB_s^{-1}x^{r-s})B = C_1 \qquad \text{and} \qquad A - B(B_s^{-1}A_rx^{r-s}) = C_2$$

in $F[x]$ are either zero or have degree less than r. If we assume that the identities of the theorem are valid for all matric polynomials of degree less than r, then if C_1 and C_2 are not zero we have

$$C_1 = S_1B + R_r, \quad A = [A_rB_s^{-1}x^{r-s} + S_1]B + R_r$$
$$C_2 = BS_2 + R_l, \quad A = B[B_s^{-1}A_rx^{r-s} + S_2] + R_l,$$

which gives the identities for A of degree r.

The proof of the uniqueness of the quotients and remainders follows from Theorem (73.1). If $A = Q_1B + R_r = Q_1'B + R_r'$, then $(Q_1 - Q_1')B = R_r' - R_r$. If $Q_1 - Q_1' \neq 0$, then deg $[(Q_1 - Q_1')B] \geq s$ by (iii) of (73.1) since B has nonsingular leading coefficient. If both R_r and R_r' satisfy the statement of the theorem, then either $R_r' - R_r = 0$, or deg $(R_r' - R_r) < s$ by (i) of (73.1) and a contradiction is obtained. The proof is the same for the quotient and remainder upon dividing A by B on the left.

The two forms of the division algorithm (73.2) give rise to corresponding remainder theorems and factor theorems for matric polynomials. They are obtained by taking as the divisor the matric polynomial $B = Ix - C$ of degree 1. First a word must be said about the values of an n-rowed square matric polynomial $A = \sum_{i=0}^{r} A_ix^i$. Since the polynomials x^i are scalars, A can be written either in this form or as $\sum_{i=0}^{r} x^iA_i$. However, if the indeterminate x is replaced by the n-rowed square matrix C with elements in F, the resulting matrices $\sum_{i=0}^{r} A_iC^i$ and $\sum_{i=0}^{r} C^iA_i$ in F are not necessarily equal. We will use the notation $A(C)_r$ for $\sum_{i=0}^{r} A_iC^i$ and $A(C)_l$ for $\sum_{i=0}^{r} C^iA_i$. The matrix C is called a *right zero* or a *left zero* of A according as $A(C)_r = 0$ or $A(C)_l = 0$.

(73.3) Theorem. Let $A = \sum_{i=0}^{r} A_ix^i$ be an n-rowed square matric polynomial in $F[x]$ and let C be an n-rowed square matrix with elements in F. Then

$$A = Q_1(Ix - C) + R_r \qquad \text{where } R_r = A(C)_r$$

and

$$A = (Ix - C)Q_2 + R_l \qquad \text{where } R_l = A(C)_l.$$

PROOF. By (73.2), there exist matrices Q_1 and R_r, where R_r has elements in F, such that $A = Q_1(Ix - C) + R_r$. Now

$$Q_1 = S_0 + S_1x + S_2x^2 + \cdots + S_{r-1}x^{r-1},$$

so that

$$\begin{aligned} R_r &= A - Q_1(Ix - C) \\ &= A - (S_0 + S_1x + \cdots + S_{r-1}x^{r-1})(Ix - C) \\ &= \sum_{i=0}^{r} A_ix^i - [(S_0x - S_0C) + (S_1x^2 - S_1Cx) + \cdots \\ &\qquad + (S_{r-1}x^r - S_{r-1}Cx^{r-1})]. \end{aligned}$$

Replacing x by C in this identity gives

$$\begin{aligned} R_r = A(C)_r - [(S_0C - S_0C) + (S_1C^2 - S_1C^2) + \cdots \\ + (S_{r-1}C^r - S_{r-1}C^r)] = A(C)_r. \end{aligned}$$

The proof of the second statement is similar.

The factor theorems for a matric polynomial are obtained immediately from Theorems (73.2) and (73.3).

(73.4) Corollary. The matrix C in F is a right zero (left zero) of $A = \sum_{i=0}^{r} A_ix^i$ in $F[x]$ if and only if $Ix - C$ is a right factor (left factor) of A.

Exercise (73.1). Find

$$\begin{pmatrix} 2x^2 - 5x & 3x & 5 \\ 3x - 4 & 2x^2 + 7 & -3x \\ x^2 - 4x + 5 & x^2 & 2x + 2 \end{pmatrix} + \begin{pmatrix} 2x & 3x^2 - 3x & 7x - 3 \\ 3x - 4 & x + 2 & 5 \\ 4x + 2 & -2x^2 & -x^2 \end{pmatrix},$$

both by adding the matrices and by adding the corresponding matric polynomials. Similarly treat the products

$$\begin{pmatrix} 2x-5 & -7x+4 & -x-2 \\ 3x+2 & -x-1 & 4x-4 \\ 4x-1 & x-7 & 7x+2 \end{pmatrix} \cdot \begin{pmatrix} 2x-1 & 3x+2 & 2x+1 \\ x-1 & -2x-4 & 3x-5 \\ x-5 & -2x+6 & x-4 \end{pmatrix}$$

and

$$\begin{pmatrix} x^2 & 4x+2 & 2x \\ 2x+3 & 2x+3 & -3x-5 \\ 3x-1 & x^2-7x & 3x^2+1 \end{pmatrix} \cdot \begin{pmatrix} 3x-2 & 4x-7 & 2 \\ 6x^2 & 3 & 6x \\ -2x^2-3x & 5 & -1 \end{pmatrix}.$$

Exercise (73.2). Find the quotients and remainders upon dividing A by B on the left and on the right if

(a) $A = \begin{pmatrix} 3x^2-2 & 3x^2-7x+4 \\ 2x+5 & 2x \end{pmatrix}$, $B = \begin{pmatrix} x & 4 \\ -3x+2 & 2x \end{pmatrix}$;

(b) $A = \begin{pmatrix} 2x-4 & 4x-3 \\ -2x+2 & -4x+6 \end{pmatrix}$, $B = \begin{pmatrix} x-5 & -x+1 \\ 3x+2 & -4x \end{pmatrix}$;

(c) $A = \begin{pmatrix} 3x^2-7 & 4x-3 \\ 2x & 2x \end{pmatrix}$, $B = \begin{pmatrix} 3 & 1 \\ 0 & -4 \end{pmatrix}$.

Exercise (73.3). Find $A(C)_r$ and $A(C)_l$ if

$$A = \begin{pmatrix} 3x^3+2x & x^2+3x+2 & 3x^2+3x \\ 4x-5 & -x^3+x^2+x-1 & -2 \\ 2x^2 & 2x^2 & -6 \end{pmatrix}$$

and

(a) $C = \begin{pmatrix} 2 & 4 & 3 \\ -1 & 0 & 1 \\ 2 & 4 & 0 \end{pmatrix}$, **(b)** $C = \begin{pmatrix} 2 & 5 & 3 \\ 6 & 2 & 5 \\ -4 & 3 & -2 \end{pmatrix}$,

(c) $C = \begin{pmatrix} 3 & 0 & 0 \\ 0 & 1 & 0 \\ 0 & 0 & -1 \end{pmatrix}$, **(d)** $C = \begin{pmatrix} 2 & 4 & 0 \\ 0 & 1 & 0 \\ 0 & 0 & 0 \end{pmatrix}$,

(e) $C = \begin{pmatrix} -2 & 0 & 0 \\ 0 & -2 & 0 \\ 0 & 0 & -2 \end{pmatrix}$, **(f)** $C = \begin{pmatrix} 3 & 0 & 0 \\ 0 & 3 & 0 \\ 0 & 0 & 0 \end{pmatrix}$.

Exercise (73.4). Test whether each of the following is a right zero or a left zero of

$$A = \begin{pmatrix} 2x^2 - 8 & x^3 - 5x^2 - 3x & -6x \\ 3x^3 - 3x^2 - 2x - 4 & -x^2 - 5x + 1 & -4x \\ -9x^2 & x^3 + x^2 - 6x + 3 & 2x^2 \end{pmatrix}:$$

(a) $C = \begin{pmatrix} 2 & 0 & 0 \\ 0 & 1 & 0 \\ 0 & 1 & 0 \end{pmatrix}$; (b) $C = \begin{pmatrix} 2 & 0 & 3 \\ 1 & 1 & 2 \\ 0 & 3 & 0 \end{pmatrix}$.

Exercise (73.5). Test whether each of the following is a right zero or a left zero of

$$A = \begin{pmatrix} x^3 - 2x^2 + 13x + 3 & -3x^2 + 6x + 3 & -5x^2 - 2x - 8 \\ -4x^2 - 10x - 12 & -2x^2 - 7x - 12 & x^3 + 3x^2 + 5x + 2 \\ -x^2 + 2x + 3 & 2x + 3 & x - 2 \end{pmatrix}:$$

(a) $C = \begin{pmatrix} 0 & 3 & -1 \\ 0 & -2 & -1 \\ 2 & 1 & 0 \end{pmatrix}$; (b) $C = \begin{pmatrix} 2 & 3 & 2 \\ -1 & 0 & -2 \\ 4 & 3 & 0 \end{pmatrix}$.

Exercise (73.6). Find $A(C)_r$ and $A(C)_l$ by two methods if

(a) $A = \begin{pmatrix} x^4 - 3x^2 & x^4 + x^3 - 4x \\ 3x^3 - 5x + 2 & 3x^4 - 7x^3 - 2x - 1 \end{pmatrix}$, $C = \begin{pmatrix} 2 & -1 \\ 5 & 3 \end{pmatrix}$;

(b) $A = \begin{pmatrix} 2x^2 - x & -4x & x^3 - 4x^2 - x \\ x^3 - 4x^2 & -2x & -2x^2 \\ 3x^2 & x^3 + 3x & 4x^2 \end{pmatrix}$, $C = \begin{pmatrix} 4 & -2 & 1 \\ 2 & 4 & 0 \\ -3 & -2 & 0 \end{pmatrix}$.

Exercise (73.7). Given $A = \sum_{i=0}^{r} A_i x^i$ and $B = \sum_{i=0}^{s} B_i x^i$ with A_r, B_s not zero, prove that $A = B$ if and only if $r = s$ and $A_i = B_i$ for all $i = 0, 1, 2, \cdots, r$.

Exercise (73.8). Let A, B, and C be n-rowed square matrices in $F[x]$ where A has nonsingular leading coefficient. Prove that $AB = AC$ implies $B = C$.

Section 74. Scalar Matric Polynomials

If the coefficients A_i in the n-rowed square matrix polynomial $A = \sum_{i=0}^{r} A_i x^i$ are scalar matrices $A_i = a_i I$ with $a_i \in F$, the results of the preceding section can be simplified. If C is any n-rowed square matrix with elements in F, then the scalar matrices $a_i I$ commute with C and we have

$$A(C)_r = \sum_{i=0}^{r} a_i I C^i = \sum_{i=0}^{r} C^i a_i I = A(C)_l.$$

Thus we can write $A(C)$ for both the right and left values of A and by Corollary (73.4), C is a *zero* of A if and only if $Ix - C$ is either a right or left factor of A.

Each scalar matric polynomial A uniquely determines a polynomial $a(x) = \sum_{i=0}^{r} a_i x^i \in F[x]$, and conversely, for

$$A = \sum_{i=0}^{r} a_i I x^i = \left(\sum_{i=0}^{r} a_i x^i\right) I = a(x)I.$$

A scalar matrix polynomial $a(x)I$ is called *monic* if $a(x)$ is a monic polynomial.

Since the set $\mathfrak{A}_n(F)$ of all n-rowed square matrices with elements in F can be thought of as the sequence vector space $V_{n^2}(F)$, the matrices

$$I, C, C^2, \cdots, C^{n^2}$$

are linearly dependent over F for every $C \in \mathfrak{A}_n(F)$. This means that there is a relation

$$a_0 I + a_1 C + a_2 C^2 + \cdots + a_r C^r = 0$$

with $a_i \in F$ and not every $a_i = 0$. In other words, C is a zero of the scalar matric polynomial $\sum_{i=0}^{r} a_i I x^i$ in $F[x]$ of degree less than or equal to n^2. In this section we will find the scalar matric polynomial in $F[x]$ of minimum degree of which C is a zero.

Corresponding to each n-rowed square $C = (c_{ij})$ in F, there is a linear matric polynomial

$$Ix - C = \begin{pmatrix} x - c_{11} & -c_{12} & \cdots & -c_{1n} \\ -c_{21} & x - c_{22} & \cdots & -c_{2n} \\ \cdot & \cdot & & \cdot \\ \cdot & \cdot & & \cdot \\ \cdot & \cdot & & \cdot \\ -c_{n1} & -c_{n2} & \cdots & x - c_{nn} \end{pmatrix} \text{ in } F[x].$$

Since the determinant of a square matrix is a sum of all products of n elements with exactly one from each row and one from each column, the only term of $|Ix - C|$ which involves x^n is the main diagonal term

$(x - c_{11})(x - c_{22}) \cdots (x - c_{nn})$. Therefore $|Ix - C|$ is a monic polynomial in $F[x]$ of degree n. In particular, $Ix - C$ is nonsingular and $|Ix - C| = e_n(x) = d_1(x)d_2(x) \cdots d_n(x)$ where the $d_i(x)$ are the invariant factors of $Ix - C$.

(74.1) Definition. If C is an n-rowed square matrix in F, the matrix $Ix - C$ in $F[x]$ is called the *characteristic matrix* of C, and $|Ix - C|$ is called the *characteristic polynomial* of C.

As an example, consider the matrix

$$C = \begin{pmatrix} 4 & 3 & 1 \\ 0 & 0 & -2 \\ 0 & 1 & -2 \end{pmatrix} \in R.$$

The characteristic matrix of C is

$$\begin{pmatrix} x-4 & -3 & -1 \\ 0 & x & 2 \\ 0 & -1 & x+2 \end{pmatrix} \in R[x]$$

and the characteristic polynomial of C is $(x - 4)[x(x + 2) + 2] = x^3 - 2x^2 - 6x - 8$. It may be shown that the invariant factors of $Ix - C$ are $d_1(x) = 1$, $d_2(x) = 1$, and $d_3(x) = x^3 - 2x^2 - 6x - 8$, so that $|Ix - C| = d_1(x)d_2(x)d_3(x) = d_3(x)$. Now

$$C^2 = \begin{pmatrix} 16 & 13 & -4 \\ 0 & -2 & 4 \\ 0 & -2 & 2 \end{pmatrix}, \quad C^3 = \begin{pmatrix} 64 & 44 & -2 \\ 0 & 4 & -4 \\ 0 & 2 & 0 \end{pmatrix},$$

and

$$\begin{pmatrix} 64 & 44 & -2 \\ 0 & 4 & -4 \\ 0 & 2 & 0 \end{pmatrix} - 2\begin{pmatrix} 16 & 13 & -4 \\ 0 & -2 & 4 \\ 0 & -2 & 2 \end{pmatrix} - 6\begin{pmatrix} 4 & 3 & 1 \\ 0 & 0 & -2 \\ 0 & 1 & -2 \end{pmatrix}$$
$$- 8\begin{pmatrix} 1 & 0 & 0 \\ 0 & 1 & 0 \\ 0 & 0 & 1 \end{pmatrix} = \begin{pmatrix} 0 & 0 & 0 \\ 0 & 0 & 0 \\ 0 & 0 & 0 \end{pmatrix}$$

so that C is a zero of the scalar matric polynomial $(x^3 - 2x^2 - 6x - 8)I = d_3(x)I$. This is an example of the following theorem.

(74.2) Theorem. Each n-rowed square matrix C in F is a zero of the scalar matric polynomial $d_n(x)I$ where $d_n(x)$ is the last invariant factor of the characteristic matrix $Ix - C$ of C.

PROOF. It has been remarked that if A is a matrix in $F[x]$, then adj A is a matrix in $F[x]$, and that Theorem (11.4) holds for polynomial matrices. We have

$$(Ix - C) \cdot \text{adj } (Ix - C) = |Ix - C| \cdot I = d_1(x)d_2(x) \cdots d_n(x) \cdot I$$
$$= e_{n-1}(x)d_n(x)I.$$

Since the elements of adj $(Ix - C)$ are the cofactors of the elements of $Ix - C$, these elements, except for sign, are just the set of all $(n - 1)$-rowed minors of $Ix - C$. Therefore by (72.1), the g.c.d. of the elements of adj $(Ix - C)$ is $e_{n-1}(x)$, and adj $(Ix - C) = e_{n-1}(x)B$ where B is a matrix in $F[x]$. We now have

$$(Ix - C) \cdot e_{n-1}(x)B = e_{n-1}(x)(Ix - C)B = e_{n-1}(x)d_n(x)I.$$

Since $e_{n-1}(x)$ is a non-zero polynomial in $F[x]$, the above equality implies that $(Ix - C)B = d_n(x)I$. Thus $Ix - C$ is a factor of the scalar matric polynomial $d_n(x)I$, and by (73.4), C is a zero of $d_n(x)I$.

(74.3) Corollary. (Cayley-Hamilton Theorem.) Each n-rowed square matrix C in F is a zero of its characteristic polynomial.

PROOF. For $|Ix - C| \cdot I = e_{n-1}(x)d_n(x)I = (e_{n-1}(x)I)(d_n(x)I)$, and C is a zero of the factor $d_n(x)I$ by the above theorem.

We call the monic scalar polynomial of least degree which has the matrix C in F as a zero the *minimum polynomial* of C. Using the division algorithm, we may prove that $d_n(x)I$ is the minimum polynomial of C.

(74.4) Theorem. The minimum polynomial of a square matrix C in F is $d_n(x)I$ where $d_n(x)$ is the last invariant factor of the characteristic matrix of C.

PROOF. Let $m(x)I$ be the minimum polynomial of C. By the division algorithm (60.1) for polynomials, $d_n(x) = q(x)m(x) + r(x)$ where either $r(x) = 0$ or $\deg r(x) < \deg m(x)$. This implies that $d_n(x)I = (q(x)I)(m(x)I) + r(x)I$, and that C is a zero of $r(x)I$ since it is a zero of $m(x)I$ by hypothesis and of $d_n(x)I$ by Theorem (74.2). But since $m(x)$ is the minimum polynomial of C, this implies that $r(x) = 0$ and that $d_n(x) = q(x)m(x)$.

In the equation $d_n(x)I = (Ix - C)B$ which was derived in the proof of (74.2), the g.c.d. of the elements of B is 1. For B was obtained from adj $(Ix - C)$ by factoring out $e_{n-1}(x)$ which is the g.c.d. of the elements of adj $(Ix - C)$. Since $m(x)I = (Ix - C)M$ by the factor theorem (73.4),

$$(Ix - C)B = d_n(x)I = (q(x)I)(m(x)I) = (q(x)I)(Ix - C)M$$
$$= (Ix - C)(q(x)I)M.$$

Thus $B = (q(x)I)M = q(x)M$ by the uniqueness of the division algorithm (73.2) on dividing $d_n(x)I$ on the left by the matrix $Ix - C$ which has nonsingular leading coefficient. Thus the polynomial $q(x)$, which is a common factor of the elements of B, is a constant in F, and since $d_n(x)$ and $m(x)$ are monic, $q(x) = 1$. Therefore $d_n(x) = q(x)m(x) = m(x)$ and $d_n(x)I = m(x)I$.

Exercise (74.1). Find the quotients and remainders on dividing $A = (x^3 - x^2 + 4x + 4)I_3$ by $B = (2x - 1)I_3$ on the right and on the left.

Exercise (74.2). Show that

$$C = \begin{pmatrix} 4 & -1 & -6 \\ 2 & 3 & 5 \\ -1 & 2 & 2 \end{pmatrix}$$

is a zero of $(x^3 - 9x^2 + 12x - 49)I_3$.

Exercise (74.3). Prove that the non-negative powers of an n-rowed square matrix C in F, $n \geq 2$, generate a subspace of $V_{n^2}(F)$ of dimension k, where $2 \leq k \leq n$, if and only if C is not a scalar matrix.

Exercise (74.4). Prove that if $A = \sum_{i=0}^{r} A_i x^i$ where A_r is nonsingular in F, then A is nonsingular in $F[x]$. Give an example of a nonsingular matrix in $F[x]$ with a singular leading coefficient.

Exercise (74.5). Find the characteristic polynomial and minimum polynomial of

(a) $\begin{pmatrix} 4 & 0 & 0 \\ 0 & 4 & 0 \\ 0 & 0 & 4 \end{pmatrix}$, (b) $\begin{pmatrix} 0 & 1 & 0 \\ 0 & 0 & 1 \\ -2 & 2/3 & 3 \end{pmatrix}$,

(c) $\begin{pmatrix} 3 & -2 & 5 \\ 4 & 1 & 6 \\ -2 & -4 & 2 \end{pmatrix}$, (d) $\begin{pmatrix} 3+i & -i & 0 \\ 2-i & 0 & 2+i \\ 0 & i & 3-i \end{pmatrix}$.

Exercise (74.6). Show that the constant term of the characteristic polynomial of an n-rowed square matrix C is $(-1)^n|C|$.

Exercise (74.7). If A and B are square matrices with elements in F, then B is similar to A over F if there exists a nonsingular square matrix P in F such that $B = PAP^{-1}$ (see Section 30).

(a) Prove that similar matrices have the same determinant.
(b) Prove that similar matrices have the same characteristic polynomial.
(c) Prove that the characteristic matrices of similar matrices have the same invariant factors.

Exercise (74.8). If $f(x)$ is a scalar matric polynomial and if A and B are similar matrices, prove that $f(A)$ and $f(B)$ are similar.

VIII CANONICAL FORMS FOR GROUPS OF MATRIX TRANSFORMATIONS

Section 75. Introduction

In Chapter II we obtained a set of canonical forms for the group $\mathcal{E}({}_m\mathfrak{A}_n(F))$ of equivalence transformations of the set of all m by n matrices with elements in the number field F. We recall that $\mathcal{E}({}_m\mathfrak{A}_n(F))$ consists of all transformations $T_{P,Q}$, defined by $T_{P,Q}(A) = PAQ$ for all $A \in {}_m\mathfrak{A}_n(F)$, where P and Q are nonsingular matrices in $\mathfrak{A}_m(F)$ and $\mathfrak{A}_n(F)$ respectively; and that the canonical forms of this group are the matrices D_r with the number 1 in the first r positions of the main diagonal and zeros elsewhere. The integer r in the canonical form D_r of a matrix A is the rank of A and is the only significant property of A with respect to the group $\mathcal{E}({}_m\mathfrak{A}_n(F))$.

Problems with a solution which depends only on the rank of some rectangular matrix with elements in F are associated with the group of matrix transformations $\mathcal{E}({}_m\mathfrak{A}_n(F))$. As examples of such problems, we have considered the solution of m linear equations in n unknowns, the simplification of a linear mapping of $V_n(F)$ into $V_m(F)$, and the simplification of a bilinear mapping from $V_m(F)$ and $V_n(F)$ into F.

In the study of a linear transformation $\mathcal{L}$ of $V_n(F)$ into itself, we found that the associated group of matrix transformations is the collineatory group, which consists of those equivalence transformations $T_{P,Q}$ of $\mathfrak{A}_n(F)$ for which $Q = P^{-1}$. Thus a complete discussion of the simplification of a linear transformation $\mathcal{L}$ requires finding a set of canonical forms for the matrices in $\mathfrak{A}_n(F)$ under the collineatory group. Because of its length, we will not give this reduction here.* The ground work for the theory of canonical forms for the collineatory group was given in Chapter VII, as the principal theorem is that there exists a collineatory transformation mapping a matrix A onto B (that is, A and B are

---

* Discussions of similarity may be found in

A. A. Albert, *Introduction to Algebraic Theories* (Chicago, 1941), Chap. V.

A. A. Albert, *Modern Higher Algebra* (Chicago, 1937), Chap. IV.

Sam Perlis, *Theory of Matrices* (Cambridge, Mass., 1953), Chap. 8 and following.

R. R. Stoll, *Linear Algebra and Matrix Theory* (New York, 1952), Chap. 6 and following.

similar) if and only if the characteristic matrices $Ix - A$ and $Ix - B$ of A and B are equivalent in $\mathfrak{A}_n(F[x])$. Several exercises in the previous chapter indicated the relation between the collineatory group of transformations of $\mathfrak{A}_n(F)$ and the equivalence group $\mathcal{E}(\mathfrak{A}_n(F[x]))$.

The problem of simplifying a bilinear mapping $\mathcal{B}$ from $V_m(F)$ and $V_n(F)$ into F can be approached in a different way. We consider the bilinear form $f(x_i,y_j) = \sum_{i=1}^{m} \sum_{j=1}^{n} a_{ij}x_iy_j = XAY'$ with $a_{ij} \in F$. This form in $m + n$ variables, or indeterminates, $X = (x_1, x_2, \cdots, x_m)$ and $Y = (y_1, y_2, \cdots, y_n)$ was defined in Section 66. For suitable nonsingular matrices P and Q' in F, $PAQ' = D_r$, where r is the rank of A, so that if the form $f(x_i,y_j)$ is subjected to a change of variables $X = \bar{X}P$, $Y = \bar{Y}Q$, it can be put in the canonical form

$$f(x_i,y_j) = XAY' = \bar{X}PAQ'\bar{Y}' = \bar{X}D_r\bar{Y}'$$
$$= \bar{x}_1\bar{y}_1 + \bar{x}_2\bar{y}_2 + \cdots + \bar{x}_r\bar{y}_r = \bar{f}(\bar{x}_i,\bar{y}_j).$$

The form $f(x_i,y_j)$ defines a bilinear mapping $\mathcal{B}$ of $V_m(F)$ and $V_n(F)$ into F. This mapping is given by $\mathcal{B}(\alpha,\beta) = \sum_{i=1}^{m} \sum_{j=1}^{n} a_{ij}a_ib_j \in F$ where the variables $x_1, x_2, \cdots, x_m$ and $y_1, y_2, \cdots, y_n$ are replaced by the coordinates $a_1, a_2, \cdots, a_m$ of $\alpha \in V_m(F)$ and $b_1, b_2, \cdots, b_n$ of $\beta \in V_n(F)$ with respect to given bases in the two spaces. If we define new bases in the two spaces by the nonsingular matrices P and Q as in Theorem (27.1), the new form $\bar{f}(\bar{x}_i,\bar{y}_j)$ defines the same mapping $\mathcal{B}$ if the variables $\bar{x}_1, \bar{x}_2, \cdots, \bar{x}_m$ and $\bar{y}_1, \bar{y}_2, \cdots, \bar{y}_n$ are replaced by the coordinates of α and β with respect to the new bases.

Since it was seen in Section 29 that each bilinear mapping $\mathcal{B}$ is defined by a form $f(x_i,y_j)$ relative to given bases in $V_m(F)$ and $V_n(F)$, the problem of simplifying a bilinear mapping by changes of bases is the same as that of reducing a bilinear form to canonical form by nonsingular changes of variable.

If the bilinear form $f(x_i,y_j) = XAY'$ has an n-rowed square matrix A, and if the same nonsingular change of variables $X = \bar{X}P$ and $Y = \bar{Y}P$ is made for the x's and the y's,

$$f(x_i,y_j) = XAY' = \bar{X}PAP'\bar{Y}' = \bar{f}(\bar{x}_i,\bar{y}_j),$$

where the matrix of the new form is obtained from A by an equivalence transformation $T_{P,Q}$ with $Q = P'$. The corresponding vector space problem is that of simplifying a bilinear mapping of ordered pairs of vectors $\alpha,\beta \in V_n(F)$ into F by a change of basis in $V_n(F)$. The associated matrix transformations defined by $T_{P,P'}(A) = PAP'$ where P is a nonsingular matrix in F, form a subgroup of $\mathcal{E}(\mathfrak{A}_n(F))$ called the congruence group. In the next sections we will be concerned with the effect of this group on symmetric matrices $A = A' \in \mathfrak{A}_n(F)$.

Exercise (75.1). Find nonsingular changes of variables which reduce the bilinear form $f(x_1,x_2,x_3;y_1,y_2) = 2x_1y_1 + 3x_1y_2 - x_2y_2 - 3x_3y_1 + 4x_3y_2$ to its canonical form.

Exercise (75.2). What are the conditions on P and Q for the equivalence transformation $T_{P,Q}$ of $\mathfrak{A}_n(F)$ to be both a collineatory transformation and a congruence transformation? Give several examples of such a transformation of $\mathfrak{A}_2(R^\#)$.

Section 76. The Congruence Subgroup of $\mathcal{E}(\mathfrak{A}_n(F))$

A quadratic form, $\sum_{\substack{i=1\\ (j\geq i)}}^{n} \sum_{j=1}^{n} c_{ij}x_ix_j$, is a homogeneous polynomial of degree 2 in the indeterminates $x_1, x_2, \cdots, x_n$ with coefficients c_{ij} in a number field F. It was shown in Section 66 that by defining $d_{ii} = c_{ii}$ and $d_{ij} = d_{ji} = 1/2\, c_{ij}$ for $i \neq j$, the quadratic form can be written as a matrix product

$$\sum_{\substack{i=1\\ (j\geq i)}}^{n} \sum_{j=1}^{n} c_{ij}x_ix_j = \sum_{i=1}^{n} \sum_{j=1}^{n} x_id_{ij}x_j = XDX',$$

where $X = (x_1, x_2, \cdots, x_n)$ and $D = (d_{ij})$ is an n-rowed square symmetric matrix in F called the *matrix of the form.*

For example, the quadratic form

$$\begin{aligned} 2x^2 - 3xy + 1/2\, y^2 - 6xz + z^2 \\ &= 2x^2 - 3/2\, xy - 3/2\, yx + 1/2\, y^2 - 3xz - 3zx + z^2 \\ &= (x,y,z)\begin{pmatrix} 2 & -3/2 & -3 \\ -3/2 & 1/2 & 0 \\ -3 & 0 & 1 \end{pmatrix}\begin{pmatrix} x \\ y \\ z \end{pmatrix}. \end{aligned}$$

If each x_i in the quadratic form XDX' is replaced by a number $a_i \in F$, then $\sum_{i=1}^{n} \sum_{j=1}^{n} a_id_{ij}a_j \in F$ is called the *value* of the form when $(x_1, x_2, \cdots, x_n) = (a_1, a_2, \cdots, a_n)$. The complete set of values in F of the form for all choices of $a_1, a_2, \cdots, a_n$ in F is called the *range of values* of the form. If $a_1, a_2, \cdots, a_n$ are interpreted as the coordinates of a vector $\alpha = a_1u_1 + a_2u_2 + \cdots + a_nu_n \in V_n(F)$ relative to a given basis $u_1, u_2, \cdots, u_n$ of $V_n(F)$, then the range of values of a quadratic form becomes the range of a single-valued mapping $\mathfrak{Q}$ of $V_n(F)$ into F given by $\mathfrak{Q}(\alpha) = \sum_{i=1}^{n} \sum_{j=1}^{n} a_i d_{ij} a_j$. In this interpretation the symmetric matrix $D = (d_{ij})$ is called the *matrix of the mapping* $\mathfrak{Q}$ with respect to the basis $u_1, u_2, \cdots, u_n$. Since the function $\mathfrak{Q}$ is completely defined by the matrix D and the basis $u_1, u_2, \cdots, u_n$, we write $\mathfrak{Q} = \mathfrak{Q}_{D,u_i}$.

If $\bar{u}_1, \bar{u}_2, \cdots, \bar{u}_n$ is a second basis of $V_n(F)$, then $(a_1, a_2, \cdots, a_n) = (\bar{a}_1, \bar{a}_2, \cdots, \bar{a}_n)P$ where $\bar{a}_1, \bar{a}_2, \cdots, \bar{a}_n$ are the coordinates of α with respect to the basis $\bar{u}_1, \bar{u}_2, \cdots, \bar{u}_n$, and P is a nonsingular matrix in $\mathfrak{A}_n(F)$. We have

$$\begin{aligned} \mathfrak{Q}_{D,u_i}(\alpha) &= (a_1, a_2, \cdots, a_n)D(a_1, a_2, \cdots, a_n)' \\ &= (\bar{a}_1, \bar{a}_2, \cdots, \bar{a}_n)PDP'(\bar{a}_1, \bar{a}_2, \cdots, \bar{a}_n)' \\ &= \mathfrak{Q}_{B,\bar{u}_i}(\alpha) \end{aligned}$$

where the matrix $B = PDP' = PD'P' = (PDP')' = B'$ is the matrix of the mapping $\mathfrak{Q}$ with respect to the basis $\bar{u}_1, \bar{u}_2, \cdots, \bar{u}_n$.

This result may also be stated without reference to the vector space $V_n(F)$. If $(x_1, x_2, \cdots, x_n) = (y_1, y_2, \cdots, y_n)P$ is a nonsingular change of variables, then the quadratic form XDX' is carried into the form YBY' where $B = PDP'$, and the two forms have the same range of values in F. This follows from the fact that the value of YBY' when $(y_1, y_2, \cdots, y_n) = (\bar{a}_1, \bar{a}_2, \cdots, \bar{a}_n)$ is the value of XDX' when $(x_1, x_2, \cdots, x_n) = (a_1, a_2, \cdots, a_n) = (\bar{a}_1, \bar{a}_2, \cdots, \bar{a}_n)P$, and conversely, the value of XDX' when $(x_1, x_2, \cdots, x_n) = (a_1, a_2, \cdots, a_n)$ is the value of YBY' when $(y_1, y_2, \cdots, y_n) = (\bar{a}_1, \bar{a}_2, \cdots, \bar{a}_n) = (a_1, a_2, \cdots, a_n)P^{-1}$.

If we are interested in information about the range of values of a quadratic form XDX' or of a quadratic mapping $\mathfrak{Q}_{D,u_i}$, the above remarks show that we are naturally led to a study of the simplification of a symmetric matrix D by an equivalence transformation $T_{P,Q}$ of $\mathfrak{A}_n(F)$ with $Q = P'$. We will prove that there exists a nonsingular matrix P such that $T_{P,P'}(D) = PDP'$ is a diagonal matrix. This matrix P can then be used to define a change of variables or change of basis in $V_n(F)$ as in the above discussion.

(76.1) Definition. An equivalence transformation $T_{P,Q}$ of $\mathfrak{A}_n(F)$ with $Q = P'$ is called a *congruence transformation* of $\mathfrak{A}_n(F)$.

We will denote the set of all congruence transformations of $\mathfrak{A}_n(F)$ by $\mathfrak{C}(\mathfrak{A}_n(F))$.

(76.2) Theorem. The set of transformations $\mathcal{C}(\mathfrak{A}_n(F))$ is a subgroup of $\mathcal{E}(\mathfrak{A}_n(F))$.

PROOF. Since $\mathcal{C}(\mathfrak{A}_n(F)) \subseteq \mathcal{E}(\mathfrak{A}_n(F))$, the product rule (18.2) can be used to obtain

$$T_{P,P'}T_{Q,Q'} = T_{PQ,Q'P'} = T_{PQ,(PQ)'} \in \mathcal{C}(\mathfrak{A}_n(F)),$$

and
$$(T_{P,P'})^{-1} = T_{P^{-1},(P')^{-1}} = T_{P^{-1},(P^{-1})'} \in \mathcal{C}(\mathfrak{A}_n(F)).$$

Since $T_{I_n,I_n} = T_{I_n,I_n'}$ is the identity transformation of $\mathfrak{A}_n(F)$, $\mathcal{C}(\mathfrak{A}_n(F))$ is a group of transformations of $\mathfrak{A}_n(F)$ and is a subgroup of $\mathcal{E}(\mathfrak{A}_n(F))$.

(76.3) Definition. The equivalence relation induced in $\mathfrak{A}_n(F)$ by the group $\mathcal{C}(\mathfrak{A}_n(F))$ is called the *congruence of square matrices* over F.

Thus the matrices $A,B \in \mathfrak{A}_n(F)$ are congruent over F if and only if there exists a nonsingular matrix $P \in \mathfrak{A}_n(F)$ such that $B = PAP'$.

As we have seen above in the discussion of quadratic forms, if $A' = A \in \mathfrak{A}_n(F)$, then $(PAP')' = (P')'A'P' = PAP'$, so that symmetric matrices are sent into symmetric matrices by the transformations in $\mathcal{C}(\mathfrak{A}_n(F))$. Thus the group of all congruence transformations of $\mathfrak{A}_n(F)$ is also a group of transformations of the set S of all symmetric matrices in $\mathfrak{A}_n(F)$. In the next two sections we will investigate the canonical forms of S for $\mathcal{C}(\mathfrak{A}_n(F))$.

Exercise (76.1). Describe in words the effect of the congruence transformation $T_{P,P'}$ on $A = \begin{pmatrix} 5 & 3 & -1 \\ 3 & -2 & 0 \\ -1 & 0 & 4 \end{pmatrix}$ if

(a) $P = \begin{pmatrix} 1 & 0 & 0 \\ 0 & 1 & 0 \\ -3 & 0 & 1 \end{pmatrix}$, (b) $P = \begin{pmatrix} 1 & 0 & 0 \\ 0 & 0 & 1 \\ 0 & 1 & 0 \end{pmatrix}$, (c) $P = \begin{pmatrix} 3 & 0 & 0 \\ 0 & 1 & 0 \\ 0 & 0 & 1 \end{pmatrix}$.

Find a sequence of congruence transformations which map A onto a matrix B with first column $\begin{matrix} 1 \\ 0 \\ 0 \end{matrix}$.

Exercise (76.2). Show that the set S of symmetric matrices in $\mathfrak{A}_n(F)$ is a subspace of $\mathfrak{A}_n(F)$ as a vector space over F. What is the dimension of this subspace?

Exercise (76.3). What is the relation between the partition of $\mathfrak{A}_n(F)$ induced by $\mathcal{E}(\mathfrak{A}_n(F))$ and that induced by $\mathcal{C}(\mathfrak{A}_n(F))$?

Exercise (76.4). Write the quadratic form $(4 + i)x_1^2 - 7x_1x_2 + 3ix_1x_3 - 2ix_2^2 + (2 + 3i)x_2x_3$ as a matrix product.

Exercise (76.5). Prove that $\mathcal{C}(\mathfrak{A}_n(F))$ is a group of transformations of the set of all skew-symmetric matrices ($-A' = A$) in $\mathfrak{A}_n(F)$.

Section 77. Reduction of Symmetric Matrices by Congruence Transformations

A congruence transformation $T_{E,E'}$ of $\mathfrak{A}_n(F)$ where E is an elementary transformation matrix is called an *elementary congruence transformation* of $\mathfrak{A}_n(F)$. By (20.3), each nonsingular matrix $P \in \mathfrak{A}_n(F)$ is a product $P = E_1E_2 \cdots E_k$ of elementary transformation matrices, so that each congruence transformation of $\mathfrak{A}_n(F)$ can be written as a product of elementary congruence transformations

$$T_{P,P'} = T_{(E_1E_2\cdots E_k),(E_1E_2\cdots E_k)'} = T_{E_1E_2\cdots E_k,E_k'\cdots E_2'E_1'}$$
$$= T_{E_1,E_1'}T_{E_2,E_2'} \cdots T_{E_k,E_k'}.$$

Therefore the reduction of a matrix $A \in \mathfrak{A}_n(F)$ by a congruence transformation $T_{P,P'}$ is effected by a sequence of elementary congruence transformations. By considering the three types of elementary transformation matrices, the reader may verify that $T_{E,E'}(A)$ is obtained from A by applying the same elementary transformation to the rows and to the columns of A [see Exercise (19.8)].

(77.1) Theorem. Every symmetric matrix $A \in \mathfrak{A}_n(F)$ is congruent over F to a matrix $\begin{pmatrix} G_r & 0 \\ 0 & 0 \end{pmatrix}$ where G_r is an r-rowed nonsingular diagonal matrix and r is the rank of A.

PROOF. If $A = O$, there is nothing to prove, so we may suppose that $A = (a_{ij}) \neq O$. We first show that A is congruent over F to a matrix $B = (b_{ij})$ with $b_{11} \neq 0$. If $a_{11} \neq 0$, then $B = A$. If $a_{11} = 0$ but $a_{ii} \neq 0$ for some $i > 1$, then $B = T_{E_1,E_1'}(A)$ has $b_{11} = a_{ii} \neq 0$ if $T_{E_1,I}$ interchanges row 1 and row i of A. Finally if $a_{ii} = 0$ for all i, then $a_{jk} = a_{kj} \neq 0$ for some pair $j \neq k$ since A is a non-zero symmetric matrix. Then the matrix $A^{(1)} = (a_{ij}^{(1)}) = T_{E_2,E_2'}(A)$ has $a_{jj}^{(1)} = 2a_{jk} \neq 0$ if $T_{E_2,I}$ adds the elements of row k to the elements of row j. We then proceed as before to obtain B. This matrix B is, of course, symmetric as are all succeeding matrices in this reduction since congruence transformations preserve symmetry.

If $b_{j1} = b_{1j} \neq 0$ for any $j > 1$, the matrix $B^{(1)} = (b_{ij}^{(1)}) = T_{E_3,E_3'}(B)$ has $b_{j1}^{(1)} = b_{1j}^{(1)} = 0$ if $T_{E_3,I}$ adds to the elements of row j the elements of row 1 multiplied by $-b_{j1}/b_{11}$. By a sequence of elementary congruence transformations of this type, we obtain a matrix $C_1 = \begin{pmatrix} d_1 & 0 \\ 0 & A_1 \end{pmatrix}$

congruent over F to A with $d_1 = b_{11} \neq 0$ and A_1 a symmetric $(n-1)$-rowed square matrix with elements in F.

If $A_1 \neq O$, the above argument shows that A_1 is congruent to a matrix $\begin{pmatrix} d_2 & 0 \\ 0 & A_2 \end{pmatrix}$ with $d_2 \neq 0$ and A_2 a symmetric $(n-2)$-rowed square matrix. Since elementary congruence transformations of A_1 may be interpreted as elementary congruence transformations of $C_1 = \begin{pmatrix} d_1 & 0 \\ 0 & A_1 \end{pmatrix}$ which do not affect the first row or first column of C_1, A is congruent to $C_2 = \left(\begin{array}{cc|c} d_1 & 0 & 0 \\ 0 & d_2 & \\ \hline \multicolumn{2}{c|}{0} & A_2 \end{array}\right)$. This process can be continued until some block $A_r = O$ $(r < n)$, or until the diagonal matrix

$$C_n = \begin{pmatrix} d_1 & & & & \\ & d_2 & & 0 & \\ & & \cdot & & \\ & & & \cdot & \\ & 0 & & \cdot & \\ & & & & d_n \end{pmatrix} \quad \text{with} \quad d_i \neq 0, \quad i = 1, 2, \ldots, n, \text{ is obtained.}$$

Therefore A is congruent over F to a matrix $\begin{pmatrix} G_r & 0 \\ 0 & 0 \end{pmatrix}$ where G_r $(r \leq n)$ is an r-rowed nonsingular diagonal matrix. Since the latter matrix is congruent to A, it is equivalent to A. Therefore its rank r is the rank of A.

It should be emphasized that the diagonal elements of the matrix $\begin{pmatrix} G_r & 0 \\ 0 & 0 \end{pmatrix}$ are rational functions of the elements of A. In fact, only rational elementary transformations of types I and II were used in the reduction of A. The matrices $\begin{pmatrix} G_r & 0 \\ 0 & 0 \end{pmatrix}$ are not unique and therefore are not canonical forms for the symmetric matrices in $\mathfrak{A}_n(F)$ under the congruence group $\mathfrak{C}(\mathfrak{A}_n(F))$. For example, the matrix $\begin{pmatrix} 1 & 0 \\ 0 & 1 \end{pmatrix}$ is congruent to the matrix $\begin{pmatrix} 4 & 0 \\ 0 & 1 \end{pmatrix}$ over every number field F.

EXAMPLE 1. Let $A = \begin{pmatrix} 0 & 1 & -\sqrt{2} \\ 1 & 1/2 & 0 \\ -\sqrt{2} & 0 & 3\sqrt{2} \end{pmatrix}$. Then $A \in \mathfrak{A}_3(F)$ where F is the number field consisting of all numbers of the form

$a + b\sqrt{2}$ with a and b rational. With

$$E_1 = \begin{pmatrix} 0 & 1 & 0 \\ 1 & 0 & 0 \\ 0 & 0 & 1 \end{pmatrix}, \quad T_{E_1,E_1'}(A) = \begin{pmatrix} 1/2 & 1 & 0 \\ 1 & 0 & -\sqrt{2} \\ 0 & -\sqrt{2} & 3\sqrt{2} \end{pmatrix}.$$

Then with

$$E_2 = \begin{pmatrix} 1 & 0 & 0 \\ -2 & 1 & 0 \\ 0 & 0 & 1 \end{pmatrix}, \quad T_{E_2E_1,E_1'E_2'}(A) = \begin{pmatrix} 1/2 & 0 & 0 \\ 0 & -2 & -\sqrt{2} \\ 0 & -\sqrt{2} & 3\sqrt{2} \end{pmatrix}.$$

Finally, with

$$E_3 = \begin{pmatrix} 1 & 0 & 0 \\ 0 & 1 & 0 \\ 0 & -1/\sqrt{2} & 1 \end{pmatrix},$$

$$T_{E_3E_2E_1,E_1'E_2'E_3'}(A) = \begin{pmatrix} 1/2 & 0 & 0 \\ 0 & -2 & 0 \\ 0 & 0 & 1 + 3\sqrt{2} \end{pmatrix} = G_3.$$

The product $E_3E_2E_1$ can be calculated by applying the three elementary transformations to the identity matrix I_3, and we find

$$E_3E_2E_1 = \begin{pmatrix} 0 & 1 & 0 \\ 1 & -2 & 0 \\ -1/\sqrt{2} & \sqrt{2} & 1 \end{pmatrix},$$

so that

$$PAP' = \begin{pmatrix} 0 & 1 & 0 \\ 1 & -2 & 0 \\ -1/\sqrt{2} & \sqrt{2} & 1 \end{pmatrix} \begin{pmatrix} 0 & 1 & -\sqrt{2} \\ 1 & 1/2 & 0 \\ -\sqrt{2} & 0 & 3\sqrt{2} \end{pmatrix} \begin{pmatrix} 0 & 1 & -1/\sqrt{2} \\ 1 & -2 & \sqrt{2} \\ 0 & 0 & 1 \end{pmatrix}$$

$$= \begin{pmatrix} 1/2 & 0 & 0 \\ 0 & -2 & 0 \\ 0 & 0 & 1 + 3\sqrt{2} \end{pmatrix}.$$

The reader may verify also that

$$QAQ' = \begin{pmatrix} 3\sqrt{2} & 0 & 0 \\ 0 & 1/2 & 0 \\ 0 & 0 & -2 - \sqrt{2}/3 \end{pmatrix} \text{ where } Q = \begin{pmatrix} 0 & 0 & 1 \\ 0 & 1 & 0 \\ 1 & -2 & 1/3 \end{pmatrix}.$$

Applying the result of Theorem (77.1) to a quadratic form XAX', we obtain

(77.2) Corollary. If XAX' is a quadratic form with matrix $A = A' \in \mathfrak{A}_n(F)$ of rank r, there exists a nonsingular matrix $P \in \mathfrak{A}_n(F)$ such that $XAX' = Y\begin{pmatrix} G_r & 0 \\ 0 & 0 \end{pmatrix} Y' = d_1y_1^2 + d_2y_2^2 + \cdots + d_ry_r^2$ by the change of variables $X = YP$.

PROOF. By the theorem, there exists a nonsingular matrix $P \in \mathfrak{A}_n(F)$ such that $PAP' = \begin{pmatrix} G_r & 0 \\ 0 & 0 \end{pmatrix}$. Then with $X = YP, XAX' = YPAP'Y'$ $= Y\begin{pmatrix} G_r & 0 \\ 0 & 0 \end{pmatrix} Y'$.

EXAMPLE 2. The matrix A of Example 1 is the matrix of the form

$$f(x_1,x_2,x_3) = 2x_1x_2 - 2\sqrt{2}\, x_1x_3 + 1/2\, x_2^2 + 3\sqrt{2}\, x_3^2.$$

Under the nonsingular change of variables

$$(x_1,x_2,x_3) = (y_1,y_2,y_3)\begin{pmatrix} 0 & 1 & 0 \\ 1 & -2 & 0 \\ -1/\sqrt{2} & \sqrt{2} & 1 \end{pmatrix}$$
$$= (y_2 - 1/\sqrt{2}\, y_3,\ y_1 - 2y_2 + \sqrt{2}\, y_3,\ y_3)$$

the form is simplified to

$$f_1(y_1,y_2,y_3) = 1/2\, y_1^2 - 2\, y_2^2 + (1 + 3\sqrt{2})y_3^2.$$

By $X = ZQ$, the form is simplified to

$$f_2(z_1,z_2,z_3) = 3\sqrt{2}\, z_1^2 + 1/2\, z_2^2 - (2 + \sqrt{2}/3)z_3^2.$$

Exercise (77.1). Reduce to a diagonal form by congruence transformations of $\mathfrak{A}_n(F)$, where F is the smallest number field containing the elements:

(a) $\begin{pmatrix} 0 & 0 & 0 \\ 0 & 0 & -1+3i \\ 0 & -1+3i & 0 \end{pmatrix}$; (b) $\begin{pmatrix} 0 & 3 & 4\sqrt{5} \\ 3 & 2/3 & -1 \\ 4\sqrt{5} & -1 & 5 \end{pmatrix}$;

(c) $\begin{pmatrix} 2+i & 3-i & -2i \\ 3-i & -2-i & -4 \\ -2i & -4 & 1+2i \end{pmatrix}$;

(d) $\begin{pmatrix} 5 & 2-i & 4+2i & -3i \\ 2-i & 0 & 5-i & 0 \\ 4+2i & 5-i & 1/2 & -1/4\,i \\ -3i & 0 & -1/4\,i & i \end{pmatrix}$;

(e) $\begin{pmatrix} 12 & 16 & -8 & 6 \\ 16 & -2 & 0 & 4 \\ -8 & 0 & -24 & 20 \\ 6 & 4 & 20 & 0 \end{pmatrix}$.

Exercise (77.2). Find the rational nonsingular change of variables $X = YP$ which reduce the following quadratic forms to the form

$$\sum_{i=1}^{r} d_i y_i^2.$$

(a) $x_1^2 - 2x_1x_2 + 3/2\, x_1x_3 - x_2^2 + 3x_2x_3 - x_3^2$;
(b) $x_1^2 - 2x_1x_2 - 10x_1x_3 + 50x_3^2$;
(c) $x_1x_2 + x_1x_3 + x_1x_4 + x_2x_3 + x_2x_4 + x_3x_4$.

Exercise (77.3). Prove that every vector $\alpha \neq O$ in $V_3(R)$ is mapped onto a positive rational number by the quadratic mapping $\mathfrak{Q}_{A,u_i}$ where

$$A = \begin{pmatrix} 1 & 1/2 & -3 \\ 1/2 & 2 & 1 \\ -3 & 1 & 15 \end{pmatrix}$$

and

$$u_1 = (1,0,0),\ u_2 = (1,1,0),\ u_3 = (1,1,1).$$

Exercise (77.4). Verify by direct substitution that the simplifications in Example 2 are correct.

Exercise (77.5).

(a) Show how by completing the square we may obtain the new variables y and the matrix P which transform

$$f(x_1,x_2) = 3x_1^2 + 7x_1x_2 + 4x_2^2$$

into a diagonal form.

(b) Do the same for

$$f(x_1,x_2,x_3) = 2x_1^2 - 4x_1x_2 + 8x_1x_3 + 3x_2^2 + 6x_2x_3 + 17x_3^2,$$
$$f(x_1,x_2,x_3) = x_1^2 + 4x_1x_2 - 5x_1x_3 + 4x_2^2 - 10x_2x_3 - 6x_3^2,$$
$$f(x_1,x_2,x_3) = 5x_1^2 - 10x_1x_2 + 5x_2^2 - 20x_2x_3,$$
$$f(x_1,x_2,x_3) = 2x_1^2 - 12x_1x_2 + 4x_1x_3 + 15x_2^2 - 24x_2x_3 - 14x_3^2.$$

Exercise (77.6). Prove that $A \in \mathfrak{A}_2(F)$ is congruent over F to $E = \begin{pmatrix} 0 & 1 \\ -1 & 0 \end{pmatrix}$ if $A \neq O$ is skew-symmetric.

Exercise (77.7). Prove that the matrices

$$\left(\begin{array}{ccccc|c} E_1 & & & & & \\ & E_2 & & 0 & & \\ & & \cdot & & & \\ & & & \cdot & & 0 \\ & 0 & & & \cdot & \\ & & & & E_k & \\ \hline & & 0 & & & 0 \end{array}\right)$$

where $E_i = \begin{pmatrix} 0 & 1 \\ -1 & 0 \end{pmatrix}$, $i = 1, 2, \cdots, k$, are a set of canonical forms of the skew-symmetric matrices in $\mathfrak{A}_n(F)$ for $\mathfrak{C}(\mathfrak{A}_n(F))$. In particular, the rank $r = 2k$ of a skew-symmetric matrix is always even.

Section 78. Congruence over C and $R^\#$

We have seen in the preceding section that a symmetric matrix $A \in \mathfrak{A}_n(F)$ can be reduced to a diagonal matrix

$$\left(\begin{array}{ccccc|c} d_1 & & & & & \\ & d_2 & & 0 & & \\ & & \cdot & & & \\ & & & \cdot & & 0 \\ & 0 & & & \cdot & \\ & & & & d_r & \\ \hline & & 0 & & & 0 \end{array}\right)$$

by rational congruence transformations. We call this matrix a rational diagonal form of A. Since the diagonal elements d_i are not uniquely determined by A, these rational diagonal forms are not canonical forms. The problem of further reducing these rational diagonal forms to a canonical form by congruence transformations of $\mathfrak{A}_n(F)$ depends upon the properties of the number field F.

If the field F has the property that for every $c \in F$, F contains a square root of c or of $-c$, then a sequence of elementary congruence transformations of type III which multiply row i and column i of a rational diagonal form of A by $1/\sqrt{d_i}$ or $1/\sqrt{-d_i}$ ($i = 1, 2, \cdots, r$), is a congruence transformation of $\mathfrak{A}_n(F)$ which further reduces A to a diagonal matrix with each non-zero element equal to ± 1. The number fields C and $R^\#$ have this property, and we can readily obtain canonical forms for symmetric matrices in these two important cases.

Since each number $a + bi \in C$, has a square root* in C, we obtain the following theorem for congruence over C.

(78.1) Theorem. Every symmetric matrix $A \in \mathfrak{A}_n(C)$ is congruent over C to a matrix $\begin{pmatrix} I_r & 0 \\ 0 & 0 \end{pmatrix}$ where r is the rank of A.

PROOF. By Theorem (77.1), A is rationally congruent, and therefore congruent over C, to $\begin{pmatrix} G_r & 0 \\ 0 & 0 \end{pmatrix}$ where $G_r = \begin{pmatrix} d_1 & & & & 0 \\ & d_2 & & & \\ & & \cdot & & \\ & & & \cdot & \\ 0 & & & & \cdot \\ & & & & d_r \end{pmatrix}$ with each $d_i \neq 0$, and where r is the rank of A. Let $c_1, c_2, \cdots, c_r$ be numbers in C such that $c_i^2 = d_i$ for $i = 1, 2, \cdots, r$. If we subject $\begin{pmatrix} G_r & 0 \\ 0 & 0 \end{pmatrix}$ to the sequence of elementary congruence transformations $T_{E_1,E_1'}$, $T_{E_2,E_2'}$, $\cdots$, $T_{E_r,E_r'}$ where $T_{E_i,I}$ multiplies row i of $\begin{pmatrix} G_r & 0 \\ 0 & 0 \end{pmatrix}$ by $1/c_i \neq 0$, $\begin{pmatrix} G_r & 0 \\ 0 & 0 \end{pmatrix}$ is congruent over C to $\begin{pmatrix} I_r & 0 \\ 0 & 0 \end{pmatrix}$.

(78.2) Corollary. Two symmetric matrices are congruent over C if and only if they have the same rank.

PROOF. If the symmetric matrices A and B are congruent over C, they are equivalent, and therefore have the same rank by (21.5). Conversely, if A and B have the same rank r, each is congruent over C to the matrix $\begin{pmatrix} I_r & 0 \\ 0 & 0 \end{pmatrix}$, and since congruence is an equivalence relation, A and B are congruent over C.

It follows from Corollary (78.2) that the matrices $\begin{pmatrix} I_r & 0 \\ 0 & 0 \end{pmatrix}$ for $r = 0, 1, \cdots, n$ are canonical forms of the set S of symmetric matrices in $\mathfrak{A}_n(C)$ for the group $\mathfrak{C}(\mathfrak{A}_n(C))$.

Applying the result of Theorem (78.1) to a quadratic form XAX', we obtain

(78.3) Corollary. If XAX' is a quadratic form with matrix $A = A'$ of rank r, there exists a nonsingular matrix $P \in \mathfrak{A}_n(C)$ such that XAX'

---

* See Section 54, and specifically Theorem (54.6). See also Exercise (78.1).

$= Y\begin{pmatrix} I_r & 0 \\ 0 & 0 \end{pmatrix} Y' = y_1^2 + y_2^2 + \cdots + y_r^2$ by the change of variables $X = YP$.

EXAMPLE 1. By successive reduction by rational transformations we find that

$$\begin{pmatrix} 0 & 4+i & -2 \\ 4+i & 0 & 0 \\ -2 & 0 & 0 \end{pmatrix} \underset{T_{E_1,E_1'}}{\rightarrow} \begin{pmatrix} 4 & 4+i & -2 \\ 4+i & 0 & 0 \\ -2 & 0 & 0 \end{pmatrix}$$

$$\underset{T_{E_2,E_2'}}{\rightarrow} \begin{pmatrix} 4 & 0 & -2 \\ 0 & -15/4 - 2i & 2 + 1/2i \\ -2 & 2 + 1/2i & 0 \end{pmatrix}$$

$$\underset{T_{E_3E_3'}}{\rightarrow} \begin{pmatrix} 4 & 0 & 0 \\ 0 & -15/4 - 2i & 2 + 1/2i \\ 0 & 2 + 1/2i & -1 \end{pmatrix}$$

$$\underset{T_{E_4,E_4'}}{\rightarrow} \begin{pmatrix} 4 & 0 & 0 \\ 0 & 0 & 0 \\ 0 & 0 & -1 \end{pmatrix} \underset{T_{E_5,E_5'}}{\rightarrow} \begin{pmatrix} 4 & 0 & 0 \\ 0 & -1 & 0 \\ 0 & 0 & 0 \end{pmatrix}$$

where

$$E_1 = \begin{pmatrix} 1 & 0 & -1 \\ 0 & 1 & 0 \\ 0 & 0 & 1 \end{pmatrix}, E_2 = \begin{pmatrix} 1 & 0 & 0 \\ -1 - 1/4i & 1 & 0 \\ 0 & 0 & 1 \end{pmatrix},$$

$$E_3 = \begin{pmatrix} 1 & 0 & 0 \\ 0 & 1 & 0 \\ 1/2 & 0 & 1 \end{pmatrix}, E_4 = \begin{pmatrix} 1 & 0 & 0 \\ 0 & 1 & 2 + 1/2i \\ 0 & 0 & 1 \end{pmatrix}, E_5 = \begin{pmatrix} 1 & 0 & 0 \\ 0 & 0 & 1 \\ 0 & 1 & 0 \end{pmatrix}.$$

Applying $T_{E_6,E_6'}$ and $T_{E_7,E_7'}$ where

$$E_6 = \begin{pmatrix} 1/2 & 0 & 0 \\ 0 & 1 & 0 \\ 0 & 0 & 1 \end{pmatrix} \text{ and } E_7 = \begin{pmatrix} 1 & 0 & 0 \\ 0 & i & 0 \\ 0 & 0 & 1 \end{pmatrix},$$

we find that A is congruent to $\begin{pmatrix} I_2 & 0 \\ 0 & 0 \end{pmatrix}$. Thus $T_{P,'P}(A) = \begin{pmatrix} I_2 & 0 \\ 0 & 0 \end{pmatrix}$ where $P = E_7E_6E_5E_4E_3E_2E_1 = \begin{pmatrix} 1/2 & 0 & -1/2 \\ 1/2\,i & 0 & 1/2\,i \\ 0 & 1 & 2+1/2i \end{pmatrix}$. This means that the quadratic form

$$f(x_1,x_2,x_3) = (8 + 2i)x_1x_2 - 4x_1x_3$$

is reduced to the form

$$f_1(y_1,y_2,y_3) = y_1^2 + y_2^2$$

by the nonsingular change of variables

$$\begin{aligned}(x_1,x_2,x_3) &= (y_1,y_2,y_3)P \\ &= (1/2\, y_1 + 1/2\, iy_2,\ y_3,\ -1/2\, y_1 + 1/2\, iy_2 + (2 + 1/2\, i)\, y_3).\end{aligned}$$

We now use the property of the field of real numbers, $R^{\#}$, that each positive real number has a real square root to obtain the reduction theorem for congruence over $R^{\#}$.

(78.4) Theorem. Every symmetric matrix $A \in \mathfrak{A}_n(R^{\#})$ is congruent over $R^{\#}$ to a matrix $\begin{pmatrix} I_s & 0 & 0 \\ 0 & -I_{r-s} & 0 \\ 0 & 0 & 0 \end{pmatrix}$ where r is the rank of A.

PROOF. By Theorem (77.1), A is rationally congruent, and therefore congruent over $R^{\#}$, to $\begin{pmatrix} G_r & 0 \\ 0 & 0 \end{pmatrix}$ where r is the rank of A. By elementary congruence transformations of type I, we can rearrange the non-zero diagonal elements d_i for $i = 1, 2, \cdots, r$ so that the first s diagonal elements are positive and the last $r - s$ are negative. Thus A is congruent over $R^{\#}$ to a diagonal matrix B with diagonal elements d_i such that $d_i > 0$ for $i = 1, 2, \cdots, s$, $d_i < 0$ for $i = s + 1, s + 2, \cdots, r$, and $d_i = 0$ for $i > r$.

Let $c_1, c_2, \cdots, c_s, c_{s+1}, \cdots, c_r$ be real numbers such that $c_i^2 = d_i$ for $i = 1, 2, \cdots, s$ and $c_i^2 = -d_i$ for $i = s + 1, s + 2, \cdots, r$. If we subject the diagonal matrix B to the sequence of elementary congruence transformations $T_{E_1,E_1'}, T_{E_2,E_2'}, \cdots, T_{E_r,E_r'}$ where $T_{E_i,I}$ multiplies row i by $1/c_i \neq 0$, the diagonal matrix is congruent over $R^{\#}$ to $\begin{pmatrix} I_s & 0 & 0 \\ 0 & -I_{r-s} & 0 \\ 0 & 0 & 0 \end{pmatrix}$.

In order to prove that the set of matrices $\begin{pmatrix} I_s & 0 & 0 \\ 0 & -I_{r-s} & 0 \\ 0 & 0 & 0 \end{pmatrix}$ for $0 \leq s \leq r \leq n$ is a set of canonical forms of the symmetric matrices in $\mathfrak{A}_n(R^{\#})$ for the group $\mathfrak{C}(\mathfrak{A}_n(R^{\#}))$, we must show that if $B = \begin{pmatrix} I_s & 0 & 0 \\ 0 & -I_{r-s} & 0 \\ 0 & 0 & 0 \end{pmatrix}$ and $C = \begin{pmatrix} I_v & 0 & 0 \\ 0 & -I_{u-v} & 0 \\ 0 & 0 & 0 \end{pmatrix}$ are congruent then they are identical, that is, $r = u$ and $s = v$. Since congruent matrices are equivalent, we have at once that $r = \text{rank } B = \text{rank } C = u$, so that we have only to show that $s = v$.

(78.5) Theorem. If $B = \begin{pmatrix} I_s & 0 & 0 \\ 0 & -I_{r-s} & 0 \\ 0 & 0 & 0 \end{pmatrix}$ and $C = \begin{pmatrix} I_v & 0 & 0 \\ 0 & -I_{r-v} & 0 \\ 0 & 0 & 0 \end{pmatrix}$ are congruent over $R^\#$, then $s = v$.

PROOF. We assume that $s \neq v$, say $s > v$, and obtain a contradiction. If $u_1, u_2, \cdots, u_n$ is any basis of $V_n(R^\#)$, then as has been explained earlier, the quadratic form XBX' defines a mapping $\mathfrak{Q} = \mathfrak{Q}_{B,u_i}$ of $V_n(R^\#)$ into $R^\#$ where if $\alpha = a_1u_1 + a_2u_2 + \cdots + a_nu_n \in V_n(R^\#)$, then $\mathfrak{Q}_{B,u_i}(\alpha) = a_1^2 + a_2^2 + \cdots + a_s^2 - a_{s+1}^2 - a_{s+2}^2 - \cdots - a_r^2 \in R^\#$. Since B and C are congruent over $R^\#$, there exists a nonsingular matrix $P \in \mathfrak{A}_n(R^\#)$ such that $PBP' = C$. If a new basis $\bar{u}_1, \bar{u}_2, \cdots, \bar{u}_n$ of $V_n(R^\#)$ is defined by $\begin{pmatrix} \bar{u}_1 \\ \bar{u}_2 \\ \cdot \\ \cdot \\ \cdot \\ \bar{u}_n \end{pmatrix} = P \begin{pmatrix} u_1 \\ u_2 \\ \cdot \\ \cdot \\ \cdot \\ u_n \end{pmatrix}$, then $\alpha = \bar{a}_1\bar{u}_1 + \bar{a}_2\bar{u}_2 + \cdots + \bar{a}_n\bar{u}_n$ where $(a_1, a_2, \cdots, a_n) = (\bar{a}_1, \bar{a}_2, \cdots, \bar{a}_n)P$, and

$$\begin{aligned} \mathfrak{Q}_{B,u_i}(\alpha) &= (a_1, a_2, \cdots, a_n)B(a_1, a_2, \cdots, a_n)' \\ &= (\bar{a}_1, \bar{a}_2, \cdots, \bar{a}_n)PBP'(\bar{a}_1, \bar{a}_2, \cdots, \bar{a}_n)' = \mathfrak{Q}_{C,\bar{u}_i}(\alpha) \\ &= \bar{a}_1^2 + \bar{a}_2^2 + \cdots + \bar{a}_v^2 - \bar{a}_{v+1}^2 - \bar{a}_{v+2}^2 - \cdots - \bar{a}_r^2. \end{aligned}$$

The vectors $u_1, u_2, \cdots, u_s, \bar{u}_{v+1}, \bar{u}_{v+2}, \cdots, \bar{u}_n$ in $V_n(R^\#)$ are a set of $s + n - v > n$ vectors in an n dimensional space and are therefore linearly dependent by (25.4). There exist c_i and $\bar{c}_j$, not all zero, in $R^\#$ such that

$$c_1u_1 + c_2u_2 + \cdots + c_su_s + \bar{c}_{v+1}\bar{u}_{v+1} + \bar{c}_{v+2}\bar{u}_{v+2} + \cdots + \bar{c}_n\bar{u}_n = O.$$

At least one c_i is not zero since the vectors $\bar{u}_{v+1}, \bar{u}_{v+2}, \cdots, \bar{u}_n$ are a linearly independent set. Let

$$\begin{aligned} \beta &= c_1u_1 + c_2u_2 + \cdots + c_su_s + 0 \cdot u_{s+1} + 0 \cdot u_{s+2} + \cdots + 0 \cdot u_n \\ &= 0 \cdot \bar{u}_1 + 0 \cdot \bar{u}_2 + \cdots + 0 \cdot \bar{u}_v \\ &\quad + (-\bar{c}_{v+1})\bar{u}_{v+1} + (-\bar{c}_{v+2})\bar{u}_{v+2} + \cdots + (-\bar{c}_n)\bar{u}_n. \end{aligned}$$

We have

$$\begin{aligned} \mathfrak{Q}_{B,u_i}(\beta) &= c_1^2 + c_2^2 + \cdots + c_s^2 \\ &= \mathfrak{Q}_{C,\bar{u}_i}(\beta) = -\bar{c}_{v+1}^2 - \bar{c}_{v+2}^2 - \cdots - \bar{c}_r^2. \end{aligned}$$

But

$$c_1^2 + c_2^2 + \cdots + c_s^2 > 0, \text{ while } -\bar{c}_{v+1}^2 - \bar{c}_{v+2}^2 - \cdots - \bar{c}_r^2 \leq 0,$$

which is a contradiction. Therefore $s = v$.

We have now proved that the matrices $\begin{pmatrix} I_s & 0 & 0 \\ 0 & -I_{r-s} & 0 \\ 0 & 0 & 0 \end{pmatrix}$ are canonical forms of real symmetric matrices for $\mathcal{C}(\mathfrak{A}_n(R^\#))$ and therefore that the integer s is uniquely determined by A. We call s the *index* of A. Combining the results of Theorems (78.4) and (78.5) we have the following theorem.

(78.6) Theorem. Two real symmetric matrices are congruent over $R^\#$ if and only if they have the same rank and same index.

Applying the above results to the quadratic form XAX', we obtain

(78.7) Corollary. If XAX' is a quadratic form with a real symmetric matrix A of rank r and index s, there exists a nonsingular matrix $P \in \mathfrak{A}_n(R^\#)$ such that

$$XAX' = Y\begin{pmatrix} I_s & 0 & 0 \\ 0 & -I_{r-s} & 0 \\ 0 & 0 & 0 \end{pmatrix}Y' = y_1^2 + y_2^2 + \cdots + y_s^2 - y_{s+1}^2 - y_{s+2}^2 - \cdots - y_r^2$$

by the change of variables $X = YP$.

The real quadratic form XAX' is called *positive definite* if all of its values, except for $X = (0, 0, \cdots, 0)$, are positive, and the form is called *positive semidefinite* if all of its values are greater than or equal to zero. It follows from (78.7) that XAX' is positive definite if and only if $s = r = n$, and XAX' is positive semidefinite if and only if $s = r$. These definitions apply as well to quadratic mappings of $V_n(R^\#)$ into $R^\#$.

EXAMPLE 2. The quadratic form

$$XAX' = x_1^2 - 2x_1x_2 + 3/2\, x_1x_3 + 3x_2^2 + 3x_2x_3 + 4x_3^2$$

has real symmetric matrix $A = \begin{pmatrix} 1 & -1 & 3/4 \\ -1 & 3 & 3/2 \\ 3/4 & 3/2 & 4 \end{pmatrix}$. By the rational congruence transformation $T_{P,P'}$ with $P = \begin{pmatrix} 1 & 0 & 0 \\ 1 & 1 & 0 \\ -15/8 & -9/8 & 1 \end{pmatrix}$, A is congruent to $B = \begin{pmatrix} 1 & 0 & 0 \\ 0 & 2 & 0 \\ 0 & 0 & 29/32 \end{pmatrix}$, and by the real congruence transformation $T_{Q,Q'}$ with $Q = \begin{pmatrix} 1 & 0 & 0 \\ 1/\sqrt{2} & 1/\sqrt{2} & 0 \\ -15/\sqrt{58} & -9/\sqrt{58} & 8/\sqrt{58} \end{pmatrix}$, A is congruent to I_3. Thus XAX' is a positive definite form, and

$$XAX' = y_1^2 + y_2^2 + y_3^2$$

where $(x_1,x_2,x_3) = (y_1,y_2,y_3)Q$.

Exercise (78.1). Show how to calculate a square root $c + di$ of the complex number $a + bi$ by finding a solution (c,d) of the equations $x^2 - y^2 = a$, $2xy = b$.

Exercise (78.2). The real quadratic form XAX' is negative definite if all of its values, except for $X = (0, 0, \cdots, 0)$, are negative, and negative semidefinite if all of its values are less than or equal to zero. Express each definition as a condition on the matrix A.

Exercise (78.3). Prove Theorem (78.6).

Exercise (78.4). Which of the following forms are positive definite, positive semidefinite, negative definite, or negative semidefinite?

(a) $x_1^2 - 12x_1x_2 - 6x_1x_3 + 37x_2^2 + 38x_2x_3 + 10x_3^2$;
(b) $2x_1^2 + 8x_1x_2 - 12x_1x_3 + 7x_2^2 - 24x_2x_3 + 15x_3^2$;
(c) $-21x_1^2 + 30x_1x_2 - 12x_1x_3 - 11x_2^2 + 8x_2x_3 - 2x_3^2$.

Exercise (78.5). Reduce each form to a sum of squares by a nonsingular complex change of variables.

(a) $-3x_1^2 - 6(1 + i)x_1x_2 - 18ix_2^2 - 6x_2x_3 + ix_3^2$;
(b) $(-15 + 12i)x_1^2 - (12 + 34i)x_1x_2 + (2 + 6i)x_1x_3 + 17x_2^2 - 6x_2x_3 + (3/2 + i)x_3^2$;
(c) $12x_1^2 + 6x_1x_2 - 12x_1x_3 + x_2^2 - 4x_2x_3 + 3x_3^2$.

Section 79. Hermitian Forms and Hermitian Matrices

The square bilinear form $f(x_i,y_j) = \sum_{i=1}^{n} \sum_{j=1}^{n} x_ib_{ij}y_j = XBY'$, where $B = (b_{ij}) \in \mathfrak{A}_n(C)$, has been used to define bilinear and quadratic mappings. For a given basis $u_1, u_2, \cdots, u_n$ of $V_n(C)$, this form can also be used to define a single-valued mapping $\mathfrak{B}$ of $V_n(C)$ into C by the rule

$$\begin{aligned}\mathfrak{B}(\alpha) &= \mathfrak{B}(a_1u_1 + a_2u_2 + \cdots + a_nu_n) = \sum_{i=1}^{n} \sum_{j=1}^{n} a_ib_{ij}\bar{a}_j \\ &= (a_1, a_2, \cdots, a_n)B(\bar{a}_1, \bar{a}_2, \cdots, \bar{a}_n)' \in C,\end{aligned}$$

where $\bar{a}_j$ is the complex conjugate $a - bi$ of the number $a_j = a + bi \in C$. The values in C of this mapping $\mathcal{B} = \mathcal{B}_{B,u_i}$ coincide with the values of a form $f(x_i) = \sum_{i=1}^{n} \sum_{j=1}^{n} x_i b_{ij} \bar{x}_j$ where the variables $(x_1, x_2, \cdots, x_n)$ are replaced by $(a_1, a_2, \cdots, a_n)$ with $a_i \in C$. In order to discuss forms and mappings of this type, we define the conjugate of a matrix in ${}_m\mathfrak{A}_n(C)$ and note some immediate consequences of this definition.

(79.1) Definition. The *conjugate* of the m by n matrix $A = (a_{ij}) \in {}_m\mathfrak{A}_n(C)$ is the matrix $\bar{A} = (c_{ij})$ where $c_{ij} = \bar{a}_{ij}$ for all pairs i,j.

Using this definition, $\mathcal{B}(\alpha) = (a_1, a_2, \cdots, a_n)B(\bar{a}_1, \bar{a}_2, \cdots, \bar{a}_n)' = AB\bar{A}'$ where $A = (a_1, a_2, \cdots, a_n)$. The corresponding form is written as $f(x_i) = XB\bar{X}'$.

(79.2) Theorem. If A and B are in $\mathfrak{A}_n(C)$, then:

(i) $\overline{A + B} = \bar{A} + \bar{B}$, $\overline{AB} = \bar{A}\bar{B}$, and $\overline{(\bar{A})} = A$;

(ii) $\bar{A} = A$ if and only if $A \in \mathfrak{A}_n(R^\#)$;

(iii) $\overline{(A')} = (\bar{A})'$, and $\overline{(A^{-1})} = (\bar{A})^{-1}$ if A is nonsingular.

PROOF. The properties of conjugacy stated in (i) are immediate consequences of the corresponding properties $\overline{a + b} = \bar{a} + \bar{b}$, $\overline{ab} = \bar{a}\bar{b}$, and $\overline{(\bar{a})} = a$ of complex numbers. Since $\overline{a + bi} = a - bi = a + bi$ if and only if $b = 0$, (ii) follows. Finally the equality $\overline{(A')} = (\bar{A})'$ in (iii) is evident, while the fact that $\overline{(A^{-1})}$ is the inverse of $\bar{A}$ follows from $\overline{(A^{-1})}\bar{A} = \overline{(A^{-1}A)} = \bar{I}_n = I_n$.

Returning to the mapping $\mathcal{B}$ of $V_n(C)$ into C, $\mathcal{B}(\alpha) = \mathcal{B}(\alpha)'$ since $\mathcal{B}(\alpha) = AB\bar{A}'$ is a 1 by 1 matrix. Using (i) and (iii) of Theorem (79.2),

$$\overline{\mathcal{B}(\alpha)} = \overline{\mathcal{B}(\alpha)'} = \overline{(AB\bar{A}')'} = \overline{(\bar{A}B'A')} = A\bar{B}'\bar{A}'.$$

If $\bar{B}' = B$, then $\overline{\mathcal{B}(\alpha)} = \mathcal{B}(\alpha)$, and the values of the mapping $\mathcal{B}$ are real. Conversely, it can be shown that if every value of the mapping $\mathcal{B}_{B,u_i}$ is real, then $\bar{B}' = B$.

(79.3) Definition. The matrix $B \in \mathfrak{A}_n(C)$ is called *Hermitian* if $\bar{B}' = B$.

Thus $B = (b_{ij})$ is Hermitian if and only if $b_{ij} = \bar{b}_{ji}$ for all pairs i,j. In particular $a_{ii} = \bar{a}_{ii}$, so that the diagonal elements of a Hermitian matrix are real. Every real symmetric matrix is Hermitian, since if $B = B' \in \mathfrak{A}_n(R^\#)$, then $\bar{B}' = B' = B$ by (ii) of (79.2). The following matrix in $\mathfrak{A}_3(C)$ is Hermitian

$$\begin{pmatrix} 0 & \sqrt{3} + i & -1/2 \\ \sqrt{3} - i & \sqrt[3]{2} & -2i \\ -1/2 & 2i & 4/3 \end{pmatrix}$$

The form $f(x_i) = \sum_{i=1}^{n} \sum_{j=1}^{n} x_i h_{ij} \bar{x}_j = XH\bar{X}'$ is called a *Hermitian form* if $H = (h_{ij})$ is a Hermitian matrix, and the associated mapping $\mathcal{B}_{H,u_i}$, which we now denote by $\mathcal{H} = \mathcal{H}_{H,u_i}$, is called a *Hermitian mapping*. We have seen that $\overline{\mathcal{H}(\alpha)} = \mathcal{H}(\alpha)$ for all $\alpha \in V_n(C)$, so that a Hermitian mapping is a mapping of $V_n(C)$ into $R^\#$.

Following the now-familiar analysis of the change in the matrix of a mapping which results from a change of basis,

$$\begin{pmatrix} v_1 \\ v_2 \\ \cdot \\ \cdot \\ \cdot \\ v_n \end{pmatrix} = P \begin{pmatrix} u_1 \\ u_2 \\ \cdot \\ \cdot \\ \cdot \\ u_n \end{pmatrix}, \quad (a_1, a_2, \cdots, a_n) = (b_1, b_2, \cdots, b_n)P,$$

in a vector space, we find

$$\begin{aligned} \mathcal{H}_{H,u_i}(\alpha) &= (a_1, a_2, \cdots, a_n)H(\bar{a}_1, \bar{a}_2, \cdots, \bar{a}_n)' \\ &= (b_1, b_2, \cdots, b_n)PH\bar{P}'(\bar{b}_1, \bar{b}_2, \cdots, \bar{b}_n)' = \mathcal{H}_{K,v_i}(\alpha) \end{aligned}$$

where $K = PH\bar{P}'$ for a nonsingular matrix $P \in \mathfrak{A}_n(C)$. Since $\overline{(PH\bar{P}')'} = (\bar{P}\bar{H}P')' = P\bar{H}'\bar{P}' = PH\bar{P}'$, the matrix K of the mapping $\mathcal{H}$ with respect to the new basis is Hermitian. Thus the problem of simplifying a Hermitian mapping by change of basis or of simplifying a Hermitian form $XH\bar{X}'$ by a nonsingular change variables $X = YP$ is the same as that of simplifying a Hermitian matrix by an equivalence transformation $T_{P,Q}$ with $Q = \bar{P}'$.

(79.4) Definition. The equivalence transformation $T_{P,Q}$ of $\mathfrak{A}_n(C)$ with $Q = \bar{P}'$ is called a *conjunctive transformation* of $\mathfrak{A}_n(C)$.

Let $\mathcal{H}(\mathfrak{A}_n(C))$ be the set of all conjunctive transformations of $\mathfrak{A}_n(C)$.

(79.5) Theorem. $\mathcal{H}(\mathfrak{A}_n(C))$ is a group of transformations of $\mathfrak{A}_n(C)$ and is a subgroup of $\mathcal{E}(\mathfrak{A}_n(C))$.

PROOF. Since $T_{P,\bar{P}'}T_{Q,\bar{Q}'} = T_{PQ,\bar{Q}'\bar{P}'} = T_{PQ,(\overline{PQ})'}$, $\mathcal{H}(\mathfrak{A}_n(C))$ is closed with respect to multiplication. Since $\bar{I}_n' = I_n$ and $(\bar{P}')^{-1} = \overline{(P^{-1})'}$, $T_{I,I}$ and $(T_{P,\bar{P}'})^{-1}$ are in $\mathcal{H}(\mathfrak{A}_n(C))$.

We proved above that conjunctive transformations map Hermitian matrices onto Hermitian matrices, so that the group $\mathcal{H}(\mathfrak{A}_n(C))$ is a group of transformations of the subset S of all Hermitian matrices in $\mathfrak{A}_n(C)$. In the next section we will outline the reduction of Hermitian matrices to canonical forms for $\mathcal{H}(\mathfrak{A}_n(C))$.

Exercise (79.1). Complete the proof of Theorem (79.2).

Exercise (79.2). State and prove a theorem like (79.2) for rectangular matrices.

Exercise (79.3). Show that $A\bar{A}'$ is Hermitian for all $A \epsilon {}_m\mathfrak{A}_n(C)$, and that $A + \bar{A}'$ is Hermitian for all square matrices A.

Exercise (79.4). Prove that if all values of $XB\bar{X}'$ are real for $X = (a_1, a_2, \cdots, a_n)$ in C, then B is a Hermitian matrix.

Exercise (79.5). Write $4x_1\bar{x}_1 + (-7 + i)x_1\bar{x}_3 + (-7 - i)x_3\bar{x}_1 + 5i\, x_2\bar{x}_3 - 5i\, x_3\bar{x}_2 + (3 + 2i)x_3\bar{x}_4 + (3 - 2i)x_4\bar{x}_3 - 17x_4\bar{x}_4$ in matrix form.

Exercise (79.6). If we use the Hermitian form of the preceding exercise and the basis $\epsilon_1, \epsilon_2, \epsilon_3, \epsilon_4$ to define a Hermitian mapping, find the map of $\alpha = (3 + i)\epsilon_1 + (-2i)\epsilon_2 + 3\epsilon_3 + (4 - 2i)\epsilon_4$. Find the matrix representation of the mapping, the coordinates of α, and the map of α with respect to the basis $u_1 = (1,1,1,0)$, $u_2 = (0,0,1,1,)$, $u_3 = (1,0,0,1)$, and $u_4 = (1,1,0,0)$.

Exercise (79.7). If $A = \begin{pmatrix} 4 & 0 & 2i \\ 0 & 1 & 1 - i \\ -2i & 1 + i & 0 \end{pmatrix}$, describe in words the effect of a conjunctive transformation $T_{P,\bar{P}'}$ with

(a) $P = \begin{pmatrix} 0 & 0 & 1 \\ 0 & 1 & 0 \\ 1 & 0 & 0 \end{pmatrix}$, **(b)** $P = \begin{pmatrix} 1 & 0 & 0 \\ 0 & 1 & 0 \\ 0 & -1 - i & 1 \end{pmatrix}$,

(c) $P = \begin{pmatrix} 1/2\, i & 0 & 0 \\ 0 & 1 & 0 \\ 0 & 0 & 1 \end{pmatrix}$.

Section 80. The Reduction of Hermitian Matrices

Every real symmetric matrix A is Hermitian and every real congruence transformation $T_{P,P'}$, $P \epsilon \mathfrak{A}_n(R^\#)$, is conjunctive since $P = \bar{P}$ and $T_{P,P'} = T_{P,\bar{P}'}$. For example, an elementary congruence transformation $T_{U,U'}$ of type I is an elementary conjunctive transformation of the same type since U is real. Type II and type III elementary conjunctive transformations are $T_{V,\bar{V}'}$ and $T_{W,\bar{W}'}$ where V and W are elementary transformation matrices in $\mathfrak{A}_n(C)$.

The reduction of a Hermitian matrix by a conjunctive transformation is effected by a sequence of elementary conjunctive transformations following the same pattern as in the reduction of a real symmetric matrix by a sequence of elementary congruence transformations. For this reason, the proofs in this section may be abbreviated.

(80.1) Theorem. Every Hermitian matrix $A = (a_{ij}) \in \mathfrak{A}_n(C)$ is conjunctive to a matrix $\begin{pmatrix} I_s & 0 & 0 \\ 0 & -I_{r-s} & 0 \\ 0 & 0 & 0 \end{pmatrix}$, where r, the rank of A, and s, the *index* of A, are uniquely determined by A.

PROOF. Since A is Hermitian, and since a conjunctive transformation preserves Hermitian-ness, A and every matrix conjunctive to A has real diagonal elements. The first step in the reduction, as in Theorem (77.1), is to show that A is conjunctive to a matrix $\begin{pmatrix} G_r & 0 \\ 0 & 0 \end{pmatrix}$ where G_r is a nonsingular real diagonal matrix.

If $A \neq O$ has $a_{ii} = 0$ for $i = 1, 2, \cdots, n$, then $a_{jk} = a + bi \neq 0$ for some pair $j \neq k$. Moreover, $a_{kj} = \bar{a}_{jk} = a - bi \neq 0$. If $a_{jk} = a + bi$ with $a \neq 0$, then if row k is added to row j and column k is added to column j, we obtain $(a + bi) + (a - bi) = 2a \neq 0$ in the j,j position. If $a_{jk} = a + bi$ with $a = 0$, then $b \neq 0$, and if the elements of row k multiplied by bi are added to row j and the elements of column k multiplied by $-bi$ are added to column j, we obtain $bi(a + bi) - bi(a - bi) = -2b^2 \neq 0$ in the j,j position. Thus A is conjunctive to a matrix with a non-zero diagonal element by an elementary conjunctive transformation $T_{E_1,\bar{E}_1'}$ of type II. A non-zero diagonal element can then be put in the 1,1 position and row 1 and column 1 cleared exactly as in Theorem (77.1). This procedure is repeated until a diagonal matrix $\begin{pmatrix} G_r & 0 \\ 0 & 0 \end{pmatrix}$ is obtained. Since conjunctive transformations are equivalence transformations, the rank of the diagonal matrix obtained by this process must be r, the rank of A.

Real type III congruence transformations are used as in Theorem (78.4) to obtain a matrix with diagonal elements ± 1. It is now possible to prove a result parallel to Theorem (78.5) by considering Hermitian mappings of $V_n(C)$. The reason that the same argument applies as in the case of quadratic mappings of $V_n(R^\#)$ into $R^\#$ is that the values of a Hermitian mapping are in $R^\#$. Thus we can show that the matrices $\begin{pmatrix} I_s & 0 & 0 \\ 0 & -I_{r-s} & 0 \\ 0 & 0 & 0 \end{pmatrix}$ and $\begin{pmatrix} I_t & 0 & 0 \\ 0 & -I_{r-t} & 0 \\ 0 & 0 & 0 \end{pmatrix}$ are conjunctive only if $s = t$ which means that s, the number of plus ones in the diagonal form, is uniquely determined by A.

EXAMPLE. Consider the Hermitian matrix $A = \begin{pmatrix} 0 & 0 & 0 \\ 0 & 0 & -i \\ 0 & i & 0 \end{pmatrix}$.

With $E_1 = \begin{pmatrix} 1 & 0 & 0 \\ 0 & 1 & -i \\ 0 & 0 & 1 \end{pmatrix}$, then $T_{E_1,\bar{E}_1'}(A) = B = \begin{pmatrix} 0 & 0 & 0 \\ 0 & 2 & -i \\ 0 & i & 0 \end{pmatrix}$.

With $E_2 = \begin{pmatrix} 0 & 1 & 0 \\ 1 & 0 & 0 \\ 0 & 0 & 1 \end{pmatrix}$, then $T_{E_2,\bar{E}_2'}(B) = C = \begin{pmatrix} 2 & 0 & -i \\ 0 & 0 & 0 \\ i & 0 & 0 \end{pmatrix}$.

With $E_3 = \begin{pmatrix} 1 & 0 & 0 \\ 0 & 1 & 0 \\ -i/2 & 0 & 1 \end{pmatrix}$, then $T_{E_3,\bar{E}_3'}(C) = D = \begin{pmatrix} 2 & 0 & 0 \\ 0 & 0 & 0 \\ 0 & 0 & -1/2 \end{pmatrix}$.

Finally, with $E_4 = \begin{pmatrix} 1 & 0 & 0 \\ 0 & 0 & 1 \\ 0 & 1 & 0 \end{pmatrix}$, $E_5 = \begin{pmatrix} 1/\sqrt{2} & 0 & 0 \\ 0 & 1 & 0 \\ 0 & 0 & 1 \end{pmatrix}$, and $E_6 = \begin{pmatrix} 1 & 0 & 0 \\ 0 & \sqrt{2} & 0 \\ 0 & 0 & 1 \end{pmatrix}$, $T_{P,\bar{P}'}(A) = \begin{pmatrix} 1 & 0 & 0 \\ 0 & -1 & 0 \\ 0 & 0 & 0 \end{pmatrix}$ where $P = E_6E_5E_4E_3E_2E_1$ $= \begin{pmatrix} 0 & 1/\sqrt{2} & -i/\sqrt{2} \\ 0 & -i/\sqrt{2} & 1/\sqrt{2} \\ 1 & 0 & 0 \end{pmatrix}$.

Since the matrices $\begin{pmatrix} I_s & 0 & 0 \\ 0 & -I_{r-s} & 0 \\ 0 & 0 & 0 \end{pmatrix}$ for $0 \leq s \leq r \leq n$ are a set of canonical forms of the Hermitian matrices in $\mathfrak{A}_n(C)$ for the conjunctive group $\mathcal{H}(\mathfrak{A}_n(C))$, we have

(80.2) Corollary. Two Hermitian matrices are conjunctive if and only if they have the same rank and the same index.

Applying this result to the Hermitian form $XH\bar{X}'$, we obtain

(80.3) Corollary. If $XH\bar{X}'$ is a Hermitian form with a Hermitian matrix H of rank r and index s, there exists a nonsingular matrix $P \in \mathfrak{A}_n(C)$ such that

$$XH\bar{X}' = Y\begin{pmatrix} I_s & 0 & 0 \\ 0 & -I_{r-s} & 0 \\ 0 & 0 & 0 \end{pmatrix}\bar{Y}' = y_1\bar{y}_1 + y_2\bar{y}_2 + \cdots + y_s\bar{y}_s - y_{s+1}\bar{y}_{s+1} - y_{s+2}\bar{y}_{s+2} - \cdots - y_r\bar{y}_r,$$

by the change of variables $X = YP$.

Exercise (80.1). Show that the diagonal form $\begin{pmatrix} G_r & 0 \\ 0 & 0 \end{pmatrix}$ of Theorem (80.1) is obtained by a rational conjunctive transformation, that is, $T_{P,\bar{P}'}(A) = \begin{pmatrix} G_r & 0 \\ 0 & 0 \end{pmatrix}$ where the elements of P and of $\bar{P}'$ are rational functions of the elements of A.

Exercise (80.2). Reduce to canonical form by conjunctive transformations:

(a) $\begin{pmatrix} 3 & -1 \\ -1 & 2 \end{pmatrix}$; **(b)** $\begin{pmatrix} 1 & 3 \\ 3 & 2 \end{pmatrix}$;

(c) $\begin{pmatrix} 0 & a + bi \\ a - bi & 0 \end{pmatrix}$; **(d)** $\begin{pmatrix} 0 & 2 + i & -1 \\ 2 - i & -4 & -2i \\ -1 & 2i & 0 \end{pmatrix}$;

(e) $\begin{pmatrix} 0 & -3i & 0 \\ 3i & 0 & -2i \\ 0 & 2i & 0 \end{pmatrix}$; **(f)** $\begin{pmatrix} \sqrt{5} & \sqrt{3} - i & 0 \\ \sqrt{3} + i & 3 & \sqrt{15}\, i \\ 0 & -\sqrt{15}\, i & 0 \end{pmatrix}$.

Exercise (80.3). Reduce the following Hermitian forms to canonical form:

(a) $x_1\bar{x}_2 + x_2\bar{x}_3 + x_3\bar{x}_1 + x_2\bar{x}_1 + x_3\bar{x}_2 + x_1\bar{x}_3$;
(b) $3x_1\bar{x}_1 + 2ix_1\bar{x}_2 - 2ix_2\bar{x}_1 + (4 + 3i)x_2\bar{x}_3 + (4 - 3i)x_3\bar{x}_2 - 4x_3\bar{x}_3$.

Exercise (80.4). Given the basis $u_1 = (1,0,0)$, $u_2 = (1,i,0)$, and $u_3 = (1,0,i)$ of $V_3(C)$, write down the Hermitian mapping defined by the matrix of Exercise (80.2), (d). Find the map of $\alpha = iu_1 - iu_3$ and of $\beta = (3 + i)u_2 - 2u_3$. Using the matrix P which reduces the matrix of the mapping to canonical form, find the new basis, the new representation of the mapping, and the new coordinates of α and β and their maps.

Exercise (80.5). Prove that the matrices $\begin{pmatrix} I_s & 0 & 0 \\ 0 & -I_{r-s} & 0 \\ 0 & 0 & 0 \end{pmatrix}$ and $\begin{pmatrix} I_t & 0 & 0 \\ 0 & -I_{r-t} & 0 \\ 0 & 0 & 0 \end{pmatrix}$ are conjunctive if and only if $s = t$.

Section 81. Euclidean Vector Spaces

In Chapter III, the vector space $V_n(F)$ was introduced as a generalization of the geometrical vectors in the plane following the observation that the rules for addition of matrices and multiplication by a scalar agree with the formulas for adding geometrical vectors and multiplying them by a real number. The properties of vector spaces studied until now depend only on these two operations, which are defined for every number field F.

In the geometrical realization of $V_2(R^\#)$ as the vectors in the plane, the vector $\alpha = (a_1,a_2)$ is the directed line segment from the origin to

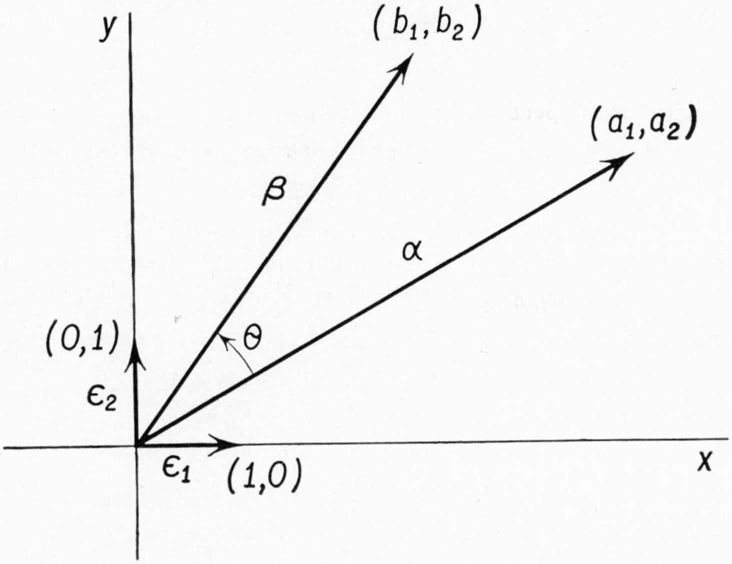

Fig. 5

the point (a_1,a_2) of a rectangular coordinate system. The components of $\alpha = (a_1,a_2)$ are the coordinates of α with respect to the basis vectors $\epsilon_1 = (1,0)$ and $\epsilon_2 = (0,1)$ in the x- and y-directions respectively (see Figure 5). In this example, the length of $\alpha = (a_1,a_2)$ is the non-negative real number $(a_1^2 + a_2^2)^{1/2} = (a_1a_1 + a_2a_2)^{1/2}$, and the distance between the terminal points of α and $\beta = (b_1,b_2)$ is the length of the vector $\alpha - \beta$, which is $[(a_1 - b_1)^2 + (a_2 - b_2)^2]^{1/2}$. The angle θ between α and β can be computed from the formula

$$\cos\theta = \frac{a_1b_1 + a_2b_2}{(a_1^2 + a_2^2)^{1/2}(b_1^2 + b_2^2)^{1/2}}.$$

In particular, by using this formula, or by examining the slopes of α and β, we see that α and β are perpendicular, or orthogonal, if and only if $a_1b_1 + a_2b_2 = 0$.

It is evident that the formulas for length and angle in this example depend upon special properties of the real field $R^\#$. In order to obtain a simple generalization of these familiar geometrical concepts, we shall at present restrict our attention to $V_n(R^\#)$, the sequence vector space with real components.

The condition for orthogonality and the formula for length for the geometrical vectors in the above example may be given in terms of a bilinear mapping $\mathfrak{N}$ of $V_2(R^\#)$ into $R^\#$. This mapping $\mathfrak{N}$ is defined for $\alpha = (a_1,a_2)$ and $\beta = (b_1,b_2)$ by

$$\mathfrak{N}(\alpha,\beta) = (a_1,a_2)I_2(b_1,b_2)' = a_1b_1 + a_2b_2.$$

The length of α is $[\mathfrak{N}(\alpha,\alpha)]^{1/2}$, and α and β are orthogonal if and only if $\mathfrak{N}(\alpha,\beta) = 0$. It is evident that such a mapping into $R^\#$ can be defined on $V_n(R^\#)$ for any n.

(81.1) Definition. The number $\mathfrak{N}(\alpha,\beta) \in R^\#$ is called the *inner product* of α and β, where $\mathfrak{N}$ is the bilinear mapping of $V_n(R^\#)$ into $R^\#$ which has matrix I_n with respect to the basis $\epsilon_1, \epsilon_2, \cdots, \epsilon_n$ of $V_n(R^\#)$.

$$\text{Thus}\quad \mathfrak{N}(\alpha,\beta) = (a_1, a_2, \cdots, a_n)I_n(b_1, b_2, \cdots, b_n)' = a_1b_1 + a_2b_2 + \cdots + a_nb_n,$$

where $a_1, a_2, \cdots, a_n$ and $b_1, b_2, \cdots, b_n$ are the components of α and β respectively. In addition to the property of bilinearity,

$$\mathfrak{N}(c_1\alpha_1 + c_2\alpha_2, d_1\beta_1 + d_2\beta_2) = c_1d_1\mathfrak{N}(\alpha_1,\beta_1) + c_1d_2\mathfrak{N}(\alpha_1,\beta_2) + c_2d_1\mathfrak{N}(\alpha_2,\beta_1) + c_2d_2\mathfrak{N}(\alpha_2,\beta_2),$$

$\mathfrak{N}$ is a symmetric mapping since $\mathfrak{N}(\alpha,\beta) = \mathfrak{N}(\beta,\alpha)$, and as a quadratic mapping, $\mathfrak{N}$ is positive definite since $\mathfrak{N}(\alpha,\alpha) \geq 0$ and $\mathfrak{N}(\alpha,\alpha) = 0$ only if $\alpha = O$, the zero vector.

(81.2) Definition. The vectors α and β in $V_n(R^\#)$ are *orthogonal* if $\mathfrak{N}(\alpha,\beta) = 0$; and $|\alpha|$, the *length* of α, is $[\mathfrak{N}(\alpha,\alpha)]^{1/2}$, the non-negative square root of $\mathfrak{N}(\alpha,\alpha)$.

As suggested by the example of the vectors in the plane, it is possible to define the distance and the angle between two vectors in terms of the inner product, but for our purposes the concepts of length and orthogonality will be sufficient.

Since $\mathfrak{N}(c\alpha,d\beta) = cd\mathfrak{N}(\alpha,\beta)$, α and β are orthogonal if and only if $c\alpha$ and $d\beta$ are orthogonal for $c \neq 0$ and $d \neq 0$. The zero vector is orthogonal to every vector of $V_n(R^\#)$. The basis $\epsilon_1, \epsilon_2, \cdots, \epsilon_n$ of $V_n(R^\#)$ has the property that $\mathfrak{N}(\epsilon_i,\epsilon_j) = \delta_{ij}$ for all pairs i,j, so that the vectors of this basis are mutually orthogonal and each has unit length.

Since we have made an obvious generalization from vectors in the

Euclidean plane (or vectors in three-space), we carry the name Euclidean to these more general spaces.

(81.3) Definition. The vector space $V_n(R^\#)$ with inner product, length, and orthogonality defined by (81.1) and (81.2) is called the *n-dimensional Euclidean space,* E_n.

Our introductory example of the vectors in the plane is the usual realization of E_2.

A rotation of the rectangular coordinate system in the plane is a change of basis from ϵ_1, ϵ_2 to a second basis u_1, u_2 with the property $\mathfrak{N}(u_i,u_j) = \delta_{ij}$. Bases with this property play a central role in the discussion of Euclidean vector spaces.

(81.4) Definition. The vectors $u_1, u_2, \cdots, u_k$ in E_n form an *orthonormal set* if $\mathfrak{N}(u_i,u_j) = \delta_{ij}$ for all pairs i,j.

Thus the basis $\epsilon_1, \epsilon_2, \cdots, \epsilon_n$ of E_n is an orthonormal basis.

A Euclidean space may be defined, more generally, as a $V_n(R^\#)$ on which there is defined a bilinear mapping f into $R^\#$ with the properties of symmetry and positive definiteness. If this is done, the basis $\epsilon_1, \epsilon_2, \cdots, \epsilon_n$ may not have the orthonormal property $f(\epsilon_i,\epsilon_j) = \delta_{ij}$. However, it can be proved that there exist bases with the orthonormal property and that

$$f(\alpha,\beta) = a_1b_1 + a_2b_2 + \cdots + a_nb_n$$

where $a_1, a_2, \cdots, a_n$ and $b_1, b_2, \cdots, b_n$ are the coordinates of α and β with respect to such a basis. But then $V_n(R^\#)$ and the mapping f are algebraically the same as the space E_n defined above.

By examining the relation between orthogonality and linear independence, we find that each subspace S of E_n has an orthonormal basis.

(81.5) Theorem. If the non-zero vectors $u_1, u_2, \cdots, u_k$ in E_n are mutually orthogonal, they are linearly independent.

PROOF. If there is a relation $c_1u_1 + c_2u_2 + \cdots + c_ku_k = O$, then for each $i = 1, 2, \cdots, k$,

$$\begin{aligned} 0 &= \mathfrak{N}(u_i,O) = \mathfrak{N}(u_i,c_1u_1 + c_2u_2 + \cdots + c_ku_k) \\ &= c_1\mathfrak{N}(u_i,u_1) + c_2\mathfrak{N}(u_i,u_2) + \cdots + c_k\mathfrak{N}(u_i,u_k) \\ &= c_i\mathfrak{N}(u_i,u_i) \end{aligned}$$

since $\mathfrak{N}(u_i,u_j) = 0$ if $i \neq j$. Since u_i is not the zero vector, $\mathfrak{N}(u_i,u_i) \neq 0$, and therefore $c_i = 0$. Thus each $c_i = 0$ and the vectors are linearly independent.

(81.6) Corollary. An orthonormal set of vectors $u_1, u_2, \cdots, u_k$ in E_n is an orthonormal basis of the subspace S of E_n which it spans.

The following theorem shows how to construct an orthonormal basis of a subspace S of E_n from a given basis.

(81.7) Theorem. If $u_1, u_2, \cdots, u_k$ are linearly independent vectors in E_n, there exists an orthonormal set of vectors $v_1, v_2, \cdots, v_k$ in E_n such that the u_i and the v_j are bases of the same subspace S of E_n.

PROOF. If $k = 1$, $v_1 = \dfrac{1}{|u_1|} u_1$ is the required basis of the subspace S spanned by u_1. If $k > 1$, assume that the theorem is true for any set of $k - 1$ linearly independent vectors. Then given the linearly independent set $u_1, u_2, \cdots, u_{k-1}, u_k$, there exists an orthonormal set $v_1, v_2, \cdots, v_{k-1}$ such that $u_1, u_2, \cdots, u_{k-1}$ and $v_1, v_2, \cdots, v_{k-1}$ are bases of the same subspace of E_n. Let S be the subspace spanned by $u_1, u_2, \cdots, u_k$ and define

$$v_k^* = u_k - c_1v_1 - c_2v_2 - \cdots - c_{k-1}v_{k-1} \in S$$

where $c_i = \mathfrak{N}(u_k,v_i)$ for $i = 1, 2, \cdots, k - 1$. Then $v_k^* \neq O$, since otherwise u_k would be in the space spanned by $u_1, u_2, \cdots, u_{k-1}$.

Now for any j such that $1 \leq j \leq k - 1$, we have

$$\begin{aligned} \mathfrak{N}(v_k^*,v_j) &= \mathfrak{N}(u_k - c_1v_1 - c_2v_2 - \cdots - c_{k-1}v_{k-1}, v_j) \\ &= \mathfrak{N}(u_k,v_j) - c_1\mathfrak{N}(v_1,v_j) - c_2\mathfrak{N}(v_2,v_j) - \cdots - c_{k-1}\mathfrak{N}(v_{k-1},v_j) \\ &= \mathfrak{N}(u_k,v_j) - c_j\mathfrak{N}(v_j,v_j) = c_j - c_j = 0. \end{aligned}$$

Thus v_k^* is orthogonal to each v_j, $j = 1, 2, \cdots, k - 1$, and the vectors $v_1, v_2, \cdots, v_{k-1}, v_k^*$ are mutually orthogonal. With $v_k = \dfrac{1}{|v_k^*|} v_k^* \in S$, the vectors $v_1, v_2, \cdots, v_k$ form an orthonormal set in S which by Theorem (81.5) is linearly independent, and therefore a basis of S.

(81.8) Corollary. Every subspace $S \neq O$ of E_n has an orthonormal basis.

PROOF. If $S \neq O$ is a subspace of E_n, S has a basis $u_1, u_2, \cdots, u_k$ where $1 \leq k \leq n$. This basis can be replaced by an orthonormal basis by the construction of Theorem (81.7).

As the following example shows, it is often convenient to first construct a basis of mutually orthogonal vectors and then "normalize" them.

EXAMPLE. Let S be the subspace of E_5 spanned by $u_1 = (2,4,0,0,0)$, $u_2 = (-1,0, 0, -1,0)$, $u_3 = (2,-1,0, -2,0)$, and $u_4 = (1,0,1,1,1)$. We take $v_1 = 1/2\ u_1 = (1,2,0,0,0)$ to simplify later computation. Since $\mathfrak{N}(v_1,v_1) = 5$ and $\mathfrak{N}(v_1,u_2) = -1$, we let $v_2^* = u_2 - (-1/5)\ v_1 = (-4/5,$

2/5, 0, −1, 0), and $v_2 = 5v_2^* = (-4,2,0,-5,0)$ to avoid fractions. Since $\mathfrak{N}(v_2,v_2) = 45$, $\mathfrak{N}(v_1,u_3) = 0$, and $\mathfrak{N}(v_2,u_3) = 0$, we let $v_3 = u_3 - 0/5\, v_1 - 0/45\, v_2 = u_3$. Since $\mathfrak{N}(v_3,v_3) = 9$, $\mathfrak{N}(v_1,u_4) = 1$, $\mathfrak{N}(v_2,u_4) = -9$, and $\mathfrak{N}(v_3,u_4) = 0$, we let $v_4 = u_4 - 1/5\, v_1 - (-9/45)\, v_2 - 0/9\, v_3 = u_4 - 1/5\, v_1 + 1/5\, v_2 = (0,0,1,0,1)$. It is readily checked that the vectors v_1, v_2, v_3, v_4 are mutually orthogonal. Then

$$w_1 = \frac{1}{|v_1|} v_1 = (1/\sqrt{5}, 2/\sqrt{5}, 0, 0, 0),$$
$$w_2 = \frac{1}{|v_2|} v_2 = (-4/\sqrt{45}, 2/\sqrt{45}, 0, -5/\sqrt{45}, 0),$$
$$w_3 = \frac{1}{|v_3|} v_3 = (2/3, -1/3, 0, -2/3, 0),$$
$$w_4 = \frac{1}{|v_4|} v_4 = (0, 0, 1/\sqrt{2}, 0, 1/\sqrt{2})$$

is an orthonormal basis of S.

Exercise (81.1). Show that for geometrical vectors α and β in ordinary three-space, the condition for orthogonality is $\mathfrak{N}(\alpha,\beta) = 0$.

Exercise (81.2). Show that

$$\cos\theta = \frac{a_1b_1 + a_2b_2}{(a_1^2 + a_2^2)^{1/2}(b_1^2 + b_2^2)^{1/2}}$$

where $\alpha = (a_1,a_2)$ and $\beta = (b_1,b_2)$ are vectors in the plane and θ is the angle between them.

Exercise (81.3). Prove that $\mathfrak{N}(\alpha,\beta) = \mathfrak{N}(\beta,\alpha)$, that $\mathfrak{N}(\alpha,\alpha) \geq 0$, and that $\mathfrak{N}(\alpha,\alpha) = 0$ only if $\alpha = O$ for $\alpha,\beta \in E_n$.

Exercise (81.4). Prove the triangle inequality $|\alpha + \beta| \leq |\alpha| + |\beta|$ for length in E_n.

Exercise (81.5). Prove that an orthonormal basis of a subspace of E_n can be extended to an orthonormal basis of E_n.

Exercise (81.6). Prove that if $u_1, u_2, \cdots, u_k$ is a basis of a subspace S of E_n and if α is orthogonal to each u_i, then α is orthogonal to every vector in S.

Exercise (81.7). Let T be the set of all vectors α such that α is orthogonal to β if β is in a given subspace S of E_n. Prove that T is a subspace of E_n. The subspace T is called the *orthogonal complement* of S and is denoted by $S^\perp$.

Exercise (81.8). If S is a subspace of E_n, prove the following properties of $S^\perp$:

(a) If $\alpha \in E_n$, there exist $\beta \in S$ and γ in $S^\perp$ such that $\alpha = \beta + \gamma$.
(b) The zero vector is the only vector in both S and $S^\perp$.
(c) $\dim S + \dim S^\perp = \dim E_n = n$.

Exercise (81.9). Prove Corollary (81.6).

Exercise (81.10). Construct an orthonormal basis for the space spanned by each of the following sets:

(a) $(3, -5, 2)$;
(b) $(3, 1, -1), (1, -2, 2)$;
(c) $(2, 2, 0), (1, -1, 1)$;
(d) $(3, 0, 1), (2, 0, -1)$;
(e) $(1, 0, 1), (0, 1, 2), (1, -1, 0)$;
(f) $(1, 0, 1, 1), (0, 2, 1, -1), (2, 1, -1, 0)$;
(g) $(1, -1, 1, -1), (0, 2, 0, 1), (2, 0, 2, -1)$.

Exercise (81.11). Find an orthonormal basis of E_5 which includes the following vectors:

(a) $(1/\sqrt{2}, 0, -1/\sqrt{2}, 0, 0)$;
(b) $(2/3, -1/3, -2/3, 0, 0), (1/3, 2/3, 0, 2/3, 0)$;
(c) $(-1/\sqrt{3}, -1/\sqrt{3}, 1/\sqrt{3}, 0, 0)$,
$(0, -1/\sqrt{3}, -1/\sqrt{3}, 1/\sqrt{3}, 0)$;
(d) $(1/2, 1/2, 1/2, 1/2, 0), (1/2, -1/2, 1/2, -1/2, 0)$,
$(0, 1/2, 0, -1/2, 1/\sqrt{2})$;
(e) $(3/4, 1/2, 1/4, 1/4, 1/4), (0, 0, 1/\sqrt{2}, -1/\sqrt{2}, 0)$,
$(1/\sqrt{10}, 0, 0, 0, -3/\sqrt{10})$,
$(\sqrt{3}/4, -\sqrt{3}/2, \sqrt{3}/12, \sqrt{3}/12, \sqrt{3}/12)$.

Section 82. Orthonormal Bases. The Orthogonal Group of Matrix Transformations

We have seen in Chapter III that the vectors $u_1, u_2, \cdots, u_n$ in $V_n(F)$ are a basis of $V_n(F)$ if and only if the matrix

$$U = \begin{pmatrix} u_1 \\ u_2 \\ \cdot \\ \cdot \\ \cdot \\ u_n \end{pmatrix} \in \mathfrak{A}_n(F)$$

is nonsingular. The following theorem gives a similar criterion for an orthonormal basis of E_n.

(82.1) Theorem. The vectors $u_1, u_2, \cdots, u_n$ in E_n are an orthonormal basis of E_n if and only if $U' = U^{-1}$ where

$$U = \begin{pmatrix} u_1 \\ u_2 \\ \cdot \\ \cdot \\ \cdot \\ u_n \end{pmatrix} \in \mathfrak{A}_n(R^{\#}).$$

PROOF. Since the ith row of U consists of the components of u_i and the jth column of U' consists of the components of u_j, the product $UU' = (a_{ij})$ where $a_{ij} = \mathfrak{N}(u_i,u_j)$ for all pairs i,j. If $u_1, u_2, \cdots, u_n$ is an orthonormal basis of E_n, $\mathfrak{N}(u_i,u_j) = \delta_{ij}$, $UU' = I_n$, and $U' = U^{-1}$. Conversely if $U' = U^{-1}$, then $UU' = I_n$, $\mathfrak{N}(u_i,u_j) = \delta_{ij}$, and the rows $u_1, u_2, \cdots, u_n$ of U form an orthonormal basis of E_n.

(82.2) Definition. A matrix $P \in \mathfrak{A}_n(R^{\#})$ is called *orthogonal* if $P' = P^{-1}$.

Thus P is orthogonal if $P = (P')^{-1} = (P^{-1})'$. By the above theorem, U is orthogonal if and only if the rows of U form an orthonormal basis of E_n. The following theorem describes a change of basis from one orthonormal basis of E_n to another. The reader should compare this theorem with (27.1).

(82.3) Theorem. Let $u_1, u_2, \cdots, u_n$ be an orthonormal basis of E_n and let $\bar{u}_1, \bar{u}_2, \cdots, \bar{u}_n$ be any set of n vectors in E_n. Then $\bar{u}_1, \bar{u}_2, \cdots, \bar{u}_n$ is an orthonormal basis of E_n if and only if there exists an orthogonal matrix $P \in \mathfrak{A}_n(R^{\#})$ such that

$$\bar{U} = \begin{pmatrix} \bar{u}_1 \\ \bar{u}_2 \\ \cdot \\ \cdot \\ \cdot \\ \bar{u}_n \end{pmatrix} = P \begin{pmatrix} u_1 \\ u_2 \\ \cdot \\ \cdot \\ \cdot \\ u_n \end{pmatrix} = PU.$$

PROOF. By Theorem (82.1), $U' = U^{-1}$. If there exists an orthogonal matrix $P \in \mathfrak{A}_n(R^{\#})$ such that $\bar{U} = PU$, then

$$\bar{U}\bar{U}' = (PU)(PU)' = P(UU')P' = PP' = I_n,$$

so that $\bar{U}$ is orthogonal, and $\bar{u}_1, \bar{u}_2, \cdots, \bar{u}_n$ is an orthonormal basis of E_n by Theorem (82.1).

Conversely, if $\bar{u}_1, \bar{u}_2, \cdots, \bar{u}_n$ is an orthonormal basis of E_n, then again by (82.1), $\bar{U}$ is orthogonal. With $P = \bar{U}U^{-1} \in \mathfrak{A}_n(R^\#)$, $\bar{U} = PU$, and

$$PP' = (\bar{U}U^{-1})(\bar{U}U^{-1})' = \bar{U}(U^{-1}U)\bar{U}' = I_n,$$

so that P is orthogonal.

In the plane, the rotations, with matrix $P = \begin{pmatrix} \cos\theta & \sin\theta \\ -\sin\theta & \cos\theta \end{pmatrix}$, and the reflections, with matrix $P = \begin{pmatrix} 1 & 0 \\ 0 & -1 \end{pmatrix}$ or $\begin{pmatrix} -1 & 0 \\ 0 & 1 \end{pmatrix}$, are examples of a change of basis which will send one orthonormal basis into another. An orthogonal change of basis in E_n is often called a *generalized rotation.*

The reason for using orthonormal bases when working with Euclidean spaces is given in the following theorem which characterizes the set of orthonormal bases of E_n. The inner-product mapping $\mathfrak{N}$ of E_n into $R^\#$ was defined in (81.1) as the bilinear mapping

$$\begin{aligned}\mathfrak{N}(\alpha,\beta) &= (a_1, a_2, \cdots, a_n)I_n(b_1, b_2, \cdots, b_n)' \\ &= a_1b_1 + a_2b_2 + \cdots + a_nb_n,\end{aligned}$$

where $a_1, a_2, \cdots, a_n$ and $b_1, b_2, \cdots, b_n$ are the components of α and β. If $u_1, u_2, \cdots, u_n$ is any basis of E_n, then by Corollary (27.3) the coordinates of α and β with respect to this basis are $\bar{a}_1, \bar{a}_2, \cdots, \bar{a}_n$ and $\bar{b}_1, \bar{b}_2, \cdots, \bar{b}_n$ where

$$\begin{aligned}(a_1, a_2, \cdots, a_n) &= (\bar{a}_1, \bar{a}_2, \cdots, \bar{a}_n)U, \\ (b_1, b_2, \cdots, b_n) &= (\bar{b}_1, \bar{b}_2, \cdots, \bar{b}_n)U,\end{aligned}$$

$$U = \begin{pmatrix} u_1 \\ u_2 \\ \cdot \\ \cdot \\ \cdot \\ u_n \end{pmatrix}.$$

Then

$$\begin{aligned}\mathfrak{N}(\alpha,\beta) &= (a_1, a_2, \cdots, a_n)(b_1, b_2, \cdots, b_n)' \\ &= (\bar{a}_1, \bar{a}_2, \cdots, \bar{a}_n)UU'(\bar{b}_1, \bar{b}_2, \cdots, \bar{b}_n)',\end{aligned}$$

and the mapping $\mathfrak{N}$ has matrix UU' with respect to the basis $u_1, u_2, \cdots, u_n$.

(82.4) Theorem. The inner-product mapping $\mathfrak{N}$ has matrix I_n with respect to the basis $u_1, u_2, \cdots, u_n$ if and only if $u_1, u_2, \cdots, u_n$ is an orthonormal basis of E_n.

PROOF. If $\mathfrak{N}$ has matrix I_n with respect to the basis $u_1, u_2, \cdots, u_n$, then $UU' = I_n$ since the matrix of a bilinear mapping with respect to a given basis is uniquely determined by the mapping and the basis. Thus U is orthogonal, and $u_1, u_2, \cdots, u_n$ is an orthonormal basis of E_n by Theorem (82.1).

Conversely, if the basis $u_1, u_2, \cdots, u_n$ is orthonormal, U is orthogonal and the matrix UU' of $\mathfrak{N}$ with respect to this basis is I_n.

We have proved that the inner product has the same form, that is, $\mathfrak{N}(\alpha,\beta) = \bar{a}_1\bar{b}_1 + \bar{a}_2\bar{b}_2 + \cdots + \bar{a}_n\bar{b}_n$, with respect to any orthonormal basis of E_n. Consequently the formulas for angle and length are left unchanged when a change of basis is made from one orthonormal basis to another.

Let XAX' be a real quadratic form with matrix $A = A'$ and let $\mathfrak{Q}_{A,u_i}$ be the associated quadratic mapping of E_n into $R^\#$ defined with respect to an orthonormal basis $u_1, u_2, \cdots, u_n$ of E_n. Under a change to a new orthonormal basis $v_1, v_2, \cdots, v_n$, $\mathfrak{Q}_{A,u_i} = \mathfrak{Q}_{PAP',v_i}$ where $P' = P^{-1}$. Similarly, the form $XAX' = YBY'$ where $B = PAP'$ under the orthogonal change of variables $X = YP$, and the simplification problem suggested here leads us to the problem of reducing a real symmetric matrix A by a real equivalence transformation $T_{P,Q}$ with $Q = P' = P^{-1}$.

(82.5) Definition. An equivalence transformation $T_{P,Q}$ of $\mathfrak{A}_n(R^\#)$ with $Q = P' = P^{-1}$ is called an *orthogonal transformation* of $\mathfrak{A}_n(R^\#)$.

As before, we may prove that the orthogonal transformations form a group $\mathcal{P}(\mathfrak{A}_n(R^\#))$. The equivalence relation in $\mathfrak{A}_n(R^\#)$ induced by this group is called *orthogonal equivalence*. From the definition we see that the orthogonal group on $\mathfrak{A}_n(R^\#)$ is a subgroup of both the congruence and the collineatory groups of matrix transformations of $\mathfrak{A}_n(R^\#)$. Finally, $\mathcal{P}(\mathfrak{A}_n(R^\#))$ is also a group of transformations of the set S of symmetric matrices in $\mathfrak{A}_n(R^\#)$. In the next sections we will discuss the reduction of a real symmetric matrix by real orthogonal transformations.

Exercise (82.1). Prove that $\mathcal{P}(\mathfrak{A}_n(R^\#))$ is a group of transformations.

Exercise (82.2). Show that if A is a symmetric matrix in $\mathfrak{A}_n(R^\#)$ and $T \in \mathcal{P}(\mathfrak{A}_n(R^\#))$, then $T(A)$ is symmetric. Also show that if A is orthogonal, $T(A)$ is orthogonal.

Exercise (82.3). Show that if $P \in \mathfrak{A}_n(R^\#)$ is orthogonal, $|P| = \pm 1$.

Exercise (82.4). Which elementary congruence transformations are orthogonal transformations?

Exercise (82.5). A linear transformation $\mathfrak{L}$ of E_n is called orthogonal if $\mathfrak{N}(\mathfrak{L}(\alpha), \mathfrak{L}(\beta)) = \mathfrak{N}(\alpha,\beta)$ for all $\alpha,\beta \in E_n$. Prove that the matrix A of a linear transformation $\mathfrak{L}$ of E_n, with respect to an orthonormal basis of E_n, is an orthogonal matrix if and only if $\mathfrak{L}$ is an orthogonal linear transformation.

Exercise (82.6). Find the condition on a, b, c, d that the 2 by 2 matrix $A = \begin{pmatrix} a & b \\ c & d \end{pmatrix}$ be orthogonal.

Exercise (82.7). As in Theorem (82.1), prove that the matrix U is orthogonal if and only if its columns form an orthonormal basis of E_n.

Section 83. Characteristic Vectors

The characteristic polynomial of a matrix $A \in \mathfrak{A}_n(F)$ is the polynomial $|Ix - A|$ of degree n with coefficients in the number field F. The complex number $r \in C$ is called a *characteristic value* of A if r is a zero of $|Ix - A|$, that is, if $|Ir - A| = 0$. In the field C, $|Ix - A|$ factors into n linear factors, so that the matrix A has n characteristic values in C if each is counted with its proper multiplicity.

EXAMPLE 1. If $A = \begin{pmatrix} 2 & m & 1 \\ 1 & -2 & -1 \\ 0 & 0 & 0 \end{pmatrix}$ with m a real number,

$$|Ix - A| = \begin{vmatrix} x - 2 & -m & -1 \\ -1 & x + 2 & 1 \\ 0 & 0 & x \end{vmatrix} = x[x^2 - (4 + m)].$$

The characteristic values of A are 0, $\sqrt{4 + m}$, and $-\sqrt{4 + m}$. If $m = -4$, each characteristic value is zero; if $m > -4$, the three characteristic values of A are real and distinct; and if $m < -4$, two of the characteristic values are pure imaginary numbers.

Similar matrices have the same characteristic polynomial [see Exercise (74.7)], for if $B = PAP^{-1}$, then $Ix - B = PP^{-1}x - PAP^{-1} = P(Ix - A)P^{-1}$ and $|Ix - B| = |P| \cdot |Ix - A| \cdot |P^{-1}| = |Ix - A|$. Therefore similar matrices have the same characteristic values, and in particular this is true of matrices which are orthogonally equivalent over $R^{\#}$.

(83.1) Definition. The non-zero vector $u = (a_1, a_2, \cdots, a_n) \in V_n(C)$ is called a *characteristic vector* of the matrix $A \in \mathfrak{A}_n(F)$ if

$$A \begin{pmatrix} a_1 \\ a_2 \\ \cdot \\ \cdot \\ \cdot \\ a_n \end{pmatrix} = c \begin{pmatrix} a_1 \\ a_2 \\ \cdot \\ \cdot \\ \cdot \\ a_n \end{pmatrix} \quad \text{for some scalar } c \in C.$$

Considering the matrix A as the matrix of a linear transformation $\mathfrak{L}$ of $V_n(C)$ with respect to the basis $\epsilon_1, \epsilon_2, \cdots, \epsilon_n$, the characteristic vectors of A are just those non-zero vectors of $V_n(C)$ which are sent into a scalar multiple of themselves by $\mathfrak{L}$.

The following theorem gives the relation between the characteristic values and the characteristic vectors of a matrix $A \in \mathfrak{A}_n(F)$.

(83.2) Theorem. If $A \in \mathfrak{A}_n(F)$, and $r \in C$ is a characteristic value of A, then there is a characteristic vector u of A such that $Au' = ru'$. Conversely, if u is a characteristic vector of A, say $Au' = su'$, then s is a characteristic value of A.

PROOF. The condition that $Au' = cu'$, or that $Icu' - Au' = (Ic - A)u' = O$ for $u \neq O$ in $V_n(C)$, is that $u = (a_1, a_2, \cdots, a_n)$ be a nontrivial solution of a system of n linear homogeneous equations with coefficients in C. But this system has a nontrivial solution if and only if $|Ic - A| = 0$, that is, if and only if c is a characteristic value of A.

This theorem enables us to find the characteristic vectors of A by solving systems of homogeneous equations.

EXAMPLE 2. In Example 1 with $m = 0$, $|Ix - A| = x^3 - 4x$ and the characteristic values are $-2, 0, 2$. Corresponding to each value is a set of homogeneous linear equations with nontrivial solutions which are the characteristic vectors of A.

$$r_1 = -2 \begin{cases} -4x_1 - x_3 = 0 \\ -x_1 + x_3 = 0 \\ -2x_3 = 0 \end{cases} \qquad \begin{matrix} x_3 = 0,\ x_1 = 0,\ x_2 \text{ arbitrary} \\ u = (0, c, 0) \text{ for any } c \in C. \end{matrix}$$

$$r_2 = 0 \begin{cases} -2x_1 - x_3 = 0 \\ -x_1 + 2x_2 + x_3 = 0 \end{cases} \qquad \begin{matrix} x_3 = -2x_1,\ x_2 = 3/2\, x_1,\ x_1 \text{ arbitrary} \\ u = (c, 3/2\, c, -2c) \text{ for any } c \in C. \end{matrix}$$

$$r_3 = 2 \begin{cases} -x_3 = 0 \\ -x_1 + 4x_2 + x_3 = 0 \\ 2x_3 = 0 \end{cases} \qquad \begin{matrix} x_3 = 0,\ x_1 = 4x_2,\ x_2 \text{ arbitrary} \\ u = (4c, c, 0) \text{ for any } c \in C. \end{matrix}$$

A matrix $A \in \mathfrak{A}_n(R^\#)$ may have complex characteristic values, as the polynomial $|Ix - A|$ with real coefficients need not factor into real linear factors. This is the case in Example 1 with $m < -4$. However, it follows from Theorem (83.2) that if $A \in \mathfrak{A}_n(R^\#)$ has real characteristic values, then A has real characteristic vectors. For if $r \in R^\#$ is a characteristic value of A, the corresponding system of homogeneous equations with matrix $Ir - A$ has coefficients in $R^\#$. Since this system has a rational solution, A has characteristic vectors in $V_n(R^\#)$. In Example 2, real characteristic vectors are obtained by choosing c in $R^\#$. It is a consequence of the following theorem that a real symmetric matrix always has a real characteristic vector.

(83.3) Theorem. The characteristic values of a Hermitian matrix (and therefore of a real symmetric matrix) are real.

PROOF. Let $r \in C$ be a characteristic value of $A = \bar{A}' \in \mathfrak{A}_n(C)$. Then by Theorem (83.2), there exists a characteristic vector $u = (a_1, a_2, \cdots, a_n) \in V_n(C)$ such that $Au' = ru'$. The vector $\bar{u} = (\bar{a}_1, \bar{a}_2, \cdots, \bar{a}_n)$ is mapped onto a real number $\bar{u}A\bar{\bar{u}}' = \bar{u}Au'$ by the Hermitian mapping $\mathcal{H}_{A,\epsilon_i}$. But $\bar{u}Au' = \bar{u}ru' = r(\bar{u}u')$ where $\bar{u}u' = \bar{a}_1a_1 + \bar{a}_2a_2 + \cdots + \bar{a}_na_n$ is a non-zero real number. Therefore $r = \dfrac{\bar{u}Au'}{\bar{u}u'}$ is real.

Exercise (83.1). Find the characteristic vectors of the matrix in Example 1 if $m = -4$, and also if $m = -8$.

Exercise (83.2). Prove that if $A \in \mathfrak{A}_n(R^\#)$ is similar to a diagonal matrix D,

(a) the characteristic values of A are the diagonal elements of D;
(b) a set of characteristic vectors of A is a basis of E_n.

(*Hint:* If $PAP^{-1} = D$, the columns of P^{-1} are characteristic vectors of A.)

Exercise (83.3). Show that if u is a characteristic vector of A and $c \neq 0$, then cu is a characteristic vector of A. Give an example to show that the sum of characteristic vectors of A need not be a characteristic vector of A.

Exercise (83.4). Show that the characteristic vectors of A which correspond to a given characteristic value r of A, together with the zero vector, form a subspace of E_n.

Exercise (83.5). Find all characteristic vectors of

(a) $\begin{pmatrix} 3 & 0 \\ 0 & 3 \end{pmatrix}$, (b) $\begin{pmatrix} 3 & 1 \\ 0 & 3 \end{pmatrix}$, (c) $\begin{pmatrix} 0 & 2i & 3+i \\ -2i & 0 & 1 \\ 3-i & 1 & 0 \end{pmatrix}$;

(d) $\begin{pmatrix} 2 & -2 & 2 & 1 \\ -1 & 3 & 0 & 3 \\ 0 & 0 & 4 & -2 \\ 0 & 0 & 2 & -1 \end{pmatrix}$, (e) $\begin{pmatrix} 0 & -1/3 & 0 & -1 \\ -1/3 & 1/2 & 2/3 & 0 \\ 0 & 2/3 & 2 & 0 \\ -1 & 0 & 0 & 1/3 \end{pmatrix}$.

Section 84. Reduction of Real Symmetric Matrices by Orthogonal Transformations

As a preliminary to the reduction theorem for real symmetric matrices by transformations in the orthogonal group $\mathcal{P}(\mathfrak{A}_n(R^\#))$, we will prove a more general reduction theorem which is itself of some importance.

(84.1) Lemma. If $u \in E_n$ has length 1, there exists a real orthogonal matrix P such that $Pu' = \epsilon_1'$.

PROOF. It follows from Theorem (81.7) [see Exercise (81.7)] that there is an orthonormal basis $u, u_2, u_3, \cdots, u_n$ of E_n which contains u.

By Theorem (82.1) the matrix $P = \begin{pmatrix} u \\ u_2 \\ u_3 \\ \cdot \\ \cdot \\ \cdot \\ u_n \end{pmatrix}$ is orthogonal, and

$$Pu' = \begin{pmatrix} uu' \\ u_2u' \\ u_3u' \\ \cdot \\ \cdot \\ \cdot \\ u_nu' \end{pmatrix} = \begin{pmatrix} 1 \\ 0 \\ 0 \\ \cdot \\ \cdot \\ \cdot \\ 0 \end{pmatrix} = \epsilon_1'.$$

(84.2) Theorem. If all of the characteristic values of $A \in \mathfrak{A}_n(R^\#)$ are real, there exists an orthogonal matrix $P \in \mathfrak{A}_n(R^\#)$ such that

$$PAP^{-1} = B = \begin{pmatrix} d_1 & a_{12}^* & a_{13}^* & \cdots & & a_{1n}^* \\ 0 & d_2 & a_{23}^* & \cdots & & a_{2n}^* \\ \cdot & \cdot & \cdot & & & \cdot \\ \cdot & \cdot & \cdot & & & \cdot \\ \cdot & \cdot & \cdot & & & \cdot \\ 0 & 0 & 0 & \cdots & d_{n-1} & a_{n-1,n}^* \\ 0 & 0 & 0 & \cdots & 0 & d_n \end{pmatrix}$$

where $d_1, d_2, \cdots, d_n$ are the characteristic values of A.

PROOF. Let d_1 be any characteristic value of A, and let $u \in E_n$ be a corresponding real characteristic vector such that $Au' = d_1u'$. The vector $v = \frac{1}{|u|} u$ of length 1 is also a characteristic vector, and $Av' = d_1v'$. By Lemma (84.1), there exists a real orthogonal matrix P_1 such that $P_1v' = \epsilon_1'$, or $v' = P_1^{-1}\epsilon_1'$. Substituting,

$$Av' = AP_1^{-1}\epsilon_1' = d_1v' = d_1P_1^{-1}\epsilon_1' = P_1^{-1}(d_1\epsilon_1'),$$

so that

$$P_1AP_1^{-1}\epsilon_1' = d_1\epsilon_1'.$$

It follows from the latter equality that the first column of $P_1AP_1^{-1}$ is $d_1, 0, 0, \cdots, 0$. Thus

$$P_1AP_1^{-1} = \left(\begin{array}{c|cccc} d_1 & a_{12}^* & \cdots & a_{1n}^* \\ \hline 0 & b_{22} & \cdots & b_{2n} \\ \cdot & \cdot & & \cdot \\ \cdot & \cdot & & \cdot \\ \cdot & \cdot & & \cdot \\ 0 & b_{n2} & \cdots & b_{nn} \end{array}\right) = \begin{pmatrix} d_1 & A_1^* \\ 0 & B_1 \end{pmatrix} = A_1.$$

Since $|Ix - A| = |Ix - A_1| = (x - d_1)|Ix - B_1|$, the characteristic values of B_1 are those of A other than d_1. Therefore we can repeat the above process on B_1 with

$$P_2^*B_1P_2^{*-1} = \begin{pmatrix} d_2 & A_2^* \\ 0 & B_2 \end{pmatrix},$$

or

$$\begin{pmatrix} 1 & 0 \\ 0 & P_2^* \end{pmatrix} A_1 \begin{pmatrix} 1 & 0 \\ 0 & P_2^* \end{pmatrix}^{-1} = \left(\begin{array}{cc|ccc} d_1 & a_{12}^* & a_{13}^* & \cdots & a_{1n}^* \\ 0 & d_2 & a_{23}^* & \cdots & a_{2n}^* \\ \hline \multicolumn{2}{c|}{0} & \multicolumn{3}{c}{B_2} \end{array}\right) = A_2.$$

Since P_2^* is a real orthogonal matrix, so are the matrices $\begin{pmatrix} 1 & 0 \\ 0 & P_2^* \end{pmatrix}$ and $P_2 = \begin{pmatrix} 1 & 0 \\ 0 & P_2^* \end{pmatrix} P_1$, and we have $P_2AP_2^{-1} = A_2$. We can continue in this way until we obtain a real orthogonal matrix P_n such that $P_nAP_n^{-1} = B$, the triangular form of the theorem.

(84.3) Corollary. If $A \in \mathfrak{A}_n(R^\#)$ is symmetric, there exists an orthogonal matrix $P \in \mathfrak{A}_n(R^\#)$ such that

$$PAP^{-1} = D = \left(\begin{array}{ccccc|c} d_1 & & & & & \\ & d_2 & & 0 & & \\ & & \cdot & & & \\ & & & \cdot & & 0 \\ & 0 & & & \cdot & \\ & & & & d_r & \\ \hline & & 0 & & & 0 \end{array}\right),$$

where r is the rank of A and $d_1, d_2, \cdots, d_r$ are the non-zero characteristic values of A.

PROOF. By (83.3), the characteristic values of A are real. Since the matrix P of Theorem (84.2) is orthogonal, $PAP^{-1} = PAP'$ is congruent to A, so that the triangular matrix B of the theorem is symmetric. Therefore the entries of B above the diagonal are also zero, and

$$PAP^{-1} = \begin{pmatrix} d_1 & & & & \\ & d_2 & & 0 & \\ & & \cdot & & \\ & & & \cdot & \\ & 0 & & \cdot & \\ & & & & d_n \end{pmatrix}$$

where the d_i are the characteristic values of A. Since orthogonally equivalent matrices have the same rank, the number of non-zero characteristic values of A must be r, the rank of A. These non-zero characteristic values of A can then be put in the first r positions of the diagonal by elementary congruence transformations of type I, which are orthogonal transformations.

The proofs of the following two results are left to the reader as an exercise.

(84.4) Corollary. A symmetric matrix in $\mathfrak{A}_n(R^\#)$ has rank r if and only if it has r non-zero characteristic values.

(84.5) Theorem. Two real symmetric matrices are orthogonally equivalent if and only if they have the same characteristic values.

While the method of Lemma (84.1) can be used to construct an orthogonal matrix P which reduces the real symmetric matrix A to diagonal form, an alternate method, which usually involves less calculation, can be based on the following theorem.

(84.6) Theorem. If $A \in \mathfrak{A}_n(R^\#)$ is symmetric, then there exists an orthonormal set of n characteristic vectors of A in E_n. Moreover, if $u_1, u_2, \cdots, u_n$ is any orthonormal set of characteristic vectors of A and $P = \begin{pmatrix} u_1 \\ u_2 \\ \cdot \\ \cdot \\ \cdot \\ u_n \end{pmatrix}$, then P is an orthogonal matrix such that $PAP^{-1} = \begin{pmatrix} d_1 & & & & \\ & d_2 & & 0 & \\ & & \cdot & & \\ & & & \cdot & \\ & 0 & & & \cdot \\ & & & & d_n \end{pmatrix}$ where $d_1, d_2, \cdots, d_n$ are the characteristic values of A.

PROOF. By (84.3) there exists an orthogonal matrix $P = \begin{pmatrix} u_1 \\ u_2 \\ \cdot \\ \cdot \\ \cdot \\ u_n \end{pmatrix}$ such that $PAP^{-1} = D = \begin{pmatrix} d_1 & & & & \\ & d_2 & & 0 & \\ & & \cdot & & \\ & & & \cdot & \\ & 0 & & & \cdot \\ & & & & d_n \end{pmatrix}$, and by (82.1) the rows $u_1, u_2, \cdots, u_n$ of P form an orthonormal set of vectors in E_n. Then $PA = DP$, or

$$\begin{pmatrix} u_1 \\ u_2 \\ \cdot \\ \cdot \\ \cdot \\ u_n \end{pmatrix} A = \begin{pmatrix} u_1A \\ u_2A \\ \cdot \\ \cdot \\ \cdot \\ u_nA \end{pmatrix} = \begin{pmatrix} d_1 & & & & \\ & d_2 & & 0 & \\ & & \cdot & & \\ & & & \cdot & \\ & 0 & & & \cdot \\ & & & & d_n \end{pmatrix} \begin{pmatrix} u_1 \\ u_2 \\ \cdot \\ \cdot \\ \cdot \\ u_n \end{pmatrix} = \begin{pmatrix} d_1u_1 \\ d_2u_2 \\ \cdot \\ \cdot \\ \cdot \\ d_nu_n \end{pmatrix}.$$

Therefore for each i, $u_iA = d_iu_i$, or $(u_iA)' = A'u_i' = Au_i' = (d_iu_i)' = d_iu_i'$, so that u_i is a characteristic vector of A corresponding to the characteristic value d_i.

If $u_1, u_2, \cdots, u_n$ is any orthonormal set of characteristic vectors of A, then $P = \begin{pmatrix} u_1 \\ u_2 \\ \cdot \\ \cdot \\ \cdot \\ u_n \end{pmatrix}$ is orthogonal by (82.1). Since for each i, u_i is a characteristic vector of A, $Au_i' = c_i u_i'$, or $(Au_i')' = u_i A' = u_i A = (c_i u_i')' = c_i u_i$, for some real scalar c_i. Then we have

$$PA = \begin{pmatrix} u_1 \\ u_2 \\ \cdot \\ \cdot \\ \cdot \\ u_n \end{pmatrix} A = \begin{pmatrix} u_1 A \\ u_2 A \\ \cdot \\ \cdot \\ \cdot \\ u_n A \end{pmatrix} = \begin{pmatrix} c_1 u_1 \\ c_2 u_2 \\ \cdot \\ \cdot \\ \cdot \\ c_n u_n \end{pmatrix} = \begin{pmatrix} c_1 & & & & \\ & c_2 & & 0 & \\ & & \cdot & & \\ & & & \cdot & \\ & 0 & & & \cdot \\ & & & & c_n \end{pmatrix} P,$$

or $PAP^{-1} = C = \begin{pmatrix} c_1 & & & & \\ & c_2 & & 0 & \\ & & \cdot & & \\ & & & \cdot & \\ & 0 & & & \cdot \\ & & & & c_n \end{pmatrix}$. But the characteristic values of C, which are $c_1, c_2, \cdots, c_n$, are the same as those of A, and this completes the proof.

It should be noticed that in the orthonormal set of n characteristic vectors of A defined by the matrix P of (84.3), there is exactly one characteristic vector u_i corresponding to each characteristic value d_i of A. In particular, if $d = d_{i_1} = d_{i_2} = \cdots = d_{i_s}$ is an s-fold characteristic value, then corresponding to d is the orthonormal set $u_{i_1}, u_{i_2}, \cdots, u_{i_s}$ of s characteristic vectors. Therefore among the characteristic vectors corresponding to d, which are the nontrivial solutions of the homogeneous linear equations $(dI - A)X' = O$, it is possible to select an orthonormal set of s vectors. Since it is easy to verify that vectors corresponding to distinct characteristic values are orthogonal [see Exercise (84.6)], we have a procedure for constructing an orthonormal set of n characteristic vectors, and therefore an orthogonal matrix P which reduces A to diagonal form. In particular, we may obtain the form D of (84.3) immediately if we choose the first r characteristic vectors to correspond to the non-zero characteristic values.

EXAMPLE 1. If $A = \begin{pmatrix} 3/2 & \sqrt{2} & -1/2 \\ \sqrt{2} & -1 & -\sqrt{2} \\ -1/2 & -\sqrt{2} & -5/2 \end{pmatrix}$, then $|Ix - A| = \begin{vmatrix} x - 3/2 & -\sqrt{2} & 1/2 \\ -\sqrt{2} & x+1 & \sqrt{2} \\ 1/2 & \sqrt{2} & x + 5/2 \end{vmatrix} = (x-3)(x+3)x.$

Corresponding to the characteristic values 3, -3, 0 are respectively the characteristic vectors $(1/\sqrt{2}, 2/3, -1/3\sqrt{2})$, $(0, 1/3, 2\sqrt{2}/3)$, and $(1/\sqrt{2}, -2/3, 1/3\sqrt{2})$ of length 1. Thus the desired matrix is

$$P = \begin{pmatrix} 1/\sqrt{2} & 2/3 & -1/3\sqrt{2} \\ 0 & 1/3 & 2\sqrt{2}/3 \\ 1/\sqrt{2} & -2/3 & 1/3\sqrt{2} \end{pmatrix}, \quad \text{and} \quad PAP^{-1} = \begin{pmatrix} 3 & 0 & 0 \\ 0 & -3 & 0 \\ 0 & 0 & 0 \end{pmatrix}.$$

EXAMPLE 2. If $A = \begin{pmatrix} -1 & -3/\sqrt{2} & 3/\sqrt{2} \\ -3/\sqrt{2} & 1/2 & 3/2 \\ 3/\sqrt{2} & 3/2 & 1/2 \end{pmatrix}$, then $|Ix - A|$ $= \begin{vmatrix} x+1 & 3/\sqrt{2} & -3/\sqrt{2} \\ 3/\sqrt{2} & x - 1/2 & -3/2 \\ -3/\sqrt{2} & -3/2 & x - 1/2 \end{vmatrix} = (x-2)^2(x+4)$. Corresponding to the characteristic value 2 is the set of equations

$$\begin{aligned} 3x_1 + 3/\sqrt{2}\, x_2 - 3/\sqrt{2}\, x_3 &= 0 \\ 3/\sqrt{2}\, x_1 + 3/2\, x_2 - 3/2\, x_3 &= 0 \\ -3/\sqrt{2}\, x_1 - 3/2\, x_2 + 3/2\, x_3 &= 0, \end{aligned}$$

which is just the equation $\sqrt{2}\, x_1 + x_2 - x_3 = 0$ repeated three times. Two independent vectors which satisfy this equation are $u_1 = (0,1,1)$ and $u_2 = (1,0,\sqrt{2})$ which can be replaced by an orthonormal set v_1, v_2 using the method of the proof of (81.7).

$$v_1 = \frac{1}{|u_1|} u_1 = (0, 1/\sqrt{2}, 1/\sqrt{2})$$

$$\begin{aligned} v_2^* = u_2 - \mathfrak{N}(u_2,v_1) \cdot v_1 &= (1,0,\sqrt{2}) - 1 \cdot (0, 1/\sqrt{2}, 1/\sqrt{2}) \\ &= (1, -1/\sqrt{2}, 1/\sqrt{2}) \end{aligned}$$

and

$$v_2 = \frac{1}{|v_2^*|} v_2^* = (1/\sqrt{2}, -1/2, 1/2).$$

Corresponding to the characteristic value -4 is $u_3 = (1/\sqrt{2}, 1/2, -1/2)$ of length 1, and v_1, v_2, u_3 is an orthonormal set of characteristic vectors. Thus

$$P = \begin{pmatrix} v_1 \\ v_2 \\ u_3 \end{pmatrix} = \begin{pmatrix} 0 & 1/\sqrt{2} & 1/\sqrt{2} \\ 1/\sqrt{2} & -1/2 & 1/2 \\ 1/\sqrt{2} & 1/2 & -1/2 \end{pmatrix}$$

is an orthogonal matrix such that $PAP^{-1} = \begin{pmatrix} 2 & 0 & 0 \\ 0 & 2 & 0 \\ 0 & 0 & -4 \end{pmatrix}$.

Applying the results of this section to quadratic mappings of E_n and to real quadratic forms, we obtain our principal theorems.

(84.7) Theorem. If $\mathfrak{Q}_{A,u_i}$ is a quadratic mapping of E_n where $u_1, u_2, \cdots, u_n$ is an orthonormal basis of E_n, then there exists an orthonormal basis $v_1, v_2, \cdots, v_n$ of E_n such that $\mathfrak{Q}_{A,u_i} = \mathfrak{Q}_{D,v_i}$ where D is the diagonal matrix of (84.3).

PROOF. Let P be the matrix of (84.3) such that $PAP^{-1} = PAP'$ $= D$ and let $\begin{pmatrix} v_1 \\ v_2 \\ \cdot \\ \cdot \\ \cdot \\ v_n \end{pmatrix} = P \begin{pmatrix} u_1 \\ u_2 \\ \cdot \\ \cdot \\ \cdot \\ u_n \end{pmatrix}$. By (82.3) $v_1, v_2, \cdots, v_n$ is an orthonormal basis of E_n since P is an orthogonal matrix, and $\mathfrak{Q}_{A,u_i} = \mathfrak{Q}_{D,v_i}$ under this change of basis.

(84.8) Corollary. A real quadratic form XAX' can be reduced by a real orthogonal change of variables $X = YP$ to the form

$$YDY' = d_1y_1^2 + d_2y_2^2 + \cdots + d_ry_r^2$$

where $d_1, d_2, \cdots, d_r$ are the non-zero characteristic values of A.

PROOF. Under any nonsingular change of variables $X = YP$,

$$XAX' = (YP)A(YP)' = YPAP'Y',$$

and by (84.3) we can find a real orthogonal P such that $PAP' = D$, a diagonal matrix with the non-zero characteristic values of A in the first r positions.

The set of all vectors in E_n which are mapped onto the constant a by the quadratic mapping $\mathfrak{Q}_{A,\epsilon_i}$ is a quadric surface (in E_2, a conic). We say that we have referred the quadric to its principal axes when we choose an orthonormal basis $u_1, u_2, \cdots, u_n$ of E_n so that $\mathfrak{Q}_{A,\epsilon_i} = \mathfrak{Q}_{D,u_i}$ where D is the diagonal matrix of (84.3). Then the equation of the quadric surface with respect to the new basis, that is, the condition that $\alpha = y_1u_1 + y_2u_2 + \cdots + y_nu_n \in E_n$ is mapped onto $a \in R^\#$, has the form $\mathfrak{Q}_{D,u_i} = d_1y_1^2 + d_2y_2^2 + \cdots + d_ry_r^2 = a$, where $\sqrt{|a/d_i|}$ for $i = 1, 2, \cdots, r$ is a semiaxis of the quadric.

EXAMPLE 3. The conic with equation $5x^2 - 6xy - 3y^2 = 4$ with respect to the ϵ_1, ϵ_2 basis is defined by $\mathfrak{Q}_{A,\epsilon_i}(\alpha) = 4$ where $A = \begin{pmatrix} 5 & -3 \\ -3 & -3 \end{pmatrix}$. Then $|Ix - A| = \begin{vmatrix} x-5 & 3 \\ 3 & x+3 \end{vmatrix} = (x-6)(x+4)$ gives characteristic values 6 and -4, and $u_1 = (3/\sqrt{10}, -1/\sqrt{10})$ and $u_2 = (1/\sqrt{10}, 3/\sqrt{10})$ are corresponding characteristic vectors of length 1. With respect to the basis u_1, u_2 of E_2, the conic has the equation $6x'^2 - 4y'^2 = 4$, where $\alpha = x\epsilon_1 + y\epsilon_2 = x'u_1 + y'u_2$.

EXAMPLE 4. Since the problem of referring the quadric $\mathfrak{Q}_{A,\epsilon_i} = a$ to its principal axes is that of finding an orthogonal change of variables $X = YP$ such that the form $XAX' = YDY'$, we may use the method discussed above to eliminate the cross-product terms in the general equation of the second degree. Consider the equation $x^2 + 2xy + y^2 - 3x + 4y + 2 = 0$. The quadratic form $x^2 + 2xy + y^2$ has matrix $A = \begin{pmatrix} 1 & 1 \\ 1 & 1 \end{pmatrix}$. Then $|Ix - A| = \begin{vmatrix} x-1 & -1 \\ -1 & x-1 \end{vmatrix} = (x-2)x$ gives characteristic values 2 and 0, and $u_1 = (1/\sqrt{2}, 1/\sqrt{2})$, $u_2 = (-1/\sqrt{2}, 1/\sqrt{2})$ are corresponding characteristic vectors of length 1. Thus

$$(x,y) = (x',y')\begin{pmatrix} 1/\sqrt{2} & 1/\sqrt{2} \\ -1/\sqrt{2} & 1/\sqrt{2} \end{pmatrix} = ((x'-y')/\sqrt{2}, (x'+y')/\sqrt{2})$$

reduces the equation to $2x'^2 + 1/\sqrt{2}\,x' + 7/\sqrt{2}\,y' + 2 = 0$. The orthogonal change of variables in this example is a rotation in the plane through 45°.

Exercise (84.1). Prove (84.4) and (84.5).

Exercise (84.2). Show that the characteristic values of $A = \begin{pmatrix} A_1 & B \\ 0 & A_2 \end{pmatrix}$, where A_1 and A_2 are square submatrices, are the characteristic values of A_1 together with those of A_2.

Exercise (84.3). Show that $\begin{pmatrix} I_t & 0 \\ 0 & P \end{pmatrix}$ is orthogonal if P is orthogonal.

Exercise (84.4). Find an orthogonal matrix P such that $Pu' = \epsilon_1'$ if

(a) $u = (1/\sqrt{2}, 1/\sqrt{2}, 0)$, **(b)** $u = (1/\sqrt{3}, -1/\sqrt{3}, 1/\sqrt{3})$,
(c) $u = (1/\sqrt{3}, -1/\sqrt{3}, -1/\sqrt{3})$, **(d)** $u = (0, 3/5, 0, -4/5)$.

Exercise (84.5). Reduce by the method of Theorem (84.2) to the form with zeros below the main diagonal

(a) $\begin{pmatrix} 3 & 2 \\ 6 & 4 \end{pmatrix}$, (b) $\begin{pmatrix} 5 & 2 \\ -1 & -1 \end{pmatrix}$,

(c) $\begin{pmatrix} 2 & 0 & 2 \\ -2 & -1 & -1 \\ -2 & -3 & -3 \end{pmatrix}$, (d) $\begin{pmatrix} 0 & 0 & 1 \\ 0 & 4 & 3 \\ 1 & 3 & 0 \end{pmatrix}$.

Exercise (84.6). Prove that if u_1 and u_2 are characteristic vectors which correspond to distinct characteristic values of a real symmetric matrix A, then u_1 and u_2 are orthogonal.

Exercise (84.7). Find an orthonormal basis of E_n which reduces the quadratic mapping $\mathfrak{Q}_{A,\epsilon_i}$ to simplest form if

(a) $A = \begin{pmatrix} 2 & -2 \\ -2 & 5 \end{pmatrix}$, (b) $\begin{pmatrix} -1 & 0 & -\sqrt{3} \\ 0 & 0 & -2 \\ -\sqrt{3} & -2 & 3 \end{pmatrix}$.

Exercise (84.8). Find the semi-axes of the quadric $\mathfrak{Q}_{A,\epsilon_i} = 6$ for the two matrices A of the preceding exercise.

Exercise (84.9). Refer the following conics and quadric surfaces to their principal axes:

(a) $4x^2 - 2xy - y^2 = 3$;
(b) $30x^2 + 200xy - 24xz - 75y^2 + 150yz - 59z^2 = 25$.

Exercise (84.10). Find an orthogonal change of variables which eliminates the cross-product term of

(a) $4xy - y^2 + 2x + 3 = 0$;
(b) $3x^2 - 8xz + y^2 + 2z^2 - 4x - 6y = 7$.

Exercise (84.11). Restate (84.3) in terms of the group $\mathcal{P}(\mathfrak{A}_n(R^\#))$. Give a set of canonical forms for the set of real symmetric matrices under the orthogonal group $\mathcal{P}(\mathfrak{A}_n(R^\#))$.

Exercise (84.12). (a) Show that the maximum value of the quadratic form XAX' for a vector X of unit length is d_1, where $d_1 \geq d_2 \geq \cdots \geq d_n$ are the characteristic values of A. (b) Find the maximum value of the following quadratic forms with matrix A for vectors of unit length where (i) $A = \begin{pmatrix} 7 & -2 \\ -2 & -3 \end{pmatrix}$; (ii) $A = \begin{pmatrix} -2 & 2 & 10 \\ 2 & -11 & 8 \\ 10 & 8 & 5 \end{pmatrix}$.

Section 85. Unitary Vector Spaces. Unitary Transformations

The material of the preceding sections carries over without difficulty to $V_n(C)$, the sequence vector space with complex components. In order to obtain a length for vectors with complex components which has suitable properties, we define the *complex inner product* $\mathfrak{N}_c$ of vectors $\alpha = (a_1, a_2, \cdots, a_n)$ and $\beta = (b_1, b_2, \cdots, b_n)$ in $V_n(C)$ by $\mathfrak{N}_c(\alpha, \beta) = (a_1, a_2, \cdots, a_n)(\bar{b}_1, \bar{b}_2, \cdots, \bar{b}_n)' = a_1\bar{b}_1 + a_2\bar{b}_2 + \cdots + a_n\bar{b}_n \in C$. Then $\mathfrak{N}_c(\alpha,\alpha) = \sum_{i=1}^{n} a_i\bar{a}_i$ defines a positive definite Hermitian mapping of $V_n(C)$ into $R^\#$, so that $\mathfrak{N}_c(\alpha,\alpha)$ is a non-negative real number and $|\alpha| = [\mathfrak{N}_c(\alpha,\alpha)]^{1/2}$, the non-negative square root, has the usual properties of *length*.

Although the mapping $\mathfrak{N}_c$ is not symmetric, since $\mathfrak{N}_c(\beta,\alpha) = \overline{\mathfrak{N}_c(\alpha,\beta)}$, $\mathfrak{N}_c(\alpha,\beta) = 0$ if and only if $\mathfrak{N}_c(\beta,\alpha) = 0$, so that we may define α and β to be *orthogonal* if the complex inner product (in either order) is zero.

(85.1) Definition. The vector space $V_n(C)$ with inner product, orthogonality, and length as defined above is called the *n-dimensional unitary space* U_n.

The Euclidean vector space E_n is contained in U_n (but not as a subspace) since the complex inner product reduces to the ordinary inner product $\mathfrak{N}(\alpha,\beta) = \sum_{i=1}^{n} a_ib_i$ for vectors α and β with real components.

As before, the set $u_1, u_2, \cdots, u_k \in U_n$ is an *orthonormal set* if $\mathfrak{N}_c(u_i,u_j) = \delta_{ij}$ for all pairs i,j, and the theorems of Section 81 are valid for unitary spaces. For these proofs it should be noted that

$$\begin{aligned}\mathfrak{N}_c(c_1\alpha_1 + c_2\alpha_2, d_1\beta_1 + d_2\beta_2) &= c_1\bar{d}_1\mathfrak{N}_c(\alpha_1,\beta_1) + c_1\bar{d}_2\mathfrak{N}_c(\alpha_1,\beta_2)\\ &\quad + c_2\bar{d}_1\mathfrak{N}_c(\alpha_2,\beta_1) + c_2\bar{d}_2\mathfrak{N}_c(\alpha_2,\beta_2),\end{aligned}$$

and that $\bar{c} = 0$ if and only if $c = 0$. The following theorem replaces (82.1).

(85.2) Theorem. The vectors $u_1, u_2, \cdots, u_n \in U_n$ are an orthonormal basis of U_n if and only if $\bar{U}' = U^{-1}$ where

$$U = \begin{pmatrix} u_1 \\ u_2 \\ \cdot \\ \cdot \\ \cdot \\ u_n \end{pmatrix} \in \mathfrak{A}_n(C).$$

PROOF. Since the ith row of U consists of the components of u_i and the jth column of $\bar{U}'$ consists of the components of $\bar{u}_j$, the product

$U\bar{U}' = (a_{ij})$ where $a_{ij} = \mathfrak{N}_c(u_i,u_j)$ for all pairs i,j. Thus $\mathfrak{N}_c(u_i,u_j) = \delta_{ij}$ if and only if $U\bar{U}' = I_n$, that is, if and only if $\bar{U}' = U^{-1}$.

Any orthonormal basis of E_n is an orthonormal basis of U_n, for in this case, $\bar{U}' = U' = U^{-1}$.

(85.3) Definition. A matrix $P \in \mathfrak{A}_n(C)$ is *unitary* if $\bar{P}' = P^{-1}$, and an equivalence transformation $T_{P,Q}$ of $\mathfrak{A}_n(C)$ with $Q = \bar{P}' = P^{-1}$ is a *unitary transformation* of $\mathfrak{A}_n(C)$.

The matrix $P = \begin{pmatrix} 1/\sqrt{3} & (1+i)/\sqrt{3} \\ (1-i)/\sqrt{3} & -1/\sqrt{3} \end{pmatrix}$ is unitary, as is any real orthogonal matrix. The following theorem, the proof of which is left to the reader as an exercise, replaces (83.3).

(85.4) Theorem. If $u_1, u_2, \cdots, u_n$ is an orthonormal basis of U_n, then the vectors $v_1, v_2, \cdots, v_n$ form an orthonormal basis of U_n if and only if there exists a unitary matrix $P \in \mathfrak{A}_n(C)$ such that $\begin{pmatrix} v_1 \\ v_2 \\ \cdot \\ \cdot \\ \cdot \\ v_n \end{pmatrix} = P \begin{pmatrix} u_1 \\ u_2 \\ \cdot \\ \cdot \\ \cdot \\ u_n \end{pmatrix}$.

The set of all unitary transformations of $\mathfrak{A}_n(C)$ is a group $\mathfrak{U}(\mathfrak{A}_n(C))$, called the *unitary group* on $\mathfrak{A}_n(C)$. This group is a subgroup of both the collineatory and the conjunctive subgroups of $\mathcal{E}(\mathfrak{A}_n(C))$. The unitary group $\mathfrak{U}(\mathfrak{A}_n(C))$ is also a group of transformations on the set of Hermitian matrices in $\mathfrak{A}_n(C)$, and it bears the same relation to Hermitian mappings and forms as the orthogonal group $\mathcal{O}(\mathfrak{A}_n(R^{\#}))$ does to real quadratic mappings and forms.

From Theorem (85.2) and the fact that any orthonormal set of vectors in U_n is contained in an orthonormal basis of U_n, it follows that the analogue of Lemma (84.1) is valid for a vector $u = (a_1, a_2, \cdots, a_n) \in U_n$ of length 1 and a unitary matrix P. Then using the argument of (84.2) and (84.3), we obtain the following reduction theorem.

(85.5) Theorem. If $A \in \mathfrak{A}_n(C)$ is Hermitian, there exists a unitary matrix $P \in \mathfrak{A}_n(C)$ such that

$$PAP^{-1} = D = \left(\begin{array}{ccccc|c} d_1 & & & & & \\ & d_2 & 0 & & & \\ & & \cdot & & & \\ & & & \cdot & & 0 \\ & 0 & & & \cdot & \\ & & & & d_r & \\ \hline & & 0 & & & 0 \end{array}\right)$$

where r is the rank of A and $d_1, d_2, \cdots, d_r$ are the non-zero characteristic values of A.

The matrix D is, of course, real since the characteristic values of a Hermitian matrix are real by (83.3). This reduction theorem when applied to Hermitian mappings and forms gives the following results.

(85.6) Theorem. If $\mathcal{H}_{A,u_i}$ is a Hermitian mapping of U_n where $u_1, u_2, \cdots, u_n$ is an orthonormal basis of U_n, then there exists an orthonormal basis $v_1, v_2, \cdots, v_n$ of U_n such that $\mathcal{H}_{A,u_i} = \mathcal{H}_{D,v_i}$ where D is the diagonal matrix of Theorem (85.5).

(85.7) Corollary. A Hermitian form $XA\bar{X}'$ can be reduced by a unitary change of variables $X = YP$ to the form

$$YD\bar{Y}' = d_1y_1\bar{y}_1 + d_2y_2\bar{y}_2 + \cdots + d_ry_r\bar{y}_r$$

where $d_1, d_2, \cdots, d_r$ are the non-zero characteristic values of A.

EXAMPLE. Consider the Hermitian form $x_1\bar{x}_1 - ix_2\bar{x}_3 + ix_3\bar{x}_2 = XA\bar{X}'$, where $x = (x_1,x_2,x_3)$ and $A = \begin{pmatrix} 1 & 0 & 0 \\ 0 & 0 & -i \\ 0 & i & 0 \end{pmatrix}$ is a Hermitian matrix. Since

$$|Ix - A| = \begin{vmatrix} x-1 & 0 & 0 \\ 0 & x & i \\ 0 & -i & x \end{vmatrix} = (x-1)(x^2-1) = (x-1)^2(x+1),$$

the characteristic values of A are 1, 1, and -1. Corresponding to the value 1 is the set of equations

$$\begin{cases} 0 = 0 \\ x_2 + ix_3 = 0 \\ -ix_2 + x_3 = 0, \end{cases}$$

which has two independent solutions $u_1 = (1,0,0)$ and $u_2 = (0, i/\sqrt{2}, -1/\sqrt{2})$ which are orthonormal. Corresponding to the value -1 is $u_3 = (0, i/\sqrt{2}, 1/\sqrt{2})$. Thus

$$(x_1,x_2,x_3) = (y_1,y_2,y_3)\begin{pmatrix} 1 & 0 & 0 \\ 0 & i/\sqrt{2} & -1/\sqrt{2} \\ 0 & i/\sqrt{2} & 1/\sqrt{2} \end{pmatrix}$$

is a unitary change of variables which reduces the form to $y_1\bar{y}_1 + y_2\bar{y}_2 - y_3\bar{y}_3$.

Exercise (85.1). Show that if $A \in \mathfrak{A}_n(C)$ is Hermitian or unitary and $T_{P,Q} \in \mathfrak{U}(\mathfrak{A}_n(C))$, then $T_{P,Q}(A)$ is respectively Hermitian or unitary.

Exercise (85.2). Find a unitary transformation which reduces each form to $\Sigma d_i y_i \bar{y}_i$.

(a) $x_1\bar{x}_1 + 2ix_1\bar{x}_2 - 2ix_2\bar{x}_1$;
(b) $(1 + 3i)x_1\bar{x}_2 + (1 - 3i)x_2\bar{x}_1$;
(c) Exercise (80.3), b.

Exercise (85.3). What is the diagonal form of

$$x_1\bar{x}_1 + ix_1\bar{x}_2 - ix_2\bar{x}_1 + (1 + i)x_1\bar{x}_3 + (1 - i)x_3\bar{x}_1 + 2x_2\bar{x}_2 + x_2\bar{x}_3 + x_3\bar{x}_2 + 3x_3\bar{x}_3?$$

Exercise (85.4). Find an orthonormal basis of E_3 which includes $(1/3 + 2/3\, i,\ 2/3,\ 0)$ and $(-1/2,\ 1/4 - 1/2\, i,\ \sqrt{7}/4)$.

Exercise (85.5). Prove that the form of the complex inner product $\mathfrak{M}_c(\alpha,\beta)$ is unchanged by a change of basis from one orthonormal basis of U_n to another.

INDEX

INDEX

NOTE: The designation "Ex." after a page reference indicates that the entry is to be found in an Exercise.